D0065136

QD
506
S78
V.5

Surface and colloid science. Editor: Egon
   Matijević, consulting editor: Frederick
   R. Eirich.   New York, Wiley-Interscience,
   1969-
      v. illus.
   Includes bibliographies.

   1. Surface chemistry - Collected works.
2. Colloids - Collected works. I. Matijević,
Egon, 1922-   ed.

SURFACE AND COLLOID SCIENCE

Volume 5

Advisory Board

ARTHUR W. ADAMSON, *University of Southern California, Los Angeles, California*

STEPHEN BRUNAUER, *Clarkson College of Technology, Potsdam, New York*

STIG CLAESSON, *University of Uppsala, Uppsala, Sweden*

B. V. DERJAGUIN, *Institute of Physical Chemistry, Academy of Science, Moscow, U.S.S.R.*

DIKRAN G. DERVICHIAN, *Institut Pasteur, Paris, France*

GERT EHRLICH, *General Electric Research Laboratory, Schenectady, New York*

FREDERICK R. EIRICH, *Polytechnic Institute of Brooklyn, Brooklyn, New York*

FRANK C. GOODRICH, *Clarkson College of Technology, Potsdam, New York*

WILFRIED HELLER, *Wayne State University, Detroit, Michigan*

STANLEY G. MASON, *McGill University, Montreal, Quebec, Canada*

ALAN S. MICHAELS, *Pharmetrics, Palo Alto, California*

ANTON PETERLIN, *Camille Dreyfus Laboratory, Triangle Research Institute, Durham, North Carolina*

BRIAN A. PETHICA, *Unilever Research Laboratory, Port Sunlight, Cheshire, England*

KOZO SHINODA, *Yokohama National University, Minamiku, Yokohama, Japan*

ARTHUR VEIS, *The Medical School, Northwestern University, Chicago, Illinois*

ALBERT C. ZETTLEMOYER, *Lehigh University, Bethlehem, Pennsylvania*

WILLIAM A. ZISMAN, *Naval Research Laboratory, Washington, D.C.*

SURFACE AND
COLLOID SCIENCE

Volume 5

Editor: EGON MATIJEVIĆ

Institute of Colloid and Surface Science
Clarkson College of Technology
Potsdam, New York 13676

Fairleigh Dickinson
University Library

Teaneck, New Jersey

177118

1972
WILEY—INTERSCIENCE
a division of John Wiley & Sons, Inc.
New York—London—Sydney—Toronto

Copyright © 1972, by John Wiley & Sons, Inc.

All rights reserved.   Published simultaneously in Canada.

No part of this book may be reproduced by any means, nor
transmitted, nor translated into a machine language without the written permission of the publisher.

Library of Congress Catalog Card Number: 67-29459

ISBN 0-471-57634-4

Printed in the United States of America.

10 9 8 7 6 5 4 3 2 1

QD
506
S78
V.5

Preface

A need for a comprehensive treatise on *surface and colloid science* has been felt for a long time. Our series endeavors to fill this need. Its format has been shaped by the features of this widely roaming science. Since the subjects to be discussed represent such a broad spectrum, no single person could write a critical review on more than a very limited number of topics. Thus, the volumes will consist of chapters written by specialists. We expect this series to represent a treatise by offering texts and critical reviews which will describe theories, systems, and processes, handle these in a rigorous way, and indicate solved problems and problems which still require further research. Purely descriptive colloid chemistry will be limited to a minimum. Qualitative observations of poorly defined systems, which in the past have been so much in evidence, will be avoided. Thus, the chapters are neither supposed to possess the character of *Advances*, nor to represent reviews of authors' own work. Instead, it is hoped that each contribution will treat a subject critically giving the historic development as well as a digest of the newest results. Every effort will be made to include chapters on novel systems and phenomena.

It is impossible to publish a work of this magnitude with all chapters in a logical order. Rather, the contributions will appear as they arrive, as soon as the editor receives sufficient material for a volume. Every effort will be made to group related chapters into the same volume. A certain amount of overlap is unavoidable, but will be kept to a minimum. Also, uniform treatment and style cannot be expected in a work that represents the effort of so many. Notwithstanding these anticipated difficulties, the series presented here appears to be the only practical way to accomplish the task of a high level and modern treatise on surface and colloid science.

A few general remarks may be in order. In modern times, few disciplines fluctuated in "popularity" as much as colloid and surface science. However, it seems that these sporadic declines in interest in the science of "neglected dimensions" were only apparent. In reality, there has been a steady increase in research through the years, especially in industrial laboratories. The fluctuations were most noticeable in academic institutions, especially with regard to teaching of specialized courses. It is thus only natural that the university professors with surface and colloid science as their abiding interest were frequently concerned and have repeatedly warned of the need for better and more intensive education, especially on the graduate level.

There are several reasons for the discrepancy between the need of industrial and of academic research laboratories in well trained surface and colloid scientists and the efforts of the academic institutions to provide specialization in these disciplines. Many instructors believe that a good background in the basic principles of chemistry, physics, and mathematics will enable a professional person to engage in research in surface and colloid science. This may be true, but only after much additional professional growth. Indeed, many people active in this area are self-educated. Furthermore, this science deals with an unusually wide range of systems and principles. This makes a uniform treatment of problems in surface and colloid science, not only challenging, but also a very difficult task. As a matter of fact certain branches of colloid science have grown into separate, independent disciplines which only in a broad sense are now considered a part of the "parent" science. Finally, there is often a stigma associated with the name "colloids." To many, the term symbolizes empirically and poorly described, irreproducible, etc., systems to which exact science cannot as yet be applied. The latter impression is in part based upon the fact that a considerable number of papers were and are published which leave much to be desired in regard to the rigorousness of the approach.

Yet, during the first half of this century some of the most acclaimed scientists have occupied themselves with colloid and surface science problems. One needs to mention only a few like Einstein, von Smoluchowski, Debye, Perrin, Loeb, Freundlich, Vzsigmondy, Pauli, Langmuir, McBain, Harkins, Donnan, Kruyt, Svedberg, Tiselius, Frumkin, Adam, and Rideal, who have made substantial contributions to the classical foundations of colloid and surface science. This work has led to many fundamental theoretical advances and to a tremendous number of practical applications in a variety of systems such as natural and synthetic polymers, proteins and nucleic acids, ceramics, textiles, coatings, detergents, lubricants, paints, catalysts, fuels, foams, emulsions, membranes, pharmaceuticals, ores, composites, soils, air and water pollutants, and many others.

It is therefore our hope that this treatise will be of value to scientists of all descriptions, and that it will provide a stimulating reference work for those who do not need to be convinced of the importance of colloid and surface science in nature and in application.

EGON MATIJEVIĆ

February, 1969

Contents

SURFACE AND COLLOID SCIENCE

Volume 5

Rheological Properties of Monomolecular Films. Part I: Basic Concepts and Experimental Methods

M. JOLY

Service de Biophysique, Institut Pasteur, Paris, France

I. INTRODUCTION

Surface rheology has been the subject of numerous publications and of several specialized reviews. A considerable amount of space has been devoted to it in recent monographs on monomolecular films (1, 2). Despite this fact, the broad aspects of surface rheology have not yet been treated systematically in a general, critical survey. We propose to present such a review here. It goes without saying that there will be no attempt to summarize the totality of all investigations that have been published concerning the rheology of monolayers. Our objective is not an annotated bibliography of research into the mechanical properties of surface and interfacial phases. What we hope to achieve is, on the one hand, an exposition of the general principles that constitute the foundation of surface rheology, and on the other hand, a synthesis of results obtained in the various specialized studies in which the measurement of surface rheology has played a role, either as an end in itself or as an auxiliary technique. We attempt to give a pedagogic character to this chapter without concealing the complexity of surface rheology. In short, our objective in this presentation is to demonstrate that this portion of surface science has progressed sufficiently to constitute henceforth a coherent body of knowledge. We shall also see that this specialized aspect of rheology can make a not inconsiderable contribution to other areas of science.

One of the first questions that presents itself is to understand precisely what is meant by surface rheology. What relationship has it with classical bulk rheology?

A brief historical review will assist our understanding of the subject of surface rheology. About a century ago Plateau (3–6) compared the damping of the oscillations of a magnetic needle depending upon whether it was immersed in a liquid or only placed upon the surface of that liquid. He thus confirmed that the surface of the liquid presents a resistance to deformation relatively higher than that of the bulk liquid. He claimed to have thus demonstrated a "surface viscosity" peculiar to the liquid surface but analogous to the ordinary bulk viscosity of liquids. Plateau was unaware that the surfaces of liquids are almost always contaminated by an adsorbed layer of impurities. It was Marangoni (7–10) who recognized that it was this layer that is responsible for the effect observed by Plateau.

Rheology is, by definition, the science of deformation. In particular, classical rheology studies the deformation of bulk matter, that is, of three-dimensional systems, be they continuous or discontinuous media, homogeneous or heterogeneous. The existence of a special resistance to deformation due to the presence of a surface covered with an adsorbed monomolecular layer, whether soluble or insoluble, leads to a definition of surface rheology. Surface rheology is the science of deformations of monomolecular films spread or adsorbed at interfaces between bulk phases. One can characterize it as the rheology of two-dimensional systems.

The first precise interpretation of the deformational resistance of surface films was proposed by Gibbs (11, 12) and amplified by Rayleigh (13–15). As for bulk systems, it is necessary to consider shear as well as dilational strains (16). At the same time we must distinguish between elastic, viscous, and plastic deformations.

The systematic study of surface rheology has developed over the last thirty years. There is no space within the confines of this monograph to follow the detailed history of this development. We may nevertheless single out among the principal contributions to this study the work of Langmuir (17, 18), Harkins (19–22), Joly (23–30), Eyring (31), Trapeznikov (32–41), Inokuchi (42–45), Ewers (46), de Bernard (47–48), Davies (49–50), Jaffé (51–53), Isemura (54–56), Motomura (57, 58), and of their collaborators.

The rheology of monomolecular layers can be studied for its own sake, but it can also be regarded as a research tool for the general study of surface and interfacial films. It is in this way that the data of surface rheology have been used to interpret the hydrodynamic behavior of interfaces (59–69). Among the principal applications of surface rheology, we may cite also the characterization of the physical state of monomolecular films (29, 70), the classification of films (71–73), the determination of molecular weights (51, 74), the study of different-order phase transitions in monolayers (22, 35, 70, 75–80), and the measurement of the energies of molecular interaction and of deformation in macromolecules (81, 82).

In the following pages we discuss first the definitions and general principles that lie at the foundation of surface rheology (Section II). We next describe the various experimental methods used in the measurement of the rheological parameters of monomolecular layers, that is, coefficients of surface viscosity and elasticity (Section III). In a second part we analyze the rheological behavior of the principal types of surface and interfacial films: insoluble monomolecular films and adsorbed films of small amphiphilic molecules, films of synthetic high polymers, films of polypeptides, and films of proteins (Part II, Section I). In a third part we present the theoretical interpretations that have been proposed up to the present time to explain the mechanical properties of surface and interfacial films (Part II, Section II). Finally, in the last part, we indicate the principal effects of the rheological properties of films upon the dynamics of interfaces (Part II, Section III), and we describe the most frequently used applications of surface rheology (Part II, Section IV).

II. GENERAL CONCEPTS REGARDING THE MECHANICAL PROPERTIES OF MONOMOLECULAR FILMS

A. Two-Dimensional Systems

1. Interface and Interfacial Phase

Before we study the rheology of two-dimensional systems, it is important to be precise about the meaning of a two-dimensional system in the context of the physical chemistry of surfaces.   Such a system is composed of a surface phase or a group of surface phases occupying a more or less extended region of the interface separating two immiscible, bulk phases.   These bulk phases can be a liquid and a gas, two liquids, a solid and a gas, a solid and a liquid, or even two solids.   Those surface phases associated with interfaces of which one of the bulk phases is a solid have not been the subject of investigation so far as surface rheology is concerned.   In this article we are therefore concerned only with surface phases located between fluid phases, liquid/gas and liquid/liquid.   It is first necessary to define with precision what is meant by a surface or interfacial phase.   This requires from the outset a clear distinction between an interface and a surface phase.

From the geometric point of view, an interface is easily conceived as the surface of separation between two conjoining volumes, surfaces and volumes being understood in their mathematical sense.   From a physical point of view, the idea of an interface on the molecular level is somewhat less precise. It corresponds to the frontier region between two homogeneous bulk phases in thermodynamic equilibrium.   It is in fact the transition zone between two phases, that is, that portion of space in the interior of which the composition, the structure, or the properties of each of the phases are modified from what they are in the bulk because of the proximity of the other phase. Because the two phases that we are discussing are presumed immiscible, the thickness of the transition zone is very small, approximately of the order of one or two molecular diameters (83, 84).   One must not forget, moreover, that the mean "geometric" surface, on either side of which is established that transition zone which constitutes an interface between two immiscible liquids, can be defined with rigor only statistically.   In actuality, as a result of thermal agitation, there are constant alterations in the positions of molecules in the transition region.   The mean lifetime of a molecule in an equilibrium position either within the interior or at the surface of a liquid is very small. Thus for water, for which the self-diffusion coefficient at 20°C is 2.2×10^{-5} cm²/sec, this mean lifetime is of the order of 10^{-11} sec. It has recently been demonstrated in a chapter of this series (85) that the precise location of the surface of separation is not necessary for the rigorous derivation of the thermodynamic relations satisfied by fluid interfaces. This result greatly simplifies the introduction of the idea of a surface or interfacial phase.

A surface or interfacial phase I is by definition a nonbulk phase that is enclosed within the interfacial transition region between two adjoining immiscible bulk phases A and B. It is of necessity characterized by the fact that its composition is different from that of either of the adjacent bulk phases A and B, a fact that does not exclude the possibility of sharing common constituents with these phases. A preliminary question that arises is to know if by such a definition the existence of an interface automatically implies the existence of an interfacial phase. In the limiting case of a single constituent, that is, a liquid in equilibrium with its vapor and hence univariant, the laws of thermodynamics demonstrate that there exists within the interfacial transition zone an excess concentration Γ moles/cm² of the single constituent: $\Gamma = -d\gamma/d\mu$, γ being the surface tension of the liquid and μ the chemical potential of the single constituent. Because of the existence of this difference in composition between the mass of the liquid and its surface region, we define the interfacial transition zone of abnormal composition as a surface phase. From the point of view of surface rheology and for reasons that we examine in Section III, this type of interface has been almost completely ignored.

A much more interesting case is that of systems of two constituents, such as that of solutions in equilibrium with their vapors. Denoting the solvent by s and the solute by S, the Gibbs equation states

$$\Gamma_S = -\left(\frac{\partial \gamma}{\partial \mu_S}\right)_T$$

for the excess concentration in moles/cm² in the interfacial region. In the same fashion the excess concentration of solvent is

$$\Gamma_s = -\left(\frac{\partial \gamma}{\partial \mu_s}\right)_T$$

Depending upon the nature of the components of the solution, Γ_S and Γ_s may be positive or negative. The two quantities Γ_S and Γ_s are not independent (85), and we have

$$(c_S{}^B - c_S{}^A)\Gamma_s + (c_s{}^B - c_s{}^A)\Gamma_S = 0$$

$c_s{}^A$, $c_s{}^B$, $c_S{}^A$, and $c_S{}^B$ being the molar concentrations of the two components in the bulk phases A and B.   In the case of a nonvolatile solute, the preceding equation reduces in first approximation to

$$x_s\Gamma_S + x_S\Gamma_s = 0$$

where x_S and x_s are the mole fractions of solute and solvent in the solution. It is the difference in composition between the interfacial region and the bulk phases that permits the description of the transition zone as a surface phase. For the case of extremely dilute solutions for which one has the well-known relation

$$\Gamma_S = - \frac{c_S}{RT} \frac{d\gamma}{dc_S}$$

the difference in concentration of solute between the bulk solution and the surface region is very large.   The accumulation of molecules of S at the interface constitutes an adsorbed surface film.   These systems have been studied extensively for large numbers of organic compounds, and it has been shown, by supposing that all the molecules in excess of those occupying the bulk of the solution are spread in a single monomolecular layer, that the molecular dimensions required are entirely compatible with the chemical structure of the solute.   It is therefore reasonable to accept the hypothesis that the adsorbed film which comprises the surface phase consists of a layer of solute one molecule thick and spread at the surface of the solution.   This hypothesis is the more acceptable when one realizes that the properties of adsorbed films are analogous to those of insoluble monomolecular films spread upon a liquid surface (86).   A very important limiting case of an interfacial phase is, in fact, that of thin films of substances insoluble in water but spread upon a water surface by means of a dilute solution in a volatile solvent.   Their strictly monomolecular character has been known for a long time (84, 87).   These surface films have been exhaustively studied from many points of view (2).

From the preceding discussion we perceive that the essential character of a two-dimensional system is that its thickness is limited in principle to a single molecule.   This is why surface or interfacial phases are commonly designated as monomolecular films whether or not they are composed of soluble or insoluble films.   In the case of liquid/gas interfaces, the bulk liquid phase plays the role of a substrate for the monomolecular film.   In the case of liquid/liquid interfaces, it is generally the denser liquid that is considered as the substrate for the film.   However, for adsorbed films of a substance soluble in one of the two adjacent bulk phases, it is the solvent phase that is regarded as the substrate.   So far as surface rheology is concerned, it is insoluble, monomolecular films that have been the most thoroughly investigated.

2. Amphiphilic Molecules and Surface Films

It is important to understand that it is not sufficient that a substance S be insoluble in two immiscible, adjacent bulk phases A and B in order that it give birth to an insoluble surface phase $I(S)$ at the interface. For this to take place, the substance must be capable of spreading at the interface (spontaneously or otherwise) and of remaining spread. This requires that the substance, however insoluble in phases A and B, possess a sufficiently strong affinity for them so that the system $A + B + I(S)$ is more stable than $A + B + C(S)$, where $C(S)$ represents a bulk phase adjacent to both A and B. Spreading must therefore be accompanied by a diminution of the free energy of the entire system (88–93). This is possible only if the molecules of S are amphiphilic. It is consequently necessary that they possess functional groups of which some are soluble in A and insoluble in B, while others are insoluble in A and soluble in B. In particular, in the case where the substrate phase is water, a substance can exist as a stable film at the interface only if its molecules possess polar groups having a sufficient affinity for water to overcome the molecular self-cohesion of a phase $C(S)$ and to disperse it as a film at the interface. It is necessary, moreover, after having been spread as a monomolecular film, that the film thus formed does not dissolve in one of the two phases A or B. This last condition is not necessarily met because S in bulk form is insoluble in A and B. The insolubility of S in essence results largely from the cohesive energy of its molecules when they are assembled in bulk form. As a result of the new molecular environment after spreading, this cohesion can be significantly reduced and no longer forms any hindrance to solution. It is for this reason that lauric acid, although practically insoluble in water whose pH is on the acidic side (1.3 mg/l at saturation at 21°C), is unstable as a monolayer spread upon 0.01 M HCl and diffuses into its substrate (94).

An "insoluble" monomolecular film is stable only if the difference in free energy of the system $A + B + I$, depending upon whether a molecule of S is localized in the interfacial region or has diffused into A or B, is large enough so that at equilibrium the number of diffused molecules is negligible compared with those fixed at the interface. This implies that the free energy of activation for diffusion from the interfacial film into the adjacent phases is very large. Put in another way, the free energy of adsorption must be sufficiently large, a circumstance which depends sensitively upon the chemical constitution of S and upon the composition of A and B. Thus at the air/water interface, amphipathic molecules possessing a paraffin chain of 16 carbon atoms form stable monomolecular films when the polar groups are

—OH, —COOH, —CN, or —CONH$_2$. As a counter example, if the terminal groups are of the type —SO$_3^-$ or —OSO$_3^{2-}$, the films are soluble (95). Alternatively, at the oil/water interface it is those molecules carrying ionized groups which, for an equal length of paraffin chain, form the most stable films because of the solubility of their paraffinic moieties in the oil phase (96, 97).

This essential balance between the solubilities of functional groups in A and B is particularly obvious in the case of high polymers. Thus highly cohesive materials such as cellulose acetate and polymethyl methacrylate, which do not spread spontaneously at the air/water interface, give stable films at the benzene/water interface, even though they are soluble in benzene (72). Polyacrylic acid and polyvinyl alcohol display a different type of behavior, for they are soluble in water but nevertheless form stable films at the air/water and oil/water interfaces provided that the pH of the water is sufficiently acid. These films become unstable and dissolve when the pH of the substrate increases (71, 98, 99).

It is apparent that analogous considerations play a role in the case of adsorbed films which, to be precise, form a localized surface film only when the free energy of adsorption $(-\Delta G_0)$ is sufficiently high. For example, at liquid/gas interfaces, the equilibrium concentration of adsorbed material is an explicit function of the free energy of adsorption (100–104). Thus the activity a of S in the liquid phase A is defined by

$$\mu^A = \mu_0^A + kT \ln a$$

and its fugacity f in the interfacial phase I is defined by

$$\mu^I = \mu_0^I + kT \ln \frac{f}{f_0}$$

At equilibrium, and taking as a standard state in the film that which corresponds to $f_0 = 1$,

$$\mu_0^I - \mu_0^A = kT \ln \frac{a}{f} = \Delta G_0$$

When phase A is a very dilute solution, the number n of molecules of S/cm^2 of interface is given in first approximation by

$$n = \frac{a}{kT} \exp\left(\frac{\mu_0^A - \mu_0^I}{kT}\right) = \frac{a}{kT} \exp\left(-\frac{\Delta G_0}{kT}\right)$$

so long as the adsorbed film is sufficiently dilute so that $f \simeq nkT$.

In the more general case of a surface phase I at the interface of two liquid phases A and B in which the activities of S are a and b, respectively, the activity i of S in I at equilibrium at the temperature T is

$$i = aK_S{}^A = bK_S{}^B$$

where the coefficients $K_S{}^A$ and $K_S{}^B$ are the adsorption coefficients of S. We have

$$K_S{}^A = \exp\left(\frac{\mu_0{}^A - \mu_0{}^I}{kT}\right)$$

and

$$K_S{}^B = \exp\left(\frac{\mu_0{}^B - \mu_0{}^I}{kT}\right)$$

It is to be recalled that the ratio $K_S{}^A/K_S{}^B = K_S$ is identical to the partition coefficient of the substance S at temperature T between the adjacent bulk phases.

3. The Structure of Two-Dimensional Systems

An important consequence of the amphiphilic nature of the molecules that make up monomolecular layers at interfaces is the orientation of these molecules. From the fact that the molecules of S contained in I bear functional groups selectively soluble in A and B, the most stable thermodynamic state of the system $A + B + I$ is achieved when each of these functional groups is in contact with solvent for which it has the greatest affinity. At equilibrium this implies a preferential distribution of orientations of the molecules of S in I. Thus polar aliphatic compounds at the oil/water interface are arranged in such a fashion that the polar groups are in contact with water and that the paraffinic chains are in contact with oil. It follows that the long axes of these molecules have a mean orientation normal to the interface, the polar ends being on one side and the paraffinic ends on the other.

If we have dwelt upon these aspects of the nature of surface phases despite their apparent *a priori* remoteness from mechanical properties, it is because in fact they have very important consequences for the rheological behavior of monomolecular films. First of all, the geometry of two-dimensional systems is always simple, in contrast to that of those systems that are the concern of classical rheology. In point of fact, classical rheology studies deformations in three dimensions, whether the media be continuous or discontinuous, homogeneous or heterogeneous. When general problems of flow are considered, the geometric description of the systems studied becomes rapidly complicated. In contrast, the systems considered in surface rheology are always made up of ensembles of molecules having the same statistical orientation with respect to the interface, and all localized within the interfacial region. Be it an insoluble film or an adsorbed film, the interfacial phase is always monomolecular.   As a consequence, the portion of space which it occupies is bounded by two parallel, neighboring surfaces. The constant distance between these two surfaces, which one can define as the thickness of the interfacial phase, depends only on the nature of the molecules of S and on their number per square centimeter of interface.   It is this fact that permits one to speak in simplified language of "two-dimensional systems," although a literal interpretation of this expression has no physical meaning.

By convention, a "two-dimensional" system is a "three-dimensional" system one of whose dimensions is constant and of the order of one molecular diameter.   This definition depends upon no hypothesis concerning the geometric shape of the interface.   Moreover, the statistical character of fluid interfaces (a result of thermal agitation) can introduce an uncertainty not exceeding several angstroms for the thickness of the two-dimensional system represented by a given interfacial phase.   This thickness can thus be taken as an invariant in space as well as in time for films of a particular substance in a well-defined physical state.   It follows that the thickness will not enter as a parameter into calculations.   All the problems that arise in the deformation of monomolecular films will therefore be "two-dimensional" problems insofar as they concern geometric variables.   This will remain true whatever the shape of the interface, planar or of arbitrary curvature.   In fact, even in the case of a dispersion of fine droplets, the radius of curvature of the interface will always be sufficiently large with respect to the thickness of the adsorbed film, so that in the absence of a structural modification of the substrate, the deformation of the interfacial film will not be involved with the third dimension.   On the other hand, this argument could be incorrect if instead of the deformation of a localized film at a geometrically invariant interface, one considers the deformation of a film simultaneously with a change in the geometric shape of the bulk substrate phase (see Section II.D).

B. Mechanical Coupling Between Film and Subphase

In Section II.A we saw that one of the necessary conditions for the existence of an interfacial phase is that the amphiphilic molecules that it contains possess functional groups soluble in at least one of the adjacent bulk phases. There results a strong "coupling" between the amphiphilic molecules and the molecules of phases A or B which are in intimate contact with those functional groups for which they have an affinity.   More precisely, when a molecule of S is displaced in the phase I, it drags with it those molecules of phases A and B (or the solvent molecules of A and B if these phases are solutions) that are immediately adjacent to the respective functional groups soluble in A and B.   Molecules of A or B in direct contact with the functional groups of S which they solvate can be considered as rigidly bound to the molecules of S whenever the latter undergo displacements. We shall see the consequences of this fact (Section II.C.1) for the definition of the kinetic units of phase I, and it plays a role in the "rheological" definition of this phase itself.

It is important to understand explicitly henceforth that this strong, mechanical coupling between monomolecular films and their liquid substrates is not imaginary, but that it may be demonstrated experimentally.

In the case of fatty acid monolayers spread at a water surface, Merigoux has shown that there is perfect bonding between the molecules of fatty acid and the water molecules in contact with the carboxylate groups. No slip is detectable between the film and the water substrate (105–107). Merigoux's experiments may be summarized as follows.

A cylindrical, glass bottle containing a small amount of an aqueous solution of potassium permanganate is mounted with its axis of revolution horizontal. The bottle is rotated about its axis so as to make the velocity of the wall about 20 cm/sec. The observed phenomenon is different depending upon whether the solution and the wall are rigorously clean (in the sense of surface chemistry) or whether the solution supports a monomolecular film. In the first case the moving wall drags with it a layer of water, and the thickness of this layer is everywhere uniform. By contrast the second case shows the formation of a large flat plateau whose height is fixed for a constant rotational velocity (Figure 1a). An analogous phenomenon is observed when a solution of potassium permanganate free of adsorbing impurities is poured at constant flux upon a plate of glass inserted at an angle into a basin filled with water. Depending upon whether the surface of this water is covered or not by a monomolecular film, it will or will not form a liquid shoulder extending up into the descending stream (Figure 1b). In these two experiments it is easily verified by conventional surface chemical techniques that the monomolecular film covers the plateau but does not extend into the thin part of the mobile, liquid sheet. In the two cases, the ratio

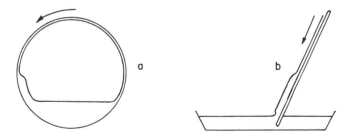

Fig. 1. Inhibition of flow by a monomolecular film: (a) rotating bottle; (b) inclined plane.

H/h of the thickness of the plateau to that of the monolayer free sheet depends upon the amount of slip between the water and the monomolecular film. Potassium permanganate being a strong, optical absorber, these thicknesses can be precisely determined by spectrophotometry. For the rotating cylinder Merigoux found $H/h = 1.964$ and for the inclined plane $H/h = 1.591$. To within experimental error, these values correspond to the case where there is no slip.

The experiment with the rotating cylinder can be treated formally as follows: a sheet of liquid of thickness h is dragged without slip at a velocity v by the plane P which supports it. A second horizontal plane R (the in-soluble monomolecular layer) capable only of vertical displacements, comes into contact with the liquid sheet (Figure 2a). The contact slows the move-ment of the liquid, revealing itself by an increased depth, and the thickness of the liquid sheet grows from h to H. There will evidently be a mass balance.

Thus

$$Q = vh = \int_0^H u(y)\,dy$$

$u(y)$ being the velocity of the liquid at an arbitrary point M of the region covered by R. The Navier-Stokes equation for this portion of the liquid is

$$\eta \frac{\partial^2 u}{\partial y^2} - \frac{\partial p}{\partial x} = 0$$

where η is the viscosity of the liquid and p the hydrostatic pressure. Now $\partial p/\partial x = 0$, whence $u = \alpha y + \beta$. If w is the velocity of slippage between R and the liquid sheet, we have

$$u = v + \frac{w - v}{H}\,y$$

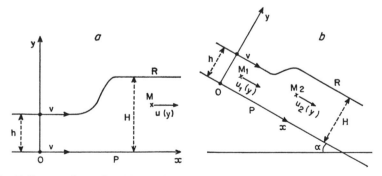

Fig. 2.   Influence of a surface film on laminar flow: (a) moving plane; (b) inclined plane.

whence

$$Q = \frac{v + w}{2} H = vh$$

and finally

$$w = v\left(2\frac{h}{H} - 1\right)$$

The experimental value of H/h being 1.964, there results $w \simeq 0.018v$.

In the case of the inclined plane making an angle α to the horizontal (Figure 2b), the Navier-Stokes equations reduce to

$$\rho g \sin \alpha + \eta \frac{\partial^2 u}{\partial y^2} = 0$$

for

$$\frac{\partial p}{\partial x} = 0$$

(ρ is the density of the liquid and g the acceleration of gravity). At $y = 0$, we must have $u = 0$, for the water wets the glass. It follows that u is of the form

$$u = Ay - \frac{\rho g \sin \alpha}{2\eta} y^2$$

In the region uncovered by R, there is zero stress at the free surface, whence

$$\left(\frac{\partial u_1}{\partial y}\right)_{y=h} = 0$$

This implies

$$u_1 = \frac{\rho g \sin \alpha}{\eta}\left(hy - \frac{y^2}{2}\right)$$

and the velocity at the free surface is

$$v = \frac{\rho g \sin \alpha}{2\eta} h^2$$

In the portion covered by R, if w is the velocity of slip between the liquid sheet and the immobile monomolecular layer, we have $u_2(H) = w$, whence

$$u_2 = \left(\frac{w}{H} + \frac{\rho g \sin \alpha}{2\eta} H\right)y - \frac{\rho g \sin \alpha}{2\eta} y^2$$

By imposing a mass balance

$$\int_0^h u_1 \, dy = \int_0^H u_2 \, dy$$

there results

$$\frac{\rho g \sin \alpha}{\eta} \frac{h^3}{3} = \frac{wH}{2} + \frac{\rho g \sin \alpha}{\eta} \frac{H^3}{12}$$

from which

$$\left(\frac{H}{h}\right)^3 = 4 - \frac{6\eta w}{\rho g \sin \alpha} \frac{H}{h^3} = 4 - \frac{3w}{v} \frac{H}{h}$$

Substituting for H/h its experimental value 1.592 we find $w \simeq -0.0023v$.

To within experimental error, the two preceding results confirm the hypothesis of no slip between monomolecular films and their substrates.

A result of the bonding between monofilms and their liquid subphases is that the expansion or flow of surface films generates a significant transport of a portion of the subphase.

This has been admirably demonstrated by an experiment of Schulman and Teorell (108). The experimental apparatus is very simple. It consists essentially of a succession of paraffined compartments placed in a trough of water at constant level (Figure 3). The source of the surface film is a drop of oleic acid floating upon the water in the cavity A. A monomolecular film spreads from this drop and extends into the compartments B and C before entering compartment D and pouring out of the end E of the apparatus. The entrance and exit of compartment D are constructed from glass rods F and G which slightly exceed the water levels in compartment C and in the trough. The spreading pressure of oleic acid is large enough to permit the film to pass barriers F and G. Compartment D was 10 cm long, 2 cm wide, and 0.5 cm deep. By means of colored dyes and by titration it was verified that water from trough was unable to enter compartment D. As the monomolecular film of oleic acid flows from A to E, a lowering of the water level in D is observed. For example, for a film flowing at a mean velocity of 5 cm/sec, compartment D initially containing 10 cm³ of water is completely emptied in 6.5 min.

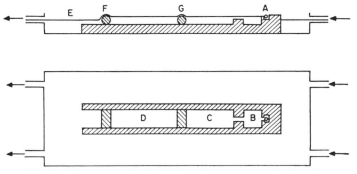

Fig. 3.   Transport of a liquid phase by a monomolecular film.

These data show unambiguously the strong coupling during flow of the molecules in surface films with the immediately adjacent molecules in the liquid substrate.

The fact that there is no slip between the molecules in a monomolecular interfacial film and those molecules of the continuous bulk phases that are in intimate contact with functional groups soluble in these phases has very important rheological consequences (see Section II.C.1).

C. Basic Concepts of Surface Rheology

1. The Kinetic Unit

When we examine the rheological behavior of an arbitrary system from the molecular point of view, we no longer study the deformation of a continuous, more or less heterogeneous medium; rather, we consider the relative displacements of kinetic units which are perfectly well defined on the molecular level. We imagine that we may push this division into structural elements of a given system up to a point such that it is proper to suppose that under deformation of the system, these structural elements undergo relative displacements without deformation. By definition, elements that move without internal deformation are the kinetic units of the deforming system. The kinetic unit of a deformable medium thus appears as the largest possible volume element of that medium which for a given state of stress moves with respect to its neighbors without internal deformation. It is obvious that the kinetic units of a system depend simultaneously upon the nature of the system and upon the magnitude and the distribution of the stress applied to it.

The results derived in Section II.B permit a more precise identification of the nature of the kinetic units of interfacial phases. The composition of the kinetic units arises from the fact that certain functional groups of the amphiphilic molecules in the interfacial film are rigidly bound to molecules which in the absence of an interfacial film would belong exclusively to the adjacent bulk phases. It follows that in general the kinetic unit of an interfacial phase is built up from an amphiphilic molecule plus those neighboring molecules of the bulk phases attached to the attracting functional groups of the amphiphile. In the case of macromolecular surface films, it is well to point out that the kinetic unit, instead of containing a complete polymer molecule, contains rather a small number of monomeric units, perhaps even a single monomer, together with the solvation shell of its functional groups.

The complex nature of the kinetic unit permits a rheological definition of interfacial films. Such a definition is in fact more precise than those presented in Section II.A. A surface phase at the interface between two immiscible bulk phases is composed of a single layer of amphiphilic molecules plus those molecules of the adjacent bulk phases firmly attached to those functional groups of the film for which they have a strong affinity.

Despite the above, let us recall the statistical character of the association between functional groups in the film and the molecules that solvate them. Thus if the mean bond energy of solvation is taken to be that of an average hydrogen bond, an application of Frenkel's (109) theory leads to a mean lifetime of the solvation bond of the order of 10^{-9} sec. Once the bond has been broken, however, there is a strong probability that it will be reformed between the same functional group–solvent molecule pair. The frequency of solvent molecule exchange upon bond rupture depends on the probability of autodiffusion at the moment of rupture. It follows that the mean lifetime of the solvation bond will be at least a microsecond. In first approximation it can be stated that the ratio of the time during which a film molecule is bound to the molecules of the subphase to the time during which it is unbound is of the order exp (vw/kT) where w is the bond energy between a subphase molecule and a functional group in the film, and v is the number of subphase molecules associated with a single molecule of the film. This ratio is generally greater than or equal to 10^6. It is this fact that explains why, practically speaking, the monomolecular film is rigidly bound to its liquid substrate.

2. Mechanical Consequences of the Nature of Surface Phases

The fundamental component of an interfacial phase is evidently the monomolecular layer of oriented, amphiphilic molecules at the interface. It follows that the characteristic parameter describing the state of an interfacial phase is the molecular area A, that is, the area of surface occupied by a molecule of the amphiphilic substance. The presence of the amphiphilic film lowers the interfacial tension, which assumes the value γ_A instead of the value γ in the absence of the interfacial phase. By definition, the difference $\pi = \gamma - \gamma_A$ is the surface pressure of the interfacial film.

Systematic study of compression isotherms $\pi = f(A)$ of insoluble monomolecular films has revealed that they can exist in a series of physical states entirely analogous to those defined for bulk phases. Between them are observed the same types of phase equilibria and first- and second-order phase changes as for three-dimensional systems (95, 110–112). Although authors disagree about a unified system of nomenclature, there is no doubt about the characterization of the various states of films (2) or about the sequence of the transitions that occur when molecular area or temperature varies (29, 113).

The mechanical properties of three-dimensional systems depend upon their physical state. According to whether we examine a gas, a liquid, a liquid crystal, or a solid, not only is the rheological behavior different, but often under ordinary experimental conditions the significant observables are also different. It is for this reason that in general for a gas we study only its compressibility and its viscosity, whereas for solids we often ignore the compressibility and concentrate largely on the elasticity and plasticity. In fact, solid and liquid three-dimensional systems under ordinary experimental conditions can without important error be treated as incompressible. Matters are quite different for two-dimensional systems. We see in Part II of this monograph that surface and interfacial films are practically without exception very compressible. For example, in the liquid state the compressibility $K = -(1/A)/(\partial A/\partial \pi)$ of films at the air/water interface is almost always greater than 0.01 cm/dyne. Even when they are in the solid state, the compressibility of films is in general greater than 0.001 cm/dyne (70).

Despite this fact, we shall shortly observe numerous parallels between the mechanical properties of surface and bulk phases. The impossibility, however, of isolating an interfacial phase from its substrate has a profound influence on its mechanical behavior. This results from the fact pointed out in Section II.B that the deformations of a surface phase are strongly coupled to those of the substrate. In all experiments there will consequently be interference between the rheological properties of the film and those of its substrate. Of course, as is shown in Section III, we may measure rheological magnitudes which are purely those of the surface phase, either by appropriate differencing or by calculation. But this will always be by more or less indirect means and often at the price of simplifying hypotheses whose validity in different cases may be questionable. For the most part, the very existence of a bulk liquid substrate limits the choice of shear strains to which the film may be subjected.

Another important limitation arises from the fact that it is possible to study the mechanical properties of surface phases only upon isolated portions of them enclosed by surface frameworks. Even in the case of solid films, it has not been possible up to the present time to construct the equivalent of the test specimens commonly used in the rheological study of bulk solids. Under ordinary experimental conditions these latter sublime so weakly that their mass can be considered invariant however long the duration of the tests. Matters are quite otherwise in the case of solid monomolecular films. We can speculate about the study of the rheological properties of a sample of solid film not directly bounded by a surface frame by placing it under conditions represented by a plateau point of the $\pi = f(A)$ isotherm for the equilibrium between a solid/liquid or a solid/gas. But the execution of experiments involving the deformation of solid portions of monolayer under such conditions seems to be prohibitively difficult. In Section II.C.3 we note the consequences of this limitation for the definition of the equivalents of the three-dimensional Young's modulus and Poisson's ratio. With this limitation, it would appear that experiments of the flexion–torsion type are hardly realizable under valid experimental conditions.

Another difficulty arises from the fact that in numerous cases the result of an interfacial deformation is an exchange of matter between the surface and bulk phases. Soluble adsorption films, for example, are of this type. For such films an equilibrium is established between the molecules in the film and those dissolved in the substrate. From this it follows that should A or π undergo local variation in the course of a mechanical deformation, a flux of matter can be established between the surface and bulk phases. The measured rheological parameters cannot then be referred to a defined system of constant mass, and their interpretation becomes obscure. Indeed, they retain rheological significance only if the deformation and the measurements are performed in a time sufficiently small so that matter exchange has had insufficient time to occur.

A rigorous insolubility is never achieved. Nevertheless, for the so-called insoluble films, their solubility is small enough that they may be considered as perfectly stable during the course of the measurements. At the same time, at high surface pressures the solubility of "insoluble" films can no longer be neglected, and their rheological properties become difficult to determine with precision. Furthermore, in the neighborhood of the saturation or collapse point of films, another source of error beyond that of dissolution may appear. This lies in the fact that with mechanical working a portion of the film can be converted more or less irreversibly into a three-dimensional form, either as small droplets or as tiny crystals. This type of instability can have a marked influence on rheological behavior and destroys any precise interpretation of the measurements.

Despite all these restrictions, it has been possible to develop surface rheology in a reasonably satisfactory manner. In Sections II.C.3 and II.C.4 we define its principal variables. Before doing this, however, it is important to understand the following facts. For the definition of these variables we assume in general that the radii of curvature of interfaces are sufficiently large with respect to the thickness of interfacial films so that deformed surface phases may in first approximation be treated as everywhere planar. We shall furthermore most frequently consider only deformations within this plane. In this sense we may with justification speak of two-dimensional rheology. This, as we establish in Section II.D and in Part II, Section III, does not necessarily exclude stresses which may be applied and strains which may be generated in directions that lie outside of the plane of the film. At the present time, however, it does not appear that sufficiently refined experimental measurements have been made except in the simple case for which the stresses and strains are localized within the plane of the film.

3. Compressional, Dilational, and Extensive Strains

Let us initially consider those rheological properties that are exhibited in the absence of all shear strains, when there is a simple compression or extension of the surface phase brought about by externally applied stresses. This type of deformation is observed, for example, when there is either a growth or diminution of the area occupied by a monomolecular film containing a fixed number of molecules. We have seen in Section II.C.2 that interfacial films can be manipulated only when enclosed by a frame. By varying the area enclosed by the frame, we may conveniently study the compression or expansion of monomolecular films, and in particular construct the isotherms $\pi = f(A)$. In this type of experiment, shear strains are in general negligible with respect to dilational-extensive strains. It will be important in what follows to distinguish between the case of the insoluble and that of the soluble film. For insoluble films, it is easy to define a compression modulus $\varkappa$ (surface compressional or area modulus) as the reciprocal of the compressibility:

$$\varkappa = -A \left(\frac{\partial \pi}{\partial A} \right)_T$$

The dimensions of $\varkappa$ are those of surface pressure MT^{-2} (g/sec² in cgs units). This modulus without further refinement is sometimes called surface elasticity (114). Its definition makes no assumption concerning the physical state of the film and is as valid for a liquid film as for a solid one. Let us recall that in rheology a solid is a body whose deformation remains finite so long as the applied stresses are within the elastic limit (see Section II.D.1). A liquid, on the other hand, will deform indefinitely however small the applied stress.

For solid films, we can imagine an experiment analogous to the extension of a three-dimensional rod. By subjecting a rectangular sample of solid film to a tension ΔF directed along the longer edge, and writing $\Delta L/L$ for the corresponding relative extension, we may define an elasticity coefficient or surface Young's modulus E by setting

$$\Delta F = E \frac{\Delta L}{L}$$

The dimensions of E are those of surface tension MT^{-2} (g/sec² in cgs units), whereas those of a bulk Young's modulus are $ML^{-1}T^{-2}$ identical with pressure. If we pursue the analogy with the three-dimensional model, we should expect that the extension of the film will be accompanied by a lateral contraction $\Delta l/l$ related to the extension by Poisson's ratio (115). The magnitude of the surface Poisson's ratio is

$$\sigma = -\frac{\Delta l}{l} \frac{L}{\Delta L}$$

It is dimensionless. In Section II.C.2 we remarked that it is in general impossible to manipulate a film without enclosing it within a framework. In Section III.A we note the resulting apparent impossibility of direct, precise experimental measurement of E and σ. It is nevertheless true that these parameters play an important role in the description of the general rheological behavior of an arbitrary interfacial phase (see Section II.D.2).

In 1878 in his study of the stability of liquid films such as those of foam (liquid lamellae partitioned from the air on each face by a surface phase), Gibbs pointed out that in order to support its own weight a film must exhibit small differences in surface tension between points at different elevations (116). This difference is a function of the vertical distance h between the two points and the thickness d of the film,

$$\Delta\gamma = f(h, d)$$

The surface tension gradient balances the weight of the film and the viscous traction which results from the drainage of liquid from the center of the film (117). $\Delta\gamma$ decreases very rapidly with h and d. Thus for $h = 50$ cm and $d = 10^{-3}$ cm, $\Delta\gamma = 25$ dyne/cm, while for $h = 1$ cm and $d = 10^{-6}$ cm, $\Delta\gamma = 5 \times 10^{-4}$ dyne/cm. Gibbs defined a film elasticity by the formula

$$E_G = 2S \frac{\partial\gamma}{\partial S}$$

in which S is the surface area of a single face of the film. The dimensions of E_G are those of surface tension MT^{-2} (g/sec^2 in cgs units). The factor 2 arises from the fact that the films have two faces. It is to be remarked that if the surface phase of the film is a solid, insoluble monolayer whose Poisson's ratio is zero, E_G is equal to twice the Young's modulus of the monolayer. We should have $\Delta L/L = \Delta S/S$ because l remains effectively constant throughout the extension.

The necessity of introducing the idea of surface viscosity in order to account for the properties of liquid interfaces was demonstrated by Boussinesq (16). His basic idea was that at equilibrium and in the absence of all external stresses, thermal agitation equalizes the mean molecular distances in all directions within the plane of the liquid surface phase, also establishing a static isotropy about every normal to this plane. Under the influence of mechanical stress, this isotropy is perturbed. It is reestablished by thermal agitation, but the relaxation always requires a certain amount of time. As a result, the molecular configuration in the fluid liquid film differs in the dynamic state from that under static conditions. The resulting forces give rise to a variation in the interfacial tension.

For deformation without shear, a coefficient of surface dilational viscosity (the area viscosity) may be defined, analogous to the volume viscosity of three-dimensional systems (118),

$$\Delta\gamma = \zeta \frac{1}{S} \frac{\partial S}{\partial t}$$

or, because the film is presumed insoluble,

$$\Delta\gamma = \zeta \frac{1}{A} \frac{\partial A}{\partial t}$$

The dimensions of ζ are MT^{-1} (g/sec in cgs units). As we see in Section I of Part II, this viscosity is exhibited principally by changes in the shape of isotherms $\pi = f(A)$ as a function of the speed of compression of a film.

For films of high polymers, some authors have introduced the idea of surface flexibility by adapting to surface phases the theory of linear, high-polymer solutions. Application of the Flory-Huggins theory to mono-molecular films has led to an expression for the force–area isotherm (119)

$$\pi = \frac{kT}{A}\left[\frac{Z-1}{Z}\frac{f}{2}\ln\left(1 - \frac{2A_0}{A}\right) - \ln\left(1 - \frac{A_0}{A}\right)\right]$$

in which π is the surface pressure, A the average area per monomer residue, A_0 the limiting molecular area of a repeating unit, Z the number of residues per polymer chain, and f the coordination number of a surface site, which is to say that f is the number of monomer units of a given polymer molecule located in the film in the immediate neighborhood of a given residue. For a rigid molecule, $f = 2$. The surface flexibility ξ has been defined (120–122) by the formula $\xi = f - 2$.

It is evident that all the preceding definitions remain valid for adsorbed films and partially soluble films. If we take account, however, of the reservations of Section II.C.2, it is well to remark that because of the flux of matter into or out of the interface, the meaning of the rheological coefficients can be considerably modified.

For Gibbs elasticity the derivative $\partial\gamma/\partial S$ is taken under the assumption of constant total mass of each constituent per square centimeter of the combined system bulk fluid plus surface films, the distribution of the constituents between surface and bulk varying during the course of the extension. E_G is a measure of the increase of surface tension resulting from an increase in area and depends upon the equilibrium surface tension. As a result of the film extension, the concentration of the amphiphilic constituent in the surface phases decreases; it is replaced by transport into the surface from the substrate; and the surface tension tends to return to its equilibrium value. Because of the flux of matter from bulk to surface, it follows that $\Delta S/S \neq \Delta A/A$, for the number of surface layer molecules has changed during the course of the extension. The reestablishment of the equilibrium surface concentration is dependent, furthermore, upon the presence of a sufficient volume of liquid substrate. In contrast to the situation for an insoluble film, E_G for an adsorbed film is not an intrinsic rheological property of the surface phase. This is to say that E_G does not depend uniquely upon the structure of the surface film. For the simple case of a solution of a single surface-active material (11, 12, 116), E_G takes the form

$$E_G = 4\Gamma^2 \frac{\partial \mu}{\partial C}$$

where Γ, μ, and C are respectively the surface density of the solute, its chemical potential, and its total amount present per unit area of film (123). Note that in this equation E_G does not depend upon any mechanical variable, so that the interpretation of E_G as a rheological coefficient is debatable. This follows presumably from the fact that Gibbs elasticity is a function only of an equilibrium state.

In actuality, during the rapid expansion or contraction of the surface of a surfactant solution, the surface tension departs from its static value and always in such a direction as to call into play restoring forces which tend to cancel the perturbation. This is the Marangoni effect, which can be explained as a consequence of the time necessary for the reestablishment of adsorption equilibrium by diffusion between the surface and substrate phases (8, 9, 124). We could probably define a Marangoni viscosity ζ_M by a relationship of the type

$$\Delta \gamma = \zeta_M \frac{1}{S} \frac{\partial S}{\partial t}$$

which is analogous to the dilational viscosity ζ of insoluble films. The dimensions of ζ_M are also MT^{-1}. But while ζ depends only on the surface phase, ζ_M depends simultaneously upon the properties of this phase and upon the rate of attainment of equilibrium between the substrate and the adsorbed film.

A precise expression for the dilational viscosity, as defined above, cannot be of the form

$$\Delta \gamma = \zeta \frac{1}{A} \frac{\partial A}{\partial t}$$

because in addition to the reestablishment of uniform molecular concentration in the film, there is exchange of matter between film and substrate. A rigorous description of the dilational viscosity of soluble films would require the replacement of ζ by a pair of parameters ζ_1 and ζ_2 corresponding to each of these mechanisms. The experimental separation of these two parameters, however, does not appear to be possible, nor perhaps does the derivation of analytical relations between them.

This is the reason why without exception the study of true dilational viscosity is limited to insoluble films. In the majority of cases this viscosity appears in association with other rheological parameters in the description of the general mechanical behavior of surface phases. The only relatively simple case in which it appears is in that of the hysteresis of force–area isotherms, during the measurement of which shear strains can be neglected.

4. Shear Strains

We shall now take up deformations that occur without appreciable change in the area occupied by the stressed film. Consider the case of simple shear in the plane of a film presumed insoluble.

For a solid film subjected in the xy plane to a laminar shear strain parallel to the x axis and generated by a force F, we may define an elastic modulus or shear modulus, sometimes called a slip or Coulomb modulus. It is the ratio between the increment of stress

$$\frac{\partial F_x}{\partial y} dy$$

and the increment of strain

$$\frac{\partial u_x}{\partial y} dy$$

between two parallel rows of kinetic units oriented along the direction of slip and separated by a distance dy. By definition we have therefore

$$G = \frac{\partial F_x}{\partial y}\left(\frac{\partial u_x}{\partial y}\right)^{-1}$$

G has the dimensions of surface tension MT^{-2} (g/sec² in cgs). For bulk solids it is known that there exist simple relations between the moduli of compression, of shear, and of Young, and Poisson's ratio (115). Similar but different relations exist for two-dimensional systems (125).

For films we have

$$\varkappa = \frac{E}{2(1-\sigma)}, \quad G = \frac{E}{2(1+\sigma)}, \quad E = \frac{4\varkappa G}{\varkappa + G}, \quad \sigma = \frac{\varkappa - G}{\varkappa + G}$$

Furthermore the maximum possible value of Poisson's ratio is $\sigma_{\max} = 1$. For a solid, incompressible film we would have $E = 4G$. The reader should not forget, however, that these relations cannot be precisely verified experimentally for reasons discussed in Sections II.C.2 and II.C.3.

For fluid films, the necessity of two and only two viscosity coefficients was confirmed by Boussinesq (16) from his demonstration that the only rates of strain which could appear in a surface element are the rates of dilation and of shear.

For bulk liquid undergoing laminar, plane shear, the viscosity is defined by the force exerted along a unit test surface within the liquid due to the relative motion of a parallel, neighboring surface. The coefficient of viscosity is the proportionality factor relating shear force to rate of shear. We generalize this definition to the case of a fluid surface phase flowing in its own plane in the x direction with a uniform velocity $v_x(y)$ driven by a pressure head F dyne/cm. Then the coefficient of surface shear viscosity η is defined by

$$\frac{\partial F}{\partial y} = \eta \frac{\partial v_x}{\partial y}$$

Note that the dimensions of η are MT^{-1} (g/sec in cgs), while those of bulk viscosity are $ML^{-1}T^{-1}$ (g/cm-sec).

In Section III.B we see that certain methods of measurement of surface viscosity lead to the determination of a value η_0 of η in the absence of a film. The quantity η_0 is the surface viscosity of the pure substrate. By analogy with bulk solutions, the definition of a relative surface viscosity

$$\eta_{\text{rel}} = \frac{\eta}{\eta_0}$$

has been proposed (51). The definition has no meaning except for extremely dilute monomolecular films (see Part II, Section II), for which it is also possible to define a specific surface viscosity

$$\eta_{\text{op}} = \frac{\eta - \eta_0}{\eta_0}$$

a reduced surface viscosity

$$\eta_{\text{red}} = \frac{\eta - \eta_0}{c\eta_0}$$

in which c is the surface concentration of the monomolecular film, and an intrinsic viscosity

$$[\eta] = \lim_{c \to 0} \eta_{\text{red}}$$

We see in Section II.D that surface phases frequently display a viscoelastic behavior. For this reason it is sometimes useful to introduce a complex surface modulus (126). So far as the film may be considered as a Maxwell body, this modulus is defined by

$$G^* = G + j\omega\eta$$

where ω is the frequency of periodic or oscillatory straining of a film and $j = \sqrt{-1}$. Its norm is the absolute surface modulus $\bar{G}$ and its phase is the loss angle or surface dissipation factor Φ. Formally,

$$\bar{G} = \frac{G}{\cos \Phi} = \frac{2\pi\eta}{T \sin \Phi} \quad \text{and} \quad \Phi = \tan^{-1}\frac{2\pi\eta}{TG}$$

in which T is the period of the oscillations in the presence of a film, $\bar{G}$ is a measure of the ratio of maximum stress to maximum strain, and Φ is the phase angle between stress and strain. It is only necessary to recall that for purely viscous systems $\Phi = \pi/2$ and that for purely elastic $\Phi = 0$.

As has been established in Section II.C.1, each kinetic unit of a surface phase is composed of an amphiphilic molecule firmly bound to a certain number of substrate molecules. It follows that all the coefficients defined above are properties of ensembles of these kinetic units. If we study small strains in rigid systems, it is evident that the experimental values of $\varkappa$, E, or G are almost uniquely the properties of the solid monomolecular film, the contribution from the substrate molecules being in first approximation negligible. For fluid films, however, and for strains which are large compared with molecular dimensions, the substrate molecules bound to the kinetic units can make the dominant contribution to ζ or η. This is particularly true for surface shear viscosity, for which the contribution of the substrate molecules can be calculated, at least for the air/water interface (see Part II, Section II). The viscosity contribution due exclusively to the amphiphilic molecules is considerably smaller than the experimental surface viscosity. We shall present examples of this in Part II, Section I. It is for this reason that when surface viscosities are rendered three dimensional by taking account of the thickness of the monomolecular film, their measured values lead to bulk viscosities far greater than the bulk viscosities actually measured for the same substances for the same value of molecular volume. If we are careful, however, to convert to three-dimensional form only that part of the surface viscosity due exclusively to the monolayer, we find bulk viscosities which are generally smaller than the measured bulk viscosities of the pure surface-active substance. This arises from the fact that the film molecules are statistically oriented with respect to the direction of flow.

For soluble films, we do not run into the same difficulties in shear deformations as are involved in dilational strains, so long as we select experimental methods which do not entail a variation in surface pressure and study only films in thermodynamic equilibrium with their substrates.

D. The Principal Types of Rheological Behavior in Surface Films

1. The General Problem of Surface Rheology

It is possible to examine two types of deformation of surface material. The first is an "external" deformation characterized by a change in the geometric form of the surface. Examples are the perturbation of an interface by vibrations normal to the surface, or the distortion or breakup of emulsion droplets in a blender. A second type of deformation, which we may describe as "internal," takes place when the kinetic units of the interfacial phase undergo relative displacements with respect to each other without modification of the global geometry of the interface. Examples are the shear or dilational deformations of a monomolecular layer within its own plane or the flowing walls of a bubble in the absence of shape or volume changes. We are almost exclusively concerned with "internal" deformations in that we limit ourselves for the most part to planar interfaces. This specialization we shall refer to as "planar" rheology.

In Section II.C we limited ourselves to systems displaying purely elementary behavior, either exclusively elastic or exclusively viscous, subjected to simple strains, either strictly dilational or strictly shear. It is obvious that such conditions are rather unusual. We must now take up more general conditions, despite the fact that most experiments are carried out in such a way as to simplify the external constraints as much as possible.

Oldroyd (63) has demonstrated the necessity of the simultaneous introduction of four rheological parameters in addition to the surface pressure in order to describe completely the rheological properties of interfacial phases. The required mathematical expressions demand the use of tensor notation (127, 128), the essential features of which will briefly be summarized.

A square matrix is a table of numbers called the components of the matrix, having the same number of rows as of columns. If we denote by a_{rs} the component located at the intersection of the rth row and the sth column, the matrix is said to be symmetric if $a_{ij} = a_{ji}$.

A matrix has a tensorial character, or is simply a tensor, if upon a coordinate transformation from one set of Cartesian axes to another the components transform according to the rule

$$a'_{kl} = \sum_{ij} \nu_{ik} \nu_{jl} a_{ij}$$

in which

$$\nu_{pq} = \cos(0x_p, 0'x'_q)$$

The a_{ij} are the Cartesian components of the tensor. In three-dimensional space, the characteristic conic surfaces associated with a tensor are those satisfying

$$\sum_{ij} a_{ij} x_i x_j = \pm 1$$

The directions of the principal axes of the conic surface lie along the characteristic vectors of the tensor.   By taking these axes as the axes of a system of
rectangular coordinates, the tensor assumes a diagonal form:

$$\begin{Vmatrix} a_1 & 0 & 0 \\ 0 & a_2 & 0 \\ 0 & 0 & a_3 \end{Vmatrix}$$

and a_1, a_2, a_3 are the principal or characteristic values of the tensor.   A
tensor is said to be isotropic or spherical if these three principal values are
equal.   From a tensor A of principal values a_1, a_2, a_3, a new tensor B said
to be the deviator of A is constructed by subtracting from A an isotropic
tensor of three equal principal values $(a_1 + a_2 + a_3)/3$.   The sum of the
three principal values b_1, b_2, b_3 of B is zero.   The quantity

$$\sqrt{b_1{}^2 + b_2{}^2 + b_3{}^2}$$

is called the norm of the deviator of A.   Quite generally, an arbitrary tensor
can be decomposed into an isotropic tensor and a deviator.   If a tensor is
symmetric, so also is its deviator, and it possesses the same principal axes.

    Classical three-dimensional rheology is commonly centered around the
strain tensor $\mathscr{S}$ and the stress tensor $\mathscr{T}$.

    With reference to a coordinate system x_1, x_2, x_3, we consider an arbitrary
deformable body and we write u_α ($\alpha = 1, 2, 3$) for the components of a vector
$\mathbf{u}$ representing the displacement of a kinetic unit P_1 whose original coordinate
location was at x_α.   The strain in the body is measured by the variation in
the vector $\mathbf{u}$ when the point of observation is shifted from P_1 to a neighboring
kinetic unit P_2 whose original position was at $x_\alpha + dx_\alpha$.   As a result of the
strain, the line segment $P_1 P_2$ whose vector components were dx_α has become
the line segment $P_1' P_2'$ with components $dx_\alpha + du_\alpha$.   It follows that one line
segment is transformed into the other by a translation dx_α followed by an
additional transformation

$$du_\alpha = \frac{\partial u_\alpha}{\partial x_1} dx_1 + \frac{\partial u_\alpha}{\partial x_2} dx_2 + \frac{\partial u_\alpha}{\partial x_3} dx_3$$

This latter expression can be decomposed into a rotation

$$\frac{1}{2}\left(\frac{\partial u_i}{\partial x_j} - \frac{\partial u_j}{\partial x_i}\right) \qquad (i = 1, 2, 3; j = 1, 2, 3)$$

plus a deformation which can be represented by a symmetric tensor called
the strain tensor, the components of which are

$$\varepsilon_{ij} = \frac{1}{2}\left(\frac{\partial u_i}{\partial x_j} + \frac{\partial u_j}{\partial x_i}\right)$$

For a surface film in the xy plane, the strain tensor reduces to

$$\mathscr{S} = \left\| \begin{array}{cc} \dfrac{\partial u_x}{\partial x} & \dfrac{1}{2}\left(\dfrac{\partial u_x}{\partial y} + \dfrac{\partial u_y}{\partial x}\right) \\ \dfrac{1}{2}\left(\dfrac{\partial u_x}{\partial y} + \dfrac{\partial u_y}{\partial x}\right) & \dfrac{\partial u_y}{\partial y} \end{array} \right\|$$

If instead of the vector displacement of a kinetic unit we examine its velocity vector **v** with components

$$v_\alpha = \frac{\partial x_\alpha}{\partial t}$$

considerations analogous to the preceding ones demand the introduction of a rate of strain tensor, the components of which are

$$\varepsilon'_{ij} = \frac{1}{2}\left(\frac{\partial v_i}{\partial x_j} + \frac{\partial v_j}{\partial x_i}\right)$$

The differential of the displacement vector in the time dt is $\mathbf{v}/dt$, and we have

$$d\varepsilon_{ij} = \varepsilon'_{ij}\, dt$$

For a plane film the rate of strain tensor is

$$\mathscr{S}' = \left\| \begin{array}{cc} \dfrac{\partial v_x}{\partial x} & \dfrac{1}{2}\left(\dfrac{\partial v_x}{\partial y} + \dfrac{\partial v_y}{\partial x}\right) \\ \dfrac{1}{2}\left(\dfrac{\partial v_x}{\partial y} + \dfrac{\partial v_y}{\partial x}\right) & \dfrac{\partial v_y}{\partial y} \end{array} \right\|$$

For bulk systems an element (or surface element) is defined to be an infinitesimal region of bounding surface enclosing a portion of matter. For surface systems we shall use "element" to mean a segment of monomolecular thickness and infinitesimal length of a boundary curve which encloses a portion of monolayer. The stress is the total force exerted on an element divided by the area (in the three-dimensional case) or by the length (in the two-dimensional case) of the element. Write p_{ij} for x_i component of the stress exerted at the point 0 upon an element normal to $0x_j$. The stress components acting on an element whose normal has direction cosines v_j are

$$p_i = \sum_j p_{ij} v_j$$

The whole stress acting in the neighborhood of a point may be represented by a tensor called the stress tensor; whole components are p_{ij}. The stress tensor is symmetric and for planar rheology reduces to

$$\mathcal{T} = \left\| \begin{array}{cc} p_{xx} & p_{xy} \\ p_{xy} & p_{yy} \end{array} \right\|$$

When the coordinate axes are those of the characteristic conic surface, $\mathcal{T}$ assumes a diagonal form, from which we conclude that the general bulk system exhibits no shear along planes normal to the principal axes. For the planar, two-dimensional case, there is no shear normal to the principal axes. The state of uniaxial stress, for example, a simple tension or compression, possesses only a single non-null principal stress component. In simple shear, there are two non-null principal stress components which are opposite in sign.

The rheological behavior of a body does not in general depend exclusively upon stress and strain. It depends also upon the rate of strain and upon the rate at which the stress develops. It follows that general rheological equations are of the form

$$\mathcal{R}(\mathcal{S}, \mathcal{S}', \mathcal{T}, \mathcal{T}') = 0$$

where $\mathcal{S}'$ and $\mathcal{T}'$ are the time derivatives of the tensors $\mathcal{S}$ and $\mathcal{T}$. When the differentiated tensors do not appear in this expression and the rheological equation reduces to

$$\mathcal{R}(\mathcal{S}, \mathcal{T}) = 0$$

the mechanical state of the system is independent of time. In this case we say that there exists a rheological equation of state. The two ideal, purely fictitious cases of greatest simplicity are either $\mathcal{S} = 0$ or $\mathcal{T} = 0$. The first describes a body incapable of deformation whatever the stress: such a body is called a Euclidean solid. The second describes a fluid whose kinetic units are without any force of interaction opposing deformation: such a fluid is called a Pascal liquid. It is obvious that neither of these two cases exists in Nature.

2. The Various Bodies and Models of Surface Rheology

In rheology it is customary to classify real bodies according to their rheological behavior. In Section II.C in the course of defining the principal rheological parameters, we were led to consider a certain number of elementary types of behavior. Specifically we investigated the case of a solid, purely elastic film (Hookean solid) and that of a liquid, purely viscous film (Newtonian liquid).

Films as simple as these are very rare, and even when they occur, the rheological equations do not always take a simple form. In general the equations of rheology are rarely simple. Thus even a law as simple as

$\mathscr{S} = k\mathscr{T}$, which states that strain is proportional to stress, is practically never verified in so general a form. For example, if a solid, rectangular film of length L in the x direction and width l in the y direction is subjected to a traction F_x along the x axis. $\mathscr{T}$ reduces to

$$\mathscr{T} = \left\| \begin{matrix} p_{xx} & 0 \\ 0 & 0 \end{matrix} \right\| = p_{xx} = \frac{F_x}{l}$$

We have seen in Section II.C.3 that the strip will lengthen in the x direction by

$$\varepsilon_{xx} = \frac{\Delta L}{L} = \frac{F_x}{lE}$$

where E is Young's modulus. But we know, as is the case for bulk solids, that there is a concomitant contraction along the y axis given by

$$\varepsilon_{yy} = -\sigma\varepsilon_{xx}$$

in which σ is Poisson's ratio. It follows that

$$\mathscr{S} = \left\| \begin{matrix} \varepsilon_{xx} & 0 \\ 0 & \varepsilon_{yy} \end{matrix} \right\| = \left\| \begin{matrix} \varepsilon_{xx} & 0 \\ 0 & -\sigma\varepsilon_{xx} \end{matrix} \right\| = \frac{p_{xx}}{E} \left\| \begin{matrix} 1 & 0 \\ 0 & -\sigma \end{matrix} \right\|$$

Hence $\mathscr{T}$ and $\mathscr{S}$ are not proportional because Poisson's ratio does not in general vanish.

To recover Hooke's law, which predicts a proportionality between stress and strain, we must suppose in the decomposition of $\mathscr{S}$ and $\mathscr{T}$ into an isotropic tensor plus a deviator that these parts are separately and respectively proportional. That is to say,

$$\mathscr{T} = \mathscr{T}_s + \mathscr{T}_0, \quad \mathscr{S} = \mathscr{S}_s + \mathscr{S}_0, \quad \mathscr{T}_s = k_s\mathscr{S}_s, \quad \text{and} \quad \mathscr{T}_0 = k_0\mathscr{S}_0$$

If in the course of the deformation of a square portion of film of side L and area S the surface pressure changes by $\Delta\pi$, the isotropic portion of the stress tensor is

$$\mathscr{T}_s = \left\| \begin{matrix} -\Delta\pi & 0 \\ 0 & -\Delta\pi \end{matrix} \right\|$$

The isotropic portion of the strain tensor is

$$\mathscr{S}_s = \left\| \begin{matrix} \dfrac{\Delta L}{L} & 0 \\ 0 & \dfrac{\Delta L}{L} \end{matrix} \right\| = \left\| \begin{matrix} \dfrac{\Delta S}{2S} & 0 \\ 0 & \dfrac{\Delta S}{2S} \end{matrix} \right\|$$

We redefine the compression modulus (Section II.C.3) by making $\mathscr{T}_s$ and $\mathscr{S}_s$ proportional to one another, which is to say

$$\Delta\pi = -K_0 \frac{\Delta S}{2S} \qquad \text{whence} \qquad \varkappa = -S \frac{\Delta\pi}{\Delta S}$$

For the deviators

$$\mathscr{S}_0 = \left\| \begin{matrix} 0 & \varepsilon_{xy} \\ \varepsilon_{yx} & 0 \end{matrix} \right\| = \left\| \begin{matrix} 0 & \dfrac{1}{2}\dfrac{\partial u_x}{\partial y} \\ \dfrac{1}{2}\dfrac{\partial u_x}{\partial y} & 0 \end{matrix} \right\|$$

and

$$\mathscr{T}_0 = \left\| \begin{matrix} 0 & p_{xy} \\ p_{xy} & 0 \end{matrix} \right\| = \left\| \begin{matrix} 0 & \dfrac{\partial F_x}{\partial y} \\ \dfrac{\partial F_x}{\partial y} & 0 \end{matrix} \right\|$$

the proportionality leads to

$$\frac{\partial F_x}{\partial y} = \frac{K_0}{2}\frac{\partial u_x}{\partial y}$$

This is equivalent to the definition of the shear modulus given in Section II.C.4

$$G = \frac{\partial F_x}{\partial y}\left(\frac{\partial u_x}{\partial y}\right)^{-1}$$

The rheology of the two-dimensional Hookean solid is therefore described by the two equations

$$\mathscr{T}_s = \varkappa\mathscr{S}_s \qquad \text{and} \qquad \mathscr{T}_0 = 2G\mathscr{S}_0$$

Such a body is rheologically defined by the two parameters $\varkappa$ and G.

Decomposing these tensors in the same way as for the traction case above, we obtain

$$\mathscr{T}_s = \left\| \begin{matrix} \dfrac{p_{xx}}{2} & 0 \\ 0 & \dfrac{p_{xx}}{2} \end{matrix} \right\| , \qquad \mathscr{T}_0 = \left\| \begin{matrix} \dfrac{p_{xx}}{2} & 0 \\ 0 & -\dfrac{p_{xx}}{2} \end{matrix} \right\|$$

and

$$\mathscr{S}_s = \left\| \begin{matrix} \dfrac{p_{xx}(1-\sigma)}{2E} & 0 \\ 0 & \dfrac{p_{xx}(1-\sigma)}{2E} \end{matrix} \right\| , \qquad \mathscr{S}_0 = \left\| \begin{matrix} \dfrac{p_{xx}(1+\sigma)}{2E} & 0 \\ 0 & -\dfrac{p_{xx}(1+\sigma)}{2E} \end{matrix} \right\|$$

Introducing these tensors into the rheological equation of state for a Hookean solid, we derive the relations

$$\varkappa = \frac{E}{2(1 - \sigma)} \quad \text{and} \quad G = \frac{E}{2(1 + \sigma)}$$

first exhibited in Section II.C.4. For a solid, incompressible film, we would have $\sigma = 1$ and $E = 4G$.

Carrying out an analogous program for the tensor $\mathscr{S}'$ there results

$$\mathscr{S}'_s = \left\| \begin{matrix} \dfrac{1}{L}\dfrac{\partial L}{\partial t} & 0 \\ 0 & \dfrac{1}{L}\dfrac{\partial L}{\partial t} \end{matrix} \right\| = \left\| \begin{matrix} \dfrac{1}{2S}\dfrac{\partial S}{\partial t} & 0 \\ 0 & \dfrac{1}{2S}\dfrac{\partial S}{\partial t} \end{matrix} \right\| , \quad \mathscr{S}'_0 = \left\| \begin{matrix} 0 & \dfrac{1}{2}\dfrac{\partial v_x}{\partial y} \\ \dfrac{1}{2}\dfrac{\partial v_x}{\partial y} & 0 \end{matrix} \right\|$$

When $\mathscr{T}_s$ and $\mathscr{S}'_s$ together with $\mathscr{T}_0$ and $\mathscr{S}'_0$ are made proportional to one another, the definitions of Sections II.C.3 and II.C.4 for the viscosity coefficients ζ and η are recovered:

$$\zeta = S\Delta F \left(\frac{\partial S}{\partial t}\right)^{-1} \quad \text{and} \quad \eta = \frac{\partial F}{\partial y}\left(\frac{\partial v}{\partial y}\right)^{-1}$$

In addition to

$$\mathscr{T}_s = \varkappa \mathscr{S}_s$$

the rheological equations of a two-dimensional Maxwell liquid therefore also require

$$\mathscr{T}_s = \zeta \mathscr{S}'_s \quad \text{and} \quad \mathscr{T}_0 = 2\eta \mathscr{S}'_0$$

It is convenient to construct simple mechanical models whose theoretical behavior is that of a rheological body of ideal behavior (127). A Hookean solid may thus be represented by a spring and a Newtonian liquid by a dashpot. For more complicated rheological bodies, it is customary to attempt their representation by a superposition of ideal elements. Such representation is a special case of Boltzmann's superposition principle and is valid so long as there exists a proportionality between cause and effect, which is to say as long as the rheological body under study can be considered as "linear." We present here several examples which occur reasonably frequently in surface rheology.

A simple case is Kelvin's or Voigt's solid in which the stress is the sum of a term proportional to the strain and another proportional to the rate of strain. It is easily pictured by the parallel coupling of a spring and a dashpot with phenomenological constants $\varkappa$, G and ζ_s, η_s. The Voigt's body is elastic, but it differs from a Hookean solid by the lack of proportionality of stress and strain and by the fact that a strain does not instantly disappear upon removal of the stress (Figure 4).   The rheological equations of the Voigt's body are

$$\mathscr{T}_s = \varkappa \mathscr{S}_s + \mathscr{T}_s \mathscr{S}'_s \quad \text{and} \quad \mathscr{S}_0 = 2G\mathscr{S}_0 + 2\eta_s\mathscr{S}'_0$$

Under a constant shear stress $[\mathscr{T}_0]$, the corresponding strain $[\mathscr{S}_0]$ is not immediately achieved.   The response is instead

$$\mathscr{S}_0(t) = [\mathscr{T}_0]G^{-1}\left[1 - \exp\left(-\frac{Gt}{\eta_s}\right)\right]$$

Upon removal of the stress, the relaxation follows the law

$$G\mathscr{S}_0 + \eta_s\mathscr{S}'_0 = 0$$

whence

$$\mathscr{S}_0 = [\mathscr{S}_0]_0 \exp\left(-\frac{Gt}{\eta_s}\right)$$

which is to say that the elastic recovery is retarded by the viscous damping. The ratio $\eta_s/G = \tau$ has the dimensions of time and is called the retardation time.

Another simple case is that of the Maxwell liquid.   This viscoelastic body can be pictured as a coupling in series of a spring of moduli $\varkappa_l$ and G_l with a dashpot of moduli ζ and η.   The strain is made up of a purely elastic and a purely viscous part.   The rheological equations of a Maxwell body are

$$\mathscr{S}'_s = \frac{\mathscr{T}'_s}{\varkappa_l} + \frac{\mathscr{T}_s}{\zeta} \quad \text{and} \quad \mathscr{S}'_0 = \frac{\mathscr{T}'_0}{2G_l} + \frac{\mathscr{T}_0}{2\eta}$$

At any time t the strain depends upon the stress history.   If the strain is maintained constant, the stress relaxes.   Thus under shear if

$$\mathscr{S}'_0 = 0$$

then

$$\mathscr{T}_0 = [\mathscr{T}_0]_0 \exp\left(-\frac{G_l t}{\eta}\right)$$

The ratio $\eta/G_l = \theta$ having the dimensions of time is called the relaxation time.   If the strain is not held constant then

$$\mathscr{T}_0 = \left\{[\mathscr{T}_0] + G_l\int_0^t \mathscr{S}'_0 \exp\left(-\frac{G_l t}{\eta}\right) dt\right\}\exp\left(-\frac{G_l t}{\eta}\right)$$

Corresponding formulas exist for dilational and compressive strains.   The behavior of the Maxwell liquid is shown schematically in Figure 5.

Three-element models are sometimes used to represent the behavior of certain films (42, 73, 129).   They are constructed by putting a spring or a

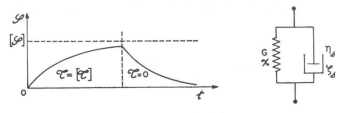

Fig. 4.   The Voigt solid.

dashpot in series with a Voigt model. The corresponding viscoelastic systems are in the first case a solid showing simultaneous instant elasticity and delayed elasticity (Figure 6), and in the second case a liquid showing delayed elasticity plus viscous flow (Figure 7). A model very frequently used in surface rheology is the four-element model of Burger's (42, 57, 73, 129). It consists of Voigt and Maxwell models in series (Figure 8). The

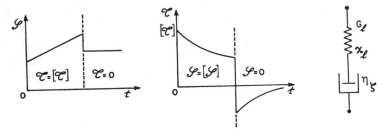

Fig. 5.   The Maxwell liquid.

corresponding body displays both instantaneous and delayed elasticity plus viscous flow (130).

Plastic bodies do not satisfy linear differential equations relating stress and strain, and Boltzmann's principle is no longer valid. A body is recognized to be plastic when no permanent strain is produced until the stress has exceeded a threshold value. For example, a perfectly plastic

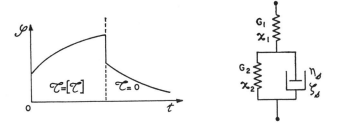

Fig. 6.   A solid showing both instantaneous and delayed elasticity.

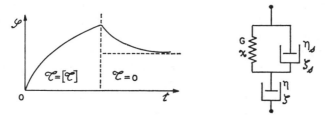

Fig. 7.   A liquid showing delayed elasticity.

body subjected to a steadily growing stress is undeformed for weak stresses, then suddenly yields without further increase in the stress.   If the stress is removed, the deformation remains at its maximum value.   A body of this type is commonly represented by a slider.   A solid both elastic and plastic is equivalent to a model consisting of a spring and slider in series.   Some plastic liquids will not flow until a stress threshold is achieved.   An equivalent model is a dashpot and slider in parallel.   The viscoelastic, plastic body is known as the Bingham body and can be represented by adding a spring in series with the previous model.   For reasons that derive largely from the difficulties of precise rheological experimentation with monomolecular films, viscoplastic or elastoplastic behavior has not been positively identified in surface phases.   On the other hand, thixotropic phenomena, shear thinning and thickening, are commonly observed in surface films.   Examples will be described in Part II, Section I.

3. Experimentation in Planar Surface Rheology

Along with the definition in Section II.C of the principal rheological co-efficients, we described experiments leading to the determination of these coefficients for surface bodies which were either purely elastic or purely viscous.   In Section III we describe the basic methodology of these experiments.   From the discussion of Section II.D.2, however, we have remarked

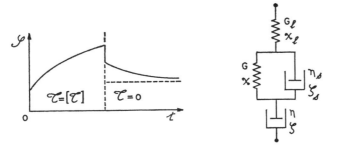

Fig. 8.   The Burgers body.

that the rheological behavior of real films is not so simple.   As a consequence, the various parameters are not easily separated, and we can only calculate them indirectly from experimental data obtained under well-defined conditions of stress or strain.   Typical experiments are of the creep (131), or of the relaxation (132) type.   We shall present here the guiding principle for experiments involving shear stress at constant film area.

In creep experiments, the stress $\mathscr{T}_0$ is maintained constant, and the strain $\mathscr{S}$ is measured as a function of time.   We define two special functions, the creep function

$$\Phi(t) = \frac{\mathscr{S}(t)}{\mathscr{T}_0}$$

and the creep recovery function

$$\mathscr{R}(t) = \frac{\mathscr{S}(t)}{\mathscr{T}_0}$$

for $t > t_0$ in which t_0 is the time at which the stress is removed.

For pure elasticity

$$\frac{d\Phi(t)}{dt} = 0$$

G is in general a function of $\mathscr{S}$, but it is often constant for large variations in $\mathscr{S}$.   In the purely viscous case

$$\frac{d\Phi(t)}{dt} = \text{constant}$$

The viscosity coefficient is defined by

$$\eta = \frac{\mathscr{T}_0}{\lim_{t \to \infty} \mathscr{S}'}$$

which in general depends sensitively on $\mathscr{T}_0$.   For delayed elasticity, it is often noted that the creep function does not reduce to

$$\Phi(t) = \frac{1 - \exp\left(-\dfrac{t}{\tau}\right)}{G}$$

which corresponds to the deformation of a Voigt model of retardation time τ under constant stress:

$$\mathscr{S}(t) = \frac{\mathscr{T}_0}{G}\left[1 - \exp\left(-\frac{t}{\tau}\right)\right]$$

or

$$\mathscr{S}(t) = J\mathscr{T}_0\left[1 - \exp\left(-\frac{t}{\tau}\right)\right]$$

where J is the compliance modulus of the film. We are therefore compelled to represent the film by an infinite series of Voigt units in which the retardation time varies continuously from 0 to ∞. For this model

$$\Phi(t) = \int_0^\infty J(\tau)\left[1 - \exp\left(-\frac{t}{\tau}\right)\right] d\tau$$

which becomes

$$\Phi(t) = \frac{1}{G_0} + \int_0^\infty J(\tau)\left[1 - \exp\left(-\frac{t}{\tau}\right)\right] d\tau$$

for a generalized Voigt body including an instantaneous elasticity of modulus G_0. The function $J(\tau)$ is the spectrum of retardation times of the monomolecular film.

For a generalized Maxwell body we have

$$\Phi(t) = \frac{1}{G_0} + \frac{1}{\eta_\infty} + \int_0^\infty J(\tau)\left[1 - \exp\left(-\frac{t}{\tau}\right)\right] d\tau$$

in which η_∞ is the viscosity coefficient for irreversible viscous flow of the surface phase. For the same body the creep recovery is

$$\mathscr{R}(t)_{t>t_0} = \frac{t_0}{\eta_\infty} + \int_0^\infty J(\tau)\left[\exp\left(\frac{t_0}{\tau}\right) - 1\right]\exp\left(-\frac{t}{\tau}\right) d\tau$$

In stress relaxation experiments, the strain $\mathscr{S}_0$ generated by the application of an initial strain $\mathscr{T}_0$ is maintained constant, and one follows the change in stress as a function of time. A relaxation function $\Psi(t)$ is defined by the formula

$$\Psi(t, \mathscr{S}_0) = \frac{\mathscr{T}(t)}{\mathscr{T}_0}$$

A generalized Maxwell body whose relaxation times θ extend from 0 to ∞ possesses a relaxation function

$$\Psi(t) = \int_0^\infty G(\theta)\exp\left(-\frac{t}{\theta}\right) d\theta$$

$G(\theta)$ is the spectrum of relaxation times of the surface phase. For the generalized Voigt body, the relaxation function is

$$\Psi(t) = G_\infty + \int_0^\infty G(\theta)\exp\left(-\frac{t}{\theta}\right) d\theta$$

in which

$$G_\infty = G_0 - \int_0^\infty G(\theta)\, d\theta$$

The study of creep and relaxation curves should in principle allow the determination of the rheological characteristics of monomolecular films. It is obvious that the general case is not simple. As was pointed out in Section II.D.2, however, when the two-element Voigt or Maxwell models do not adequately represent the mechanical properties of a given mono-molecular film, a Burgers four-element model is generally sufficient to describe the rheological behavior of these two-dimensional phases. For this model, the creep and relaxation equations assume a form which is comparatively easy to use:

$$\Phi(t) = \frac{1}{G_l} + \frac{1}{G}\left[1 - \exp\left(-\frac{Gt}{\eta_s}\right)\right] + \frac{t}{\eta}$$

$$\Psi(t) = \frac{G_l[(G - \lambda_1\eta_s)\exp(-\lambda_1 t) - (G - \lambda_2\eta_s)\exp(-\lambda_2 t)]}{\eta_s(\lambda_2 - \lambda_1)}$$

where λ_1 and λ_2 are the roots of the quadratic equation

$$\frac{\eta_s}{G_l}\lambda^2 - \left(\frac{G}{G_l} + \frac{\eta_s}{\eta} + 1\right)\lambda + \frac{G}{\eta} = 0$$

The notation is that of Figure 8.

4. Aspects of "Nonplanar" Surface Rheology

A situation which has been studied in detail (133) is that of a plane, isotropic film subjected to stresses which are not exclusively located within its own xy plane, and consequently for which the displacement vector **u**, although a function of x and y only, possesses a z component normal to the plane.

If the film acts like a purely elastic body, the components of the tensors $\mathcal{S}$ and $\mathcal{T}$ are related by

$$p_{xx} = (\varkappa + G)\varepsilon_{xx} + (\varkappa - G)\varepsilon_{yy}$$
$$p_{yy} = (\varkappa - G)\varepsilon_{xx} + (\varkappa + G)\varepsilon_{yy}$$
$$p_{zz} = 0$$
$$p_{xy} = 2G\varepsilon_{xy}, \qquad p_{xz} = 2\chi\varepsilon_{xz}, \qquad p_{yz} = 2\chi\varepsilon_{yz}$$

in which κ and G are the previously defined moduli of compression and surface elasticity; χ is an elastic modulus for shear in a direction normal to the plane of the film. If $u_z \equiv 0$, meaning the planar case, the classical two-dimensional

Hooke's law relations of Section II.D.2 are obtained. If, on the other hand

$$u_x \equiv 0, \qquad u_y \equiv 0 \qquad \text{and} \quad u_z \neq 0$$

only strains in a direction normal to the plane of the film are possible, and Hooke's law takes the simple form

$$\mathscr{T} = 2\chi\mathscr{S}$$

If the film is purely viscous, the rheological equations are

$$p_{xx} = (\zeta + \eta)\varepsilon'_{xx} + (\zeta - \eta)\varepsilon'_{yy}$$

$$p_{yy} = (\zeta - \eta)\varepsilon'_{xx} + (\zeta + \eta)\varepsilon'_{yy}$$

$$p_{zz} = 0$$

$$p_{xy} = 2\eta\varepsilon'_{xy}, \qquad p_{xz} = 2\lambda\varepsilon'_{xz}, \qquad p_{yz} = 2\lambda\varepsilon'_{yz}$$

in which ζ and η are the coefficients of surface viscosity defined in Section II.C; λ is a viscosity coefficient for shear in a direction normal to the plane of the film. Setting $v_z \equiv 0$, these equations reduce to those for purely viscous behavior in the "planar" case. For $v_x \equiv 0$, $v_y \equiv 0$, and $v_z \neq 0$, the film is unable to flow only in a direction normal to its plane and obeys the simple law

$$\mathscr{T} = 2\lambda\mathscr{S}'$$

For a general viscoelastic film, the preceding equations are augmented:

$$p_{xx} = (\varkappa + G)\varepsilon_{xx} + (\varkappa - G)\varepsilon_{yy} + (\zeta + \eta)\varepsilon'_{xx} + (\zeta - \eta)\varepsilon'_{yy}$$

$$p_{yy} = (\varkappa - G)\varepsilon_{xx} + (\varkappa + G)\varepsilon_{yy} + (\zeta - \eta)\varepsilon'_{xx} + (\zeta + \eta)\varepsilon'_{yy}$$

$$p_{zz} = 0$$

$$p_{xy} = 2(G\varepsilon_{xy} + \eta\varepsilon'_{xy})$$

$$p_{xz} = 2(\chi\varepsilon_{xz} + \lambda\varepsilon'_{xz})$$

$$p_{yz} = 2(\chi\varepsilon_{yz} + \lambda\varepsilon'_{yz})$$

A situation which has been rather well studied is that of a spherical film enclosing an emulsion droplet (63). Adopting a generalized coordinate system x, y, z such that $z = 0$ corresponds to the surface of the droplet, the geodesic distance between two neighboring kinetic units is

$$ds^2 = g_{xx}\, dx^2 + 2g_{xy}\, dx\, dy + g_{yy}\, dy^2$$

in which the g_{ij} are the components of the surface metric tensor. The components of the strain tensor are defined by

$$d(ds^2) = 2\varepsilon_{xx}\, dx^2 + 4\varepsilon_{xy}\, dx\, dy + 2\varepsilon_{yy}\, dy^2$$

The components of the rate of strain tensor are

$$\frac{d}{dt}(ds^2) = 2\varepsilon'_{xx}\,dx^2 + 4\varepsilon'_{xy}\,dx\,dy + 2\varepsilon'_{yy}\,dy^2$$

For purely elastic interfacial films the rheological equations assume the form

$$p_{\alpha\beta} = 2G\varepsilon_{\alpha\beta} + g_{\alpha\beta}[\gamma + (\varkappa - G)(\varepsilon_{xx} + \varepsilon_{yy})]$$

with $\alpha = x, y$; $\beta = x, y$; and in which γ is the interfacial tension and $\varkappa$ and G are respectively the compression and elastic moduli of the film.

If the interfacial films are purely viscous, the rheological equations reduce to

$$p_{\alpha\beta} = 2\eta\varepsilon'_{\alpha\beta} + g_{\alpha\beta}[\gamma + (\zeta - \eta)(\varepsilon'_{xx} + \varepsilon'_{yy})]$$

where ζ and η are the film viscosity coefficients for dilation and shear.

For the general viscoelastic interfacial film, we have in addition

$$p_{\alpha\beta} = 2(G\varepsilon_{\alpha\beta} + \eta\varepsilon'_{\alpha\beta}) + g_{\alpha\beta}[\gamma + (\varkappa - G)(\varepsilon_{xx} + \varepsilon_{yy}) + (\zeta - \eta)(\varepsilon'_{xx} + \varepsilon'_{yy})]$$

III. METHODS OF EXPERIMENTAL SURFACE RHEOLOGY

A. General Considerations

Up to the present time systematic rheological experimentation has been directed exclusively toward planar films.

If an experiment is performed to study the mechanical behavior of a homogeneous, two-dimensional system, the rheological parameters derived from the experiment can be considered as characterizing the film only if the experimental conditions are such that local stresses and strains throughout the system are uniform.   If this condition is not met, the measured quantities are only apparent quantities.   It is obvious that it is often difficult to satisfy completely the condition for rheological uniformity.   Nevertheless every attempt is made to approach it as completely as possible by constructing experimental apparatus with a high degree of symmetry: symmetry with respect to a plane perpendicular to the film, or symmetry around an axis normal to the film.

With some experimental equipment the rheological properties of mono-molecular films are directly determined from a calculation whose theoretical form changes with the type of apparatus, it being understood that the equations of motion of the substrate are properly taken into account.   With other equipment the properties of the surface phase are calculated by forming the difference between data taken on a clean surface in the absence of a monolayer and data obtained from the same experiment performed on a monolayer covered surface.   The latter method would seem to be *a priori* the simpler, for the calculation of the rheological constants of the film does not require an exact knowledge of the equations of motion of the substrate. This would indeed be a valid procedure if the substrate motion were identical in the presence and in the absence of the film. Unfortunately this is rarely the case, and as a consequence the additivity rule is only approximate to the extent that the contribution of the substrate is the same whether or not it is covered with a film. Only the case of the rotating ring has been studied in detail (46). Despite this fact, calculations based on differenced data are to a good approximation valid when the film is very fluid and the substrate motion is slow and of small amplitude, or especially when the film displays high rigidity or viscosity. The approximation is, in short, a good one when the substrate is only slightly disturbed by the motion of the film and the film makes the dominant contribution to the rheological behavior of the total system.

In the sections to follow we shall see that experiments are relatively easy to perform for the liquid/gas interface, and good precision is attainable. The major reason for this fact is that almost the entirety of the experimental apparatus is located in the atmosphere, that the film is, so to speak, directly accessible, and that furthermore the rheological response of the substrate to deformations of the film can be reduced to a minimum. It is the contrasting behavior of films at the liquid/liquid interface which makes experimentation under well-defined conditions much more difficult, for it is not possible to obtain access to the films without disturbing the bulk liquid phases separated by them. The contribution of the liquid phases to the total mechanical stress, furthermore, is almost always large. These difficulties generally reduce the precision of results obtained for interfacial films.

In Section II.C.3 we introduced the elastic compression modulus. The role which it plays in describing the general rheological behavior of surface phases was discussed in Section II.D. We shall, nevertheless, not speak here of methods of measuring this most commonly employed parameter, for the methods are not peculiar to rheological studies. In sum, $\varkappa$ is almost always deduced from the compression isotherm $\pi = f(A)$; and it is the measurement of this isotherm that is the fundamental physicochemical experiment performed on two-dimensional phases at fluid interfaces. The numerous techniques for determining the form of these isotherms have been frequently described in review articles (1, 2, 95, for example), and their study falls outside the scope of a monograph on surface rheology. It is better to direct our attention to methods which are of a specifically rheological nature.

B. The Measurement of Surface Elasticity

There are a number of amphiphilic materials which at convenient temperatures, surface pressures, and substrate conditions produce monomolecular films which to a reasonable approximation behave like purely elastic solids. The determination of the compression modulus $\varkappa$ from the isotherm $\pi = f(A)$ represents no difficulty aside from the necessity of assuring the stability of the film.   It is equally important to verify the absence of dilational viscosity by controlling the conditions so that the compression isotherm is independent of the rate of compression.

1. Young's Modulus

As was mentioned in Section II.C.2, measurements of Young's modulus are always contaminated with an error arising from the fact that the portion of film under study must be enclosed by a frame which restricts the freedom of transverse motion needed in principle for the measurement of E.   The result is that the quantity measured is rheologically poorly defined and is a sort of intermediate coefficient between $\varkappa$ and E.   Most techniques suggested for the measurement of E, moreover, induce possibly significant shear strains in addition to the longitudinal strain.   As a result only approximate values are obtained for E, and these "apparent" values depend upon the experimental apparatus.

In Van Waser's method (134), the force F is measured which is necessary to cause a displacement d normal to its long dimension of a float of length L placed upon the film parallel to the sides of the confining framework and at distances l_1 and l_2 from these sides.   By neglecting the transverse compression and shear even though the float is almost as long as the side of the frame to which it is parallel, the result is

$$E = \frac{F l_1 l_2}{L(l_1 + l_2)d}$$

In the method of Cheesman and Sten-Knudsen (135), the interpretation of the measured coefficient is equally uncertain (136).   Here the float is a small disc of 1.2 cm diameter bearing a small, permanent magnet 1 cm long and 1 mm^2 in cross section, aligned together with the trough along the magnetic meridian.   A solenoid is placed with its axis in the plane of the liquid surface and directed along the long axis of the little magnet, about 15 cm from it. The displacements of the float are observed through a cathetometer. E is calculated from an expression analogous to that above if for L is substituted the diameter a of the float.   If d is small and the trough sufficiently large, shear effects become negligible.   Nevertheless, the coefficient determined in this way can only with difficulty be interpreted as a true Young's modulus.

2. The Shear Modulus

The first measurements of the shear modulus G were carried out in a very direct manner (137).   A solid film is formed on a water surface between two concentric rings of radii r_1 and r_2. The outer ring is fixed, and the inner one is suspended from a torsion wire of constant C. A rotation δ_0 of the torsion head causes a small rotation δ of the inner ring. The measurement of δ and of the equilibrium turning couple permits the calculation of G:

$$G = \frac{C}{4\pi}\left(\frac{1}{r_1^2} - \frac{1}{r_2^2}\right)\frac{\delta_0 - \delta}{\delta}$$

Some solid films being very fragile, a necessary precaution is to be certain that the film does not break during the measurement, and that it does not become detached from the moving ring (138). Some workers (18) have replaced the moving ring by a needle of length l. The required formula is

$$G = \frac{2C}{l^2}\frac{\delta_0 - \delta}{\delta}$$

but it is obvious that the rheological meaning of the coefficient measured in this way is unclear and can be interpreted only crudely as a shear modulus.

The same argument holds true when surface elasticity is measured by causing a needle suspended from a torsion wire to oscillate in the plane of the film. Fourt (139) introduced an elastic index $\mathscr{E}$ defined by

$$\mathscr{E} = \frac{4\pi^2 I}{l^3}\left(\frac{1}{T^2} - \frac{1}{T_0^2}\right)$$

in which I is the moment of inertia of the moving apparatus, T_0 the period of oscillation in the absence of the film, and T the period in the presence of the film. $\mathscr{E}$, however, does not have the correct dimensions for a surface shear modulus (125). It would be better to use a relation of the form

$$G = \frac{8\pi^2 I}{l^2}\left(\frac{1}{T^2} - \frac{1}{T_0^2}\right)$$

but the rheological significance of the modulus thus determined is poorly defined. On the other hand, the oscillations of a disc (36) lead to correct values of G

$$G = \pi I\left(\frac{1}{T^2} - \frac{1}{T_0^2}\right)\left(\frac{1}{r_1^2} - \frac{1}{r_2^2}\right)$$

provided that the amplitude of the oscillations is sufficiently small so that the errors introduced by taking differences (see Section III.A) are negligible, and also of course provided that the film studied is purely elastic.

A resonance method has been suggested (134). The film is spread upon the liquid annulus between two coaxial cylinders of radii r_1 and r_3, rigidly coupled to each other and undergoing low-amplitude oscillations of adjustable frequency ω. A ring of radius r_2, coaxial with the cylinders and with a moment of inertia I is suspended without torsion from a wire and placed upon the film.   If ω_r is the resonance frequency between the oscillations of the cylinders and those of the film, the shear modulus is

$$G = \pi \omega_r^2 I \left(\frac{1}{r_1^2} - \frac{1}{r_2^2} \right) \left(\frac{1}{r_2^2} - \frac{1}{r_3^2} \right) \left(\frac{1}{r_1^2} - \frac{1}{r_3^2} \right)^{-1}$$

3. Gibbs Elasticity

Although Gibbs elasticity is not in general a property of solid films, we shall set down here methods for its measurement.   By definition (Section II.C.3), Gibbs elasticity E_G may be calculated from the plot $\gamma(l)$ of the variation in tension of a liquid lamella as a function of its extension by means of a rod moved perpendicular to the substrate surface (140, 141).   Under these conditions, one dimension of the film is held constant so that

$$\frac{\Delta S}{S} = \frac{\Delta l}{l}$$

whence

$$E_G = - \frac{\partial \gamma}{\partial \ln l}$$

It is important to recall that E_G is not an intrinsic rheological property of the surface film which covers the liquid lamella.   Thus the equilibrium tension γ depends upon the thickness of the lamella (142); and most importantly, the amount of amphiphilic material in the surface layer changes during the extension.

Equipment has been constructed to measure the curves $\gamma(l)$ either point by point (143–145), or by continuous recording in the "laminometer" of Matalon (146).   Besides the Gibbs elasticity, however, there enter into the measurements made by these devices the effects of the drainage of the lamella and the replenishment of the two surface films of the lamella by the film which covers the horizontal surface of the substrate.   The derived curves $\gamma(l)$ thus do not allow calculation of exact values of E_G because the measured displacements l are not those which enter into the expression for E_G.

The movement of the rod is not identical with the true extension of the surface film.   This extension has been determined in the following way (147, 148).   The tension variation is measured simultaneously with that of the displacement of the interference fringes observed at a reflection angle of 45° from the stretched lamella.   The movement of the interference fringes is that of the displacement of contours of equal thickness.   This movement, however, does not coincide with that of elements of the surface; and to calculate the latter it is assumed that the volume of liquid trapped in the lamella between its apex and a given level covered by the portion of film of interest is constant during the displacement of that film portion as a result of the extension of the lamella. This postulate enables one to calculate graphically with great precision the true extension of the surface film by photographing interference fringes corresponding to equal thicknesses at several different positions of the rod, and from this in turn follows a calculation of the true values of E_G. It is nevertheless true that a Marangoni effect can vitiate the results (124) by making the tension γ a function of the rate of extension.

To eliminate perturbing effects due to drainage and to the replenishment of the film from the mother solution, an isolated washer-shaped lamella may be supported by two coaxial, horizontal, platinum rings of radii r_1, r_2 (149). When the inner ring is raised a distance h, the equilibrium shape of the film is a surface of revolution whose profile is a catenary. If the force necessary to raise the inner ring to h is measured, then for each value of h it is possible to calculate the surface area S and its tension γ. Using the notation of Figure 9, the equation of a catenary is

$$y = b \cosh \frac{x - a}{b}$$

the parameters a and b being defined by

$$r_1 = b \cosh\left(-\frac{a}{b}\right) \quad \text{and} \quad r_2 = b \cosh\left(\frac{h - a}{b}\right)$$

The surface area of the film is

$$S = 2\pi[bh + r_2\sqrt{r_2{}^2 - b^2} + r_1\sqrt{r_1{}^2 - b^2}]$$

which is to say

$$S = 2\pi b\left[h + \frac{l}{2}\left\{\sinh \frac{2(h - a)}{b} + \sinh \frac{2a}{b}\right\}\right]$$

In another approach, if F is the force applied to the inner ring to raise it to h, the tension in the film is

$$\gamma = \frac{F}{4\pi r_1 \cos \theta}$$

But $\cos \theta = b/r$, whence $\gamma = F/4\pi b$. The relation between h and b is

$$h = b \ln \frac{r_2 + \sqrt{r_2{}^2 - b^2}}{r_1 + \sqrt{r_1{}^2 - b^2}}$$

By plotting this equation, one has once and for all a value of b for each value

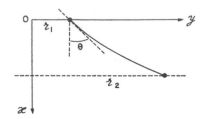

Fig. 9.   Equilibrium of a film between two coaxial rings.

of h.   It follows that by measuring F and h the values of γ and S may be calculated.   The result is a plot of $\gamma(S)$ and the determination of E_G.

C. The Measurement of Surface Viscosity

Methods of measuring surface or interfacial viscosity are more or less directly derived from those in use in three-dimensional rheology.   Only a few techniques have been advanced for the measurement of dilational viscosity.   By contrast, the number of experimental arrangements for measuring shear viscosity is large.   We shall not review in detail this equipment, but we shall give the principal mode of operation of a given apparatus and describe how the coefficients ζ or η can be calculated from the raw data. Throughout this section it will be presumed that the measurements are made upon a two-dimensional system which is purely viscous, that is, totally devoid of any elasticity.

1. Dilational Surface Viscosity

A relatively direct method for the measurement of dilational surface viscosity has been deduced from the definition of ζ:

$$\Delta\gamma = \frac{\zeta}{S}\frac{\partial S}{\partial t}$$

It consists in varying the surface occupied by the film in such a way that

$$\frac{1}{S}\frac{\partial S}{\partial t} = \text{constant}$$

and in measuring the corresponding change in the surface tension (118). The variation of the surface area is generated by the simultaneous displacement of two barriers symmetrically disposed with respect to the center of the trough containing the substrate.   In Figure 10 the barriers are moved by the rotation at constant angular velocity ω of an eccentric cam having the shape of a spiral $\rho = q \exp(K\varphi)$ in polar coordinates.   The constant q is chosen

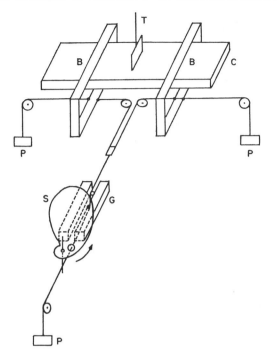

Fig. 10.   Schematic representation of the apparatus of Van Voorst Vader, Erkens, and Van den Temple.   *B*, barriers; *C*, trough; *G*, slider; *P*, counterweights; *S*, cam; *T*, hanging plate tensiometer.

equal to half the initial distance between the two barriers ($\varphi = 0$, $t = 0$). The area is then $S = 2bq \exp(K\omega t)$, with b the width of the trough.   It follows that

$$\frac{1}{S}\frac{\partial S}{\partial t} = K\omega$$

In the apparatus constructed by the authors of this method, $q = 2.1$ cm, $K = 0.0715$/degree.   The maximum attained value of $K\omega$ was 0.15/sec.

A more indirect method consists in studying the stationary rising motion of bubbles or droplets to the surface of another fluid phase (150).   The resistance to the motion of bubbles or droplets depends upon ζ and the bulk viscosities η_1 and η_2 of the two phases.   According to Boussinesq (16), the resisting force is

$$6\pi r\eta_1 \frac{\zeta + r(2\eta_1 + 3\eta_2)}{\zeta + r(3\eta_1 + 3\eta_2)} v$$

in which v is the velocity of the rising drop or bubble and r its radius. On the other hand, an equal and opposing force is

$$\tfrac{4}{3}\pi r^3(\rho_1 - \rho_2)g$$

where ρ_1 and ρ_2 are the phase densities and g the acceleration of gravity. It follows that

$$v = \frac{2r^2}{9\eta_1}(\rho_1 - \rho_2)g\,\frac{\zeta + r(3\eta_1 + 3\eta_2)}{\zeta + r(2\eta_1 + 3\eta_2)}$$

whence

$$\zeta = 3r\,\frac{2r^2 g(\rho_1 - \rho_2)(\eta_1 + \eta_2) - 3v\eta_1(2\eta_1 + 3\eta_2)}{9\eta_1 v - 2r^2(\rho_1 - \rho_2)g}$$

For gas bubbles, we may neglect η_2 and ρ_2 to find

$$\zeta \simeq 6r\eta_1\,\frac{r^2 g\rho_1 - 3v\eta_1}{9v\eta_1 - 2r^2 g\rho_1}$$

All things considered, this method is of low sensitivity, for v depends much more on η_1 than on ζ. It has in fact been shown (150) that for the same relative change in η_1 and in ζ, the variation in v is at least 8.9 times more sensitive to η_1 than it is to ζ.

2. Surface Shear Viscosity

Four principal methods have been used in the measurement of η.

a. Motion of a Floating Object

By following the pointer of a torsion balance whose head is subjected to a constant rotational velocity, a small disc undergoes uniform circular motion in a circular canal bounding the film (Figure 11). The resistance to the

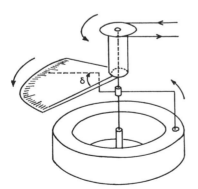

Fig. 11. Schematic representation of the surface viscometer of Kalousek.

motion of the disc is determined from the torsion δ of the balance wire and from the velocity V of the disc relative to the canal border (151, 152). The mathematical formulas needed have been derived approximately by Faxen (153) for the motion of a cylinder in a canal. The resistance F experienced by a cylinder immersed to a depth h and moving at a constant velocity V is $F = Kh\eta_v V$ in which η_v is the viscosity of the medium and

$$K = 4\pi \left[\ln \frac{l}{2a} - 0.9157 + 6.88 \frac{a^2}{l^2} - 27.68 \frac{a^4}{l^4} \right]$$

with a the radius of the cylinder and l the width of the canal. In practice, however, it has proved preferable to determine K experimentally by calibrating the apparatus in solutions of glycerol for discs of known thickness h. The viscosity of the film is obtained by differencing for a given V the resisting forces F_1 and F_0 taken in the presence and in the absence of a film. By assuming the additivity of the resistances due to the film and to the substrate, and assuming also that the resistance of the substrate is the same in the presence as in the absence of the film, there results

$$\eta = \frac{F_1 - F_0}{KV}$$

b. Damped Oscillations of a Torsion Pendulum

One of the oldest and most frequently employed techniques in surface rheology is the measurement of surface viscosity η from the damping of a moving oscillator placed in the surface (18, 21, 24, 25, 40, 53, 126, 139, 154–161).

For an oscillating needle, the mechanical conditions are not the same everywhere in the film and are furthermore often poorly defined. As a result, surface viscosities determined in this way are very approximate and indicate no more than an order of magnitude. Fourt's formula (139) used to calculate η is

$$\eta = \frac{9.21}{l^2} I \left(\frac{\Delta}{T} - \frac{\Delta_0}{T_0} \right)$$

in which I is the moment of inertia, l the length of the needle, Δ and Δ_0 the base 10 logarithmic decrements of damping in the presence and absence of a film, and T and T_0 the respective periods of oscillation.

If a ring is caused to oscillate in the plane of the surface, the rheological parameters are much better defined, particularly if the film is bounded by a fixed ring of radius r_2 concentric with the moving ring of radius r_1. For I the moment of inertia of the oscillating system and C the torsion constant of the suspending wire, the equation of motion is

$$I \frac{d^2\delta}{dt^2} + P \frac{d\delta}{dt} + C\delta = 0$$

in which δ is the deflection angle of the moving ring and P the damping constant. For damped sinusoidal oscillations, $(P^2 < 4CI)$, the base 10 logarithmic decrement is

$$\Delta = \frac{2\pi P}{2.303\sqrt{4CI - P^2}}$$

By assuming the additivity of damping factors due to the film and to its substrate, we have

$$P = P_0 + M$$

where

$$M = 4\pi\eta \frac{r_1^2 r_2^2}{r_2^2 - r_1^2}$$

and P_0 is the damping factor of the clean surface. Then the surface viscosity is (24, 25)

$$\eta = \frac{\sqrt{CI}}{2\pi} \frac{r_2^2 - r_1^2}{r_1^2 r_2^2} \left[\frac{\Delta}{\sqrt{7.4 + \Delta^2}} - \frac{\Delta_0}{\sqrt{7.4 + \Delta_0^2}} \right]$$

in which Δ and Δ_0 are the logarithmic decrements for the film-covered and film-free interfaces, respectively.

A relatively simple formula is obtained (162) by introducing the corresponding periods of oscillation T and T_0:

$$\eta = \frac{1.15}{\pi} I \left(\frac{1}{r_1^2} - \frac{1}{r_2^2} \right) \left(\frac{\Delta}{T} - \frac{\Delta_0}{T_0} \right)$$

The sensitivity of the method is notably increased (24, 25) by using a narrow, paraffined ring of mica as the moving unit floating at the liquid surface (Figure 12). Enhanced sensitivity also results if C, I, and $r_2 - r_1$ are made small and if r_1 is made large. It is consequently necessary to choose the apparatus parameters to match the film to be studied. As an example, an apparatus giving a particularly satisfactory performance (51) was characterized by $r_1 = 1.51$ cm, $I = 9.81$ g-cm^2, $C = 0.71$ g-cm^2/sec^2. It is equally essential that the trough and the torsion head be supported by vibration-free foundations and that the equipment be carefully thermostated and protected from external disturbances such as air currents, evaporation, etc. In one exceedingly elaborate apparatus (53) the movement of the floating ring was followed by a spot of light and the measurements of Δ analyzed by an electronic computer.

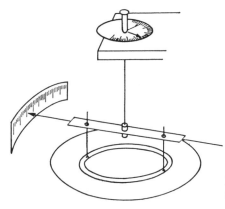

Fig. 12. The oscillating surface viscometer (schematic).

In oscillation methods, the rate of shear changes during the course of measurement. The viscosity values are consequently exact only when the surface viscosity is Newtonian, which is to say independent of the shear rate. If the viscosity is non-Newtonian, Δ changes with the amplitude of the oscillations and the values of η calculated are only values averaged over a range of shear rates. These methods for the measurement of η are, furthermore, in principle invalid for adsorbed films because of the necessity of measuring the damping on a substrate of the same solution in the absence of the film.

For adsorbed films on very dilute solutions, it is possible in first approximation to assume that the contribution of the substrate reduces to that of the pure solvent and to take for Λ_0 the logarithmic decrement measured in the absence of solute. For concentrated solutions this simplification is evidently no longer valid. For extremely viscous films one may presume that the damping due to the substrate is negligible compared to that for the film and use the simplified formula (163).

$$\eta = \frac{2.303 \, \Delta I}{\pi T} \left(\frac{1}{r_1^2} - \frac{1}{r_2^2} \right)$$

Such cases are very unusual, however, for the probability is small that a highly viscous film is purely viscous and not viscoelastic.

A method for the determination of Δ_0 has been proposed (164) in the case of a substrate which cannot be prepared free of an adsorbed film. The method is based upon the observation that when a disc oscillates within the interior of an infinite mass of liquid, the fluid velocity decreases very rapidly as one moves away from the disc. Taken as a function of the distance y

from the plane of the disc, the fluid velocity is (165)

$$v = v_0 \exp\left[-\left(\frac{i\omega\rho}{\eta_0}\right)^{\frac{1}{2}} y \right] \exp(i\omega t)$$

in which ρ and η_0 are the density and the viscosity of the liquid, respectively. It is thus possible to use a finite volume of liquid far from phase boundaries to study the damping of an oscillating disc.   One can assume furthermore that the energy dissipated by the oscillations is the same on each side of the submerged disc.   With this assumption, we may take for Δ_0 at a clean surface one half the observed decrement Δ_t measured within the interior of the liquid.   This hypothesis has been accurately verified for aqueous solutions of glycerol whose viscosities varied from 0.08 to 1.12 P.   So that true values of Δ_t are obtained, it is obviously necessary to use a trough sufficiently deep with the disc positioned sufficiently far from both the bottom and the free surface to ensure that the damping is independent of the depth of immersion of the disc.

c. Steady Rotation of a Ring

For the study of the viscosity of non-Newtonian surface phases, we require an apparatus in which the shear rate is constant for the duration of the experiment and also practically constant everywhere in that portion of the film being strained.   It is therefore advantageous to adapt the Couette viscometer to surface rheology.   In this equipment the essential element is a pair of concentric rings of which one turns about its axis with a constant rotational velocity.   The resistance of a film entrained between the two rings opposes this motion.

From the time of the first experiments (134), the principal difficulty has been the low sensitivity of the apparatus.   This feature derived from the dominant part played by the substrate in the ensemble of viscous forces brought into play.   An important improvement has resulted by using for the moving ring a thin, paraffined metal wire floating at the surface (28, 166). In this apparatus constant-speed rotational motion is communicated to the moving ring through a torsion wire or spiral spring whose deformation is a measure of the turning couple due to the viscous resistance of the film.   The principle is illustrated in Figure 13.   If C is the torsion constant, r_1 the radius of the moving ring, r_2 the radius of the fixed ring bounding the film, ω the angular velocity, and δ and δ_0 the torsions in the presence and in the absence of the film, then for $r_2 - r_1$ small compared with r_1,

$$\eta = \frac{C(\delta - \delta_0)}{4\pi\omega} \left(\frac{1}{r_1{}^2} - \frac{1}{r_2{}^2} \right)$$

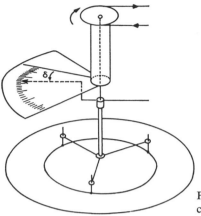

Fig. 13. The continuous rotation surface viscometer (schematic).

The shear rate is practically the same throughout the annulus of film under strain, its value being

$$g = \frac{\omega r_1}{r_2 - r_1}$$

This method obviously assumes the additivity of the turning couples due to substrate and film. We have observed in Section III.A that this is only a first approximation, but in the majority of cases of practical interest the approximation is adequate. The error committed only becomes significant for films of both high fluidity and strongly non-Newtonian behavior, and experience shows such cases to be very rare.

In one of the most sensitive of the viscometers yet constructed (47), the moving ring was made from a fine, paraffined glass filament. It was enclosed by a second ring, also a paraffined glass filament. The outer ring was connected with a torsion balance whose readings were a measure of the turning couple arising from the surface viscosity (Figure 14). To interpret the couple, it was necessary that only the portion of the film contained between the rings undergoes fluid flow. The required suppression of film motion in the region external to the outer ring was accomplished by immobilizing the substrate with a supported mica plate. For a given rotational velocity of the inner ring, it was verified that the difference $\delta - \delta_0$ of the displacements of the outer ring taken in the presence and absence of film was independent of the depth of immersion of the plate (between 0.25 and 3 mm), although δ_0 varied by a factor of 10 during this process. This result justifies the use of the differencing procedure and show that for this apparatus errors arising from the additivity rule are negligible. The formula for η is the same as when the turning couple is measured from the inner ring.

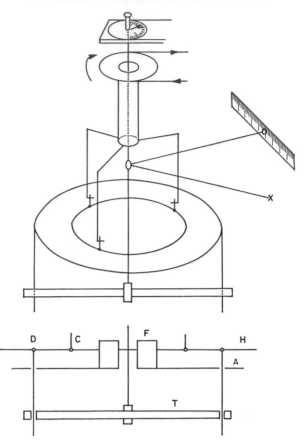

Fig. 14.   De Bernard's surface viscometer.   *A*, damping device; *C*, rotating inner ring; *D*, outer ring; *F*, float; *H*, water surface; *T*, torsion balance.

In another modification of this apparatus (167), it is the outer ring together with the substrate and the film that are subjected to a uniform rotation in analogy with the classic situation in the Couette viscometer. The turning couple on the inner ring is measured by means of a torsion balance. The relation between η and ω is identical with that used for the rotating inner ring.

d. Flow Along a Canal

The reduction to two-dimensional systems of the capillary viscometers of Poiseuille or Ostwald has led to the measurement of surface viscosity from the determination of the exit flux or the velocity of flow of films along a canal.   The method is obviously rigorously valid only for films displaying exclusively Newtonian viscosity.

Two techniques are in use depending upon whether the flow is generated by the establishment of a constant surface pressure difference between the two ends of the canal (19, 20, 23, 46, 154, 160, 168–172) or whether it is generated by the motion of the substrate (19, 49, 50, 171, 173).   The first method may evidently be applied only to insoluble monomolecular films, whereas the second may with equal validity be applied to adsorbed films at surfaces of solutions.   Equipment in which the flow depends upon a difference $\Delta\pi$ in surface pressure between the ends of a canal of length l and of width $2a$ is of two types depending upon the depth of the canal.

In the first type (23, 168) the depth of the canal is very small.   This is accomplished by two parallel plates of paraffined mica which float upon the substrate.   Figure 15 shows the design.   The measurement consists in the determination of the surface flux, which is to say the area of film ΔS per unit time, which under a constant pressure drop flows from compartment I into compartment II.   The surface pressure drop $\Delta\pi = \pi_I - \pi_{II}$ is maintained constant along with each of the pressures π_I and π_{II} by the simultaneous movement of two pistons A and B in such a way that the two surface manometers M and N remain motionless throughout the duration of the measurement.   This method has the advantage of being extremely sensitive and of being applicable to films of very low viscosity.   A formula permitting the calculation of η from the surface flux may be derived as follows.

At an arbitrary point of the surface (Figure 16), a surface element $dx\ dy$ of the film moving with velocity v parallel to the axis of the canal in the positive x direction is subjected to the viscous drag of neighboring elements,

$$\eta \left(\frac{\partial^2 v}{\partial y^2} \right)_{z=0} dx\ dy$$

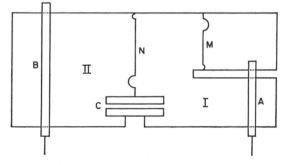

Fig. 15.   Floating canal surface viscometer (schematic).

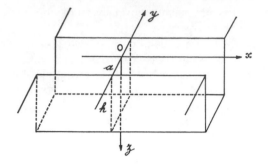

Fig. 16.   Flow in a surface canal.

to the viscous drag of the substrate,

$$\eta_0\left(\frac{\partial v}{\partial z}\right)_{z=0} dx\, dy$$

and to the force derived from the difference in surface pressure between the ends of the canal

$$\frac{\Delta\pi}{l} dx\, dy$$

At steady state

$$\eta\left(\frac{\partial^2 v}{\partial y^2}\right)_{z=0} - \eta_0\left(\frac{\partial v}{\partial z}\right)_{z=0} + \frac{\Delta\pi}{l} = 0$$

Within the interior of the substrate, the Navier-Stokes equations reduce to

$$\frac{\partial^2 v}{\partial y^2} + \frac{\partial^2 v}{\partial z^2} = 0$$

If the depth h of the canal is very small with respect to its width $2a$, the boundary conditions are

$$v = 0 \qquad \text{for } z = 0, \qquad |y| \geqslant a$$

and

$$v = 0 \qquad \text{for } y = \pm\infty \qquad \text{and} \quad z = +\infty$$

No exact solution has been developed for this system of equations (174). An approximate solution may be derived by replacing

$$\left(\frac{\partial v}{\partial z}\right)_{z=0}$$

with the first term of its series development.   The equation of motion of the film then reduces to

$$\eta\frac{d^2 v}{dy^2} - A\eta_0 v + \frac{\Delta\pi}{l} = 0$$

analogous to an equation which had been proposed previously (175). The integral of this differential equation is

$$v = \frac{\Delta \pi}{A l \eta_0}\left[1 - \left(\cosh\sqrt{\frac{\eta_0 A}{\eta}}\, y\right)\left(\cosh\sqrt{\frac{\eta_0 A}{\eta}}\, a\right)^{-1}\right]$$

whence

$$q = \frac{2}{A \eta_0}\left[a - \sqrt{\frac{\eta}{\eta_0 A}}\tanh\sqrt{\frac{\eta_0 A}{\eta}}\, a\right]$$

q being the reduced flux, $q = (\Delta S/\Delta \pi)l$, meaning that quantity of film which is delivered every second from a canal of length 1 cm under a pressure difference of 1 dyne. This formula gives a very good description of the experimental data. For very wide canals, it takes the form

$$q = \frac{2a}{\eta_0 A} - 2\sqrt{\frac{\eta}{\eta_0{}^3 A^3}}$$

For very narrow canals it simplifies to $q = 2a^3/3\mu$ which is precisely Poiseuille's formula in two dimensions. The quantity A can be determined by successive approximations from the experimental data. It varies with the width of the canal. Thus for successive values of $2a$ equal to 0.066, 0.117, 0.265, and 0.382 cm, the values of A are respectively 14.05, 11.9, 6.8, and 5.2. Practically speaking, the calculation of η from measured values of q is that of the graphical inversion of $\tanh x = Kx$.

In a second type of apparatus, the depth of the canal is no longer negligible in comparison with its width. The canal is often constructed from two paraffined microscope slides mounted parallel to each other with great precision (19, 160, 170). This method is less sensitive than the preceding one, due largely to a greater contribution from the substrate to the total resistance to flow. On the other hand, the calculation of η can be performed without any recourse to empirical coefficients. The partial differential equations of flow are obviously the same as for the canal of zero depth, but the boundary conditions are different:

$$v = 0 \quad \text{for } y = 0 \quad \text{and} \quad z > 0$$

and

$$v = 0 \quad \text{for } z = h$$

The reduced surface flux for a canal of depth h is (169, 176)

$$q = \frac{64a^3}{\pi^4 \eta}\sum_{n=0}^{\infty}(2n+1)^{-4}\left[1 + \frac{2a\eta_0}{(2n+1)\pi\eta}\coth\frac{(2n+1)\pi h}{2a}\right]^{-1}$$

which reduces to

$$q = \frac{64a^3}{\pi^4 \eta} \sum_{n=0}^{\infty} (2n + 1)^{-4} \left[1 + \frac{2a\eta_0}{(2n + 1)\pi\eta} \right]^{-1}$$

when the canal is infinitely deep $(h = \infty)$. If $h \gg 2a$, a very satisfactory approximation (169) is

$$q = \frac{2a^3}{3\eta} \left[1 + \frac{2a\eta_0}{\pi\eta} \coth \frac{\pi h}{2a} \right]^{-1}$$

A crude approximation in common use (20) is

$$q = \frac{2\pi a^3}{3(\pi\eta + 2a\eta_0)}$$

in which the depth of the canal does not occur. If in addition to $a/h \ll 1$, we have also $a\eta_0 \ll \eta$, the last equation simplifies to $q = 2a^3/3\eta$, which is the limiting case of the two-dimensional Poiseuille formula. If on the other hand $\eta \ll a\eta_0$, then $q = \pi^2 h/6\eta_0$; and the reduced flux becomes independent of the surface viscosity. It is this fact which explains why the measurement of η by flow along a deep canal is much less sensitive than that of flow along a canal of zero depth, and why it cannot be used for films of high fluidity.

Let us now examine equipment in which the flow of film in the canal is generated by bulk fluid flow in the substrate. Two types of apparatus have been used. In the oldest, the essential unit is a horizontal rectangular canal of rectangular cross section between the two ends of which is maintained a difference in hydrostatic pressure Δp. The measurement of η is achieved by measuring the velocity v_m of the film along the axis of the canal (through the observation of fine dust particles floating in the surface), and of the comparison of this velocity with the bulk flux Q of the substrate in the canal (46, 171). This is to say,

$$\frac{v_m}{Q} = f(\eta, \eta_0)$$

Using the same notation as formerly (Figure 16), at steady state at the surface

$$\eta \left(\frac{\partial^2 v}{\partial y^2} \right)_{z=0} - \eta_0 \left(\frac{\partial v}{\partial z} \right)_{z=0} = 0$$

and in the bulk

$$\eta_0 \left(\frac{\partial^2 v}{\partial y^2} + \frac{\partial^2 v}{\partial z^2} \right) + \frac{\Delta p}{l} = 0$$

The boundary conditions are

$$v = 0 \qquad \text{at} \qquad y = \pm a$$

and

$$v = 0 \quad \text{at} \quad z = h$$

Integration of these equations leads to

$$v_{z=0} = \frac{16a^2 \Delta p}{\pi^3 l \eta_0} \sum_{n=0}^{\infty} \cos \frac{(2n+1)\pi x}{2a}$$

$$\times \frac{(-1)^n \tanh[(2n+1)\pi h/4a]}{(2n+1)^3 \coth[(2n+1)\pi h/2a] + (2n+1)^4 \pi \eta/2a\eta_0}$$

For a deep canal ($h \geq 6a$, for example) this expression simplifies to

$$v_{z=0} = \frac{16a^2 \Delta p}{\pi^3 l \eta_0} \sum_0^{\infty} (-1)^n (2n+1)^{-3} \left[1 + \frac{(2n+1)\pi\eta}{2a\eta_0} \right]^{-1} \cos \left[\frac{(2n+1)\pi x}{2a} \right]$$

whence

$$v_m = \frac{16a^2 \Delta p}{\pi^3 l \eta_0} \sum_0^{\infty} (-1)^n (2n+1)^{-3} \left[1 + \frac{(2n+1)\pi\eta}{2a\eta_0} \right]^{-1}$$

The bulk flux Q is

$$Q = \frac{2a^3}{\eta_0} \frac{\Delta p}{l} \left[\frac{h}{3} - \frac{64a}{\pi^5} \sum_{n=0}^{\infty} \frac{1}{(2n+1)^5} \right.$$

$$\left. \times \frac{2a\eta_0 + 2(2n+1)\pi\eta \tanh[(2n+1)\pi h/4a]}{2a\eta_0 \coth[(2n+1)\pi h/2a] + (2n+1)\pi h} \right]$$

which for a deep canal becomes

$$Q = \frac{2a^3}{\eta_0} \frac{\Delta p}{l} \left\{ \frac{h}{3} - \frac{64a}{\pi^5} \sum_0^{\infty} \left[1 + \frac{(2n+1)\pi\eta}{a\eta_0} \right] (2n+1)^{-5} \left[1 + \frac{(2n+1)\pi\eta}{2a\eta_0} \right]^{-1} \right\}$$

whence

$$\frac{Q}{v_m} = \frac{\pi^5 ah - 192a^2 \sum_0^{\infty} (2n+1)^{-5}[1 + (2n+1)\pi\eta/a\eta_0]}{24\pi^2 \sum_0^{\infty} (-1)^n (2n+1)^{-3}[1 + (2n+1)\pi\eta/2a\eta_0]^{-1}} \times [1 + (2n+1)\pi\eta/2a\eta_0]^{-1}$$

Because flow methods for the measurement of surface viscosity are applicable only to relatively small surface viscosities, we may assume that $\eta/a\eta_0$ is always small. It is then possible to develop Q/v_m as a power series in η/η_0. The result is

$$\frac{Q}{v_m} = 1.3334ah - 0.8404a^2 + (1.9799h - 2.5812a) \frac{\eta}{\eta_0} + \cdots$$

Both v_m and Q are to be measured. With h and η_0 known, η is the result of a simple calculation. The apparatus used for these measurements is sketched in Figure 17. The method has the advantage of being applicable to adsorbed films.

The preceding formulas presume that the bulk fluid flow does not generate a drop in surface pressure $\Delta\pi$ as a result of changing the concentration of the surface layer. If this occurs, it is possible under the assumption of a linear superposition of the two effects to relate v_m, Q, $\Delta\pi$, and η at steady state, whence the surface viscosity may be calculated from experimental determinations of v_m, Q, and $\Delta\pi$. The necessary formula, however, is not in a computationally convenient form, and the precision of the calculated surface viscosity is poor.

The risk of creating a more or less ill-defined surface pressure gradient because of film flow is eliminated in apparatus in which the motion of the substrate is generated by the containing vessel. A circular vessel turns with constant angular velocity about its axis. A circular canal, formed by two cylinders coaxial with the container, either touches (49, 50) or is more or less deeply inserted into the substrate (173). As in the preceding method, the film velocity v_m in the center of the canal is observed by the motion of fine dust particles on the surface. If the canal is not submerged, the technique is relatively sensitive, but the calculation of η from v_m and the angular velocity of the trough is a difficult one. For this reason it is preferable to calibrate the apparatus by means of insoluble films whose surface viscosity has been determined by the method of the floating canal. On the other hand, this apparatus has the advantage of being capable of generalization to the measurement of the surface viscosity of films at the interface between two liquids, whether they be insoluble or adsorbed films. For interfacial films, however, the precise calibration of the viscometer is a far more delicate matter.

If the circular canal is so deep that its lower edge is in contact with the bottom of the moving vessel, it is possible to relate v_m to the mean velocity

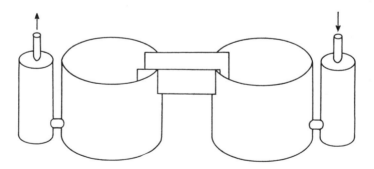

Fig. 17.   The surface viscometer of Ewers and Sack (schematic).

v_f of that portion of the base lying between the walls of the canal. Assuming (173) that the width $2a$ of the canal of depth h is small compared to the radius r of the canal, and using the same notation as above, the equations of the motion are

$$\frac{\partial^2 v}{\partial y^2} + \frac{\partial^2 v}{\partial z^2} = 0$$

$$\eta \left(\frac{\partial^2 v}{\partial y^2}\right)_{z=0} - \eta_0 \left(\frac{\partial v}{\partial z}\right)_{z=0} = 0$$

for which the boundary conditions are

$$v = 0 \quad \text{for} \quad y = \pm a$$

and

$$v = v_f \quad \text{for} \quad z = h$$

Upon integration, these equations yield

$$v_m = \frac{8a\eta_0 v_f}{\pi} \sum_{n=0}^{\infty} (-1)^n (2n+1)^{-1}$$

$$\times \left[(2n+1)\pi\eta \sinh(2n+1)\frac{\pi h}{2a} + 2a\eta_0 \cosh(2n+1)\frac{\pi h}{2a} \right]^{-1}$$

which for a narrow canal ($a < \pi h/4$) reduces to

$$v_m = \frac{8}{\pi} a\eta_0 v_f \left(\pi\eta \sinh\frac{\pi h}{2a} + 2a\eta_0 \cosh\frac{\pi h}{2a} \right)^{-1}$$

$$= \frac{16a\eta_0 r}{T} \left(\pi\eta \sinh\frac{\pi h}{2a} + 2a\eta_0 \cosh\frac{\pi h}{2a} \right)^{-1}$$

in which T is the period of rotation of the vessel. For a given canal it is thus possible to deduce the value of η from that of v_m. The method is as valid for insoluble as for adsorbed films. For insoluble films the value of v_m for the substrate surface free from surface film is

$$v_{m_0} = \frac{8r}{T \cosh\dfrac{\pi h}{2a}}$$

whence

$$\frac{v_{m_0} - v_m}{v_m} = \frac{\pi\eta}{2a\eta_0} \tanh\frac{\pi h}{2a}$$

This formula, independent of the rotational velocity of the vessel, provides an extremely simple method for the determination of η. It is, however, rather insensitive. Thus for $\eta \sim 10^{-4}$, the difference $v_{m_0} - v_m$ is only of the order $10^{-2}v_{m_0}$. On the other hand, for $\eta \sim 10^{-2}$, v_m is of the order $(\frac{1}{2})v_{m_0}$. The method thus appears to be satisfactory only for the measurement of high surface viscosities.

D. Surface Rheometry

We have just surveyed methods of measuring the elasticity or viscosity of monomolecular films when they are either purely elastic or purely viscous. Many surface phases, however, are either viscoelastic or viscoplastic (see Section II.D.2), and can be represented only by rheological models containing several elements. If the investigator is not content with measurements of the "apparent" values of viscosity and elasticity, it is important, as explained in Section II.D.3, to plan experiments from which may be determined the ensemble of rheological coefficients. We shall see that equipment used for experiments of this type often differs very little from that used for films whose rheological properties are describable in terms of a single parameter.

In the absence of any quantitative determination of the rheological coefficients, qualitative measurements may be performed using equipment which does not allow true measurements of the rheological parameters. Such experiments distinguish between systems that are almost exclusively viscous and those for which the plastic or elastic effects are dominant. They are often used to detect phase transitions at the interface as a function of, say, temperature, concentration, or pH. Thus the development of plasticity in soap films has been demonstrated by changes in the rate of damping of the oscillations of a ring suspended from a torsion wire (77), or of those of a spring whose coils support the film (177). Analogous information can be obtained with the apparatus of Cheesman and Sten-Knudsen (135) on protein films, for example, by studying the stress displacement curves of a floating object, which are in fact creep or recovery curves. The existence of plastic behavior can also be demonstrated whenever the stress–elongation curves determined from the apparatus of Grabenstetter and Corkill (149) or of Matalon (145, 146) show a perceptible hysteresis.

1. The Determination of Surface Yield Values

Some of the equipment originally designed for the measurement of surface viscosity has proved itself to be adaptable to the determination of plastic yield values. Such apparatus has in general been of the type in which a stationary flow pattern is imposed upon the substrate. In particular this is the case in the viscometer of Burton and Mannheimer (173). For such apparatus the maximum value of the stress in the film is

$$f = \frac{4\eta_0 v_f}{\pi} \sum_0^\infty \left[\frac{2a\eta_0}{\pi\eta} \cosh(2n+1)\frac{\pi h}{2a} + (2n+1)\sinh(2n+1)\frac{\pi h}{2a} \right]^{-1}$$

the notation being that of Section II.C.2.d. For deep canals, this formula reduces to

$$f = 4\eta_0 v_f \left[\frac{2a\eta_0}{\eta} \cosh \frac{\pi h}{2a} + \pi \sinh \frac{\pi h}{2a} \right]^{-1}$$

Letting v_s be the minimum value of v_f necessary for v_m not to vanish, and assuming that for stresses less than the yield value the surface viscosity may be taken as infinite, the surface plastic yield value is

$$f_s = \frac{4\eta_0 v_s}{\pi \sinh(\pi h/2a)}$$

The apparatus of Brown, Thuman, and MacBain (Figure 18) is suitable for the study of viscoplastic films. A plot is constructed of the deflection δ of the inner ring of radius r_1 against the angular velocity ω of the outer ring of radius r_2. Let δ_s be the value of δ extrapolated to $\omega = 0$ along the linear portion of $\delta(\omega)$. If $\delta_0(\omega)$ is the deflection of the ring in the absence of the film, the surface viscosity is

$$\eta = \frac{C(\delta - \delta_0 - \delta_s)}{4\pi\omega} \left(\frac{1}{r_1^2} - \frac{1}{r_2^2} \right)$$

in which C is the torsion constant of the suspension wire. The surface plastic yield value, or the surface elastic limit, is given by

$$f_s = \delta_s \frac{C}{4\pi} \left(\frac{1}{r_1^2} - \frac{1}{r_2^2} \right) \left(\ln \frac{r_2}{r_1} \right)^{-1}$$

This method has the disadvantage of not allowing the determination of the surface elastic modulus G.

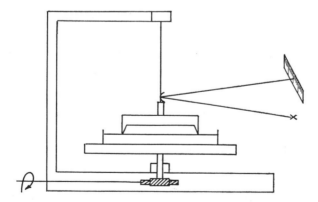

Fig. 18. The rheometer of Brown, Thuman, and McBain (schematic).

2. The Use of Oscillatory Rheometers

One of the most commonly used methods in the study of the rheological properties of films is to measure the damping of the oscillations of a body suspended from a torsion wire. For surface films, the body is a narrow ring which touches the surface. For interfacial films, the oscillating body generally has the form of a pair of opposed cones whose common base is in the plane of the interface (178).

To convert damping measurements into numerical values of the rheological parameters of two-dimensional phases, it is necessary to make assumptions concerning the nature of the "rheological body" chosen to represent the properties of a given phase. The simplest assumption would obviously be to choose either of the two-element models, the Voigt solid or the Maxwell liquid. Some authors (179) have even pushed the simplification further by assuming as a very crude approximation that for large amplitude oscillations, the viscous term is the dominant one and that we may write

$$\eta = \frac{1.15I}{\pi}\left(\frac{1}{r_1^{\,2}} - \frac{1}{r_2^{\,2}}\right)\left(\frac{\Delta}{T} - \frac{\Delta_0}{T_0}\right)$$

while for small-amplitude oscillations the elastic term is dominant and

$$G = \pi I\left(\frac{1}{r_1^{\,2}} - \frac{1}{r_2^{\,2}}\right)\left(\frac{1}{T^2} - \frac{1}{T_0^{\,2}}\right)$$

As in Section III.C.2.b, T and Δ are respectively the period of the oscillation and its logarithmic decrement in the presence of the film, T_0 and Δ_0 being the same quantities in the absence of film.

For the calculation of G a less simplified formula has been proposed (71):

$$G = \frac{I}{\pi}\left(\frac{1}{r_1^{\,2}} - \frac{1}{r_2^{\,2}}\right)\left(\frac{\pi^2 - 1.32\Delta^2}{T^2} - \frac{\pi^2 - 1.32\Delta_0^{\,2}}{T_0^{\,2}}\right)$$

but the shear modulus was taken to be the real part of the complex modulus G^* which enters into an equation of motion for the torsion pendulum reducing to (180)

$$I\frac{d^2\delta}{dt^2} + G^*\delta = 0$$

If the elastic and viscous reactions are superposed classically (162), the surface modulus is given by

$$G = \frac{1}{\pi}\left(\frac{1}{r_1^{\,2}} - \frac{1}{r_2^{\,2}}\right)\left(\frac{\pi^2 + 1.32\Delta^2}{T^2} - \frac{\pi^2 + 1.32\Delta_0^{\,2}}{T_0^{\,2}}\right)$$

and the equation of motion takes the general form

$$I \frac{d^2\delta}{dt^2} + (\alpha\eta_0 + \beta\eta) \frac{d\delta}{dt} + (C + \gamma G)\, \delta = 0$$

Instead of studying the free oscillations of a torsion pendulum, we may instead consider the forced oscillations of frequency ω imposed either through the torsion head or through the vessel containing the film. Let H be the ratio at steady state of the amplitude of the driving oscillation to that of the oscillating body, let φ be the phase angle between the two motions, and define Z by

$$Z = 4\pi \left(\frac{1}{r_1{}^2} - \frac{1}{r_2{}^2} \right)^{-1}$$

Then for G and η we obtain the following formulas (162).

If the forced oscillations are generated by the torsion head,

$$G = \frac{1}{Z} \left(C \frac{\cos \varphi}{H} - C + I\omega^2 \right)$$

$$\eta = \frac{1}{\omega Z} \left(C \frac{\sin \varphi}{H} - (C - I\omega^2)\tan \varphi_0 \right)$$

in which C is the torsion constant, I the moment of inertia, and φ_0 the phase angle in the absence of film.

When the oscillations are generated by the trough,

$$G = \frac{H}{Z} (C - I\omega^2) \frac{\cos \varphi - H}{H^2 - 2H \cos \varphi + 1}$$

$$\eta = \frac{1}{\omega Z} (C - I\omega^2) \left[\frac{H \sin \varphi}{H^2 - 2H \cos \varphi + 1} - \cot \varphi \right]$$

It does not appear that these methods of forced oscillation have been much exploited experimentally. It appears furthermore that models of greater than two elements have not been used in the interpretation of damping experiments.

3. The Use of Deflection Rheometers

A frequently employed method (42, 57, 58, 181) in the study of viscoelastic films consists in following as a function of time the movement $\delta(t)$ of a torsion pendulum whose head has initially been rotated through an angle ψ. It is important to note that in this method the stress is not constant, except as a first approximation when δ is small in comparison with ψ.

At an arbitrary point of the film, for example, the point whose polar coordinates are r, φ in Figure 19, the relation between shear strain θ and shear stress p can be expressed in the form (181)

$$L\varepsilon = Mp$$

in which L and M are operators characteristic of the mechanical model of the film. The equation of motion of the moving ring may in this case (182) be written

$$M\left[I\frac{d^2\delta}{dt^2} - C(\psi - \delta)\right] + ZL\delta = 0$$

When the resistance of the film to deformation is sufficiently large to render negligible the inertial term because of the slowness of the movement, this equation simplifies to

$$CM(\psi - \delta) - ZL\,\delta = 0$$

Explicit expressions for L and M depend upon the rheological model chosen to represent the film. In every case that has been examined from this point of view, the influence of the substrate upon the motion of the film is always neglected. The deflexion technique can consequently be used only on films that offer a large resistance to deformation.

If we take as a rheological model of the film a solid displaying both instantaneous and delayed elasticity, the operators L and M are written in terms of three parameters η_s, G_1, and G_2 as follows (the notation is that of Figure 6):

$$L = \eta_s\frac{d}{dt} + G_2$$

$$M = \frac{\eta_s}{G_1}\frac{d}{dt} + \frac{G_2}{G_1} + 1$$

Assuming that the motion is sufficiently slow to render negligible the inertial terms (181), the equation of motion becomes

$$\frac{d\delta}{dt} + \alpha\delta - \beta\psi = 0$$

with

$$\alpha = \frac{C(G_1 + G_2) + ZG_1G_2}{\eta_s(C + G_1Z)}$$

and

$$\beta = \frac{C}{\eta_s}\frac{G_1 + G_2}{C + G_1Z}$$

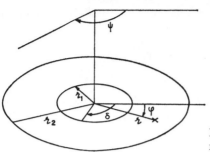

Fig. 19.   The principle of the deflection surface rheometer.

whence

$$\delta = \frac{\beta}{\alpha}\psi - Bl^{-\alpha t}$$

B being a constant whose value depends upon the initial conditions.   If the comparison with experimental curves $\delta(t)$ permits the empirical determination of α, β, and B, it may be shown that

$$G_1 = \frac{C}{Z}\frac{\left(1 - \dfrac{\beta}{\alpha}\right)\psi + B}{\psi\dfrac{\beta}{\alpha} - B}$$

$$G_2 = (\alpha - \beta)G_1\left[\frac{C + G_1 Z}{C}\beta - \alpha\right]^{-1}$$

$$\eta_s = \frac{C}{C + G_1 Z}\frac{G_1 + G_2}{\beta}$$

If the film shows only instantaneous elasticity we recover

$$G_1 = \frac{C}{Z}\frac{\psi - \delta}{\delta}$$

with δ independent of the time.

In the most general case, where the film is represented by a Burger's body, L and M are a function of four parameters η_s, η, G, and G_l (the notation is that of Figure 8):

$$L = \eta_s\frac{d^2}{dt^2} + G\frac{d}{dt}$$

$$M = \frac{\eta_s}{G_l}\frac{d^2}{dt^2} + \left(1 + \frac{G}{G_l} + \frac{\eta_s}{\eta}\right)\frac{d}{dt} + \frac{G}{\eta}$$

and the equation of motion with the neglect of the inertial terms (181) assumes the form

$$\frac{d^2\delta}{dt^2} + \alpha \frac{d\delta}{dt} + \beta(\delta - \psi) = 0$$

with

$$\alpha = \frac{C}{C + G_i Z} \left(\frac{G_l}{\eta_s} + \frac{G}{\eta_s} + \frac{G_l}{\eta} + \frac{GG_l}{ZC\eta_s} \right)$$

$$\beta = \frac{C}{C + GZ_l} \frac{GG_l}{\eta\eta_s}$$

whence

$$\delta = 4 - Be^{-at} - De^{-bt}$$

with

$$a = \frac{\alpha - \sqrt{\alpha^2 - 4\beta}}{2}, \qquad b = \frac{\alpha + \sqrt{\alpha^2 - 4\beta}}{2}$$

B and D are constants whose values are determined by the initial conditions of the motion.   If the constants α, β, B, and D can be determined from experimental curves, it is possible to show that

$$G_l = \frac{C}{Z} \frac{B + D}{\psi - B - D}$$

$$G = \frac{CB(B + D)}{\psi DZ}$$

$$\eta_s = \frac{C}{\alpha} \left[G + G_l + \frac{ZGG_l}{C} \right] [C + G_l Z]^{-1}$$

$$\eta = \frac{CGG_l}{\beta\eta_s} [C + G_l Z]^{-1}$$

If the inertial forces cannot be neglected, the equation of motion is more complicated and becomes

$$\frac{d^4\delta}{dt^4} + a\frac{d^3\delta}{dt^3} + b\frac{d^2\delta}{dt^2} + f\frac{d\delta}{dt} + h(\delta - \psi) = 0$$

in which

$$a = \frac{G_l}{\eta} + \frac{G_l}{\eta_s} + \frac{G}{\eta_s}$$

$$b = \frac{GG_l}{\eta\eta_s} + \frac{C}{I} + \frac{ZG_l}{I}$$

$$f = \frac{C}{I} \left[\frac{G_l}{\eta} + \frac{G_l}{\eta_s} + \frac{G}{\eta_s} + \frac{Z}{C} \frac{GG_l}{\eta_s} \right]$$

$$h = \frac{C}{I} \frac{GG_l}{\eta\eta_s}$$

whence

$$\delta = \psi - Be^{\alpha_1 t} - De^{\alpha_2 t} - Fe^{\alpha_3 t} - Ne^{\alpha_4 t}$$

$B, D, F,$ and N being constants determined by the initial conditions, and the α_i being the roots of

$$\alpha^4 + a\alpha^3 + b\alpha^2 + f\alpha + h = 0$$

If the experimental curves $\delta(t)$ permit the empirical determination of the coefficients, it may be shown that

$$G_l = \frac{C}{Z} \frac{B + D}{\psi - B - D}$$

$$G = \frac{C}{Z} \frac{B(B + D)}{\psi D}$$

$$\eta_s = \frac{G_l}{f} \frac{G + G_l + ZGG_l C^{-1}}{C + G_l Z}$$

$$\eta = \frac{CGG_l}{\eta_s} \frac{b}{h} (C + G_l Z)^{-1}$$

In a recently constructed apparatus (58), the instrument consisted of a Teflon ring 2.1 cm in diameter suspended by a torsion wire of torsion constant $C = 0.314$ g-cm²/sec². The exterior ring consisted of a trough of glass or of polypropylene. In the calculation of Z, a correction was made for the enlargement of the surface due to the meniscus (183, 184):

$$\Delta S = (4 - 2\sqrt{2})\pi(r - 0.25l)l$$

with

$$l^2 = \frac{\gamma}{(\rho_1 - \rho_2)g}$$

in which r is the radius of the trough, γ the interfacial tension, ρ_1 and ρ_2 the densities of the two phases, and g the acceleration of gravity.

4. The Use of Rheometers with Constant Turning Couple

In all the deflection instruments described above the stress varies with time, a fact which complicates the equations of motion and hinders the determination of creep curves in the strict sense of the term. To obtain a constant stress it is convenient to use instead of a torsion wire an electromagnetic unit (Figure 20) in which a moving coil C is placed in the radial field of a magnet M (44, 73, 131, 185). Under these conditions, the turning

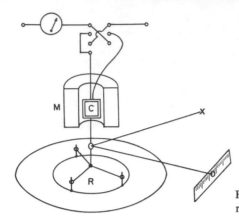

Fig. 20. The constant turning couple surface rheometer (schematic).

couple P to which the film is subjected is proportional to the current i in the moving coil, $P = Ki$. The constant K is determined by balancing the electromagnetic turning couple against a torsion wire of known torsion constant. To measure creep curves, the current i is maintained constant, and the displacement $\delta(t)$ of the ring R is recorded. Recovery curves are determined by measuring $\delta(t)$ after cessation of the current. Relaxation curves may be determined by varying i in such a way that δ remains constant. The curve $i(t)$ is then plotted and is, except for a scale factor, the relaxation curve.

If the inertial forces and the mechanical resistance of the substrate may be neglected, and if the film may be represented by a Voigt model, G is given by

$$G = \frac{Ki}{Z\delta_\infty}$$

in which δ_∞ is the limiting deflection after the achievement of equilibrium. If the film is represented by a Maxwell liquid, η is given by

$$\eta = \frac{Ki}{Z\delta'_\infty}$$

in which δ'_∞ is the slope of the curve $\delta(t)$ after the attainment of a steady state.

For films which can be represented by models containing three or four elements, the methods developed in Section III.D.3 for the determination of the rheological coefficients may easily be extended to the case in which the stress is maintained constant.

Thus for a three-element model, the equation of motion is

$$\frac{d\delta}{dt} + \alpha\delta - \beta = 0$$

whence

$$\delta = \frac{\beta}{\alpha} - Be^{-\alpha t}$$

with

$$\alpha = \frac{G_2}{\eta_s}, \qquad \beta = \left(\frac{G_2}{G_1} + 1\right)\frac{Ki}{Z\eta_s}, \qquad B = \frac{Ki}{ZG_2}$$

The coefficients α, β, and B are easily determined from experiment:

$$\alpha = \frac{\delta_0'}{\delta_\infty - \delta_0}, \qquad \beta = \frac{\delta_\infty \delta_0'}{\delta_\infty - \delta_0}, \qquad B = \delta_\infty - \delta_0$$

δ_0 being the instantaneous displacement due to an instantaneous elasticity, and δ_0' being the slope of $\delta(t)$ as $t \to 0$.   Therefore

$$G_1 = \frac{Ki}{Z\delta_0}, \qquad G_2 = \frac{Ki}{Z(\delta_\infty - \delta_0)}, \qquad \eta = \frac{Ki}{Z\delta_0'}$$

For the four-element Burger's model, the equation of motion is

$$\frac{d^2\delta}{dt^2} + \alpha\frac{d\delta}{dt} - \beta = 0$$

whence

$$\delta = A + \frac{\beta}{\alpha}t - Be^{-\alpha t}$$

with

$$\alpha = \frac{G}{\eta_s}, \qquad \beta = \frac{GKi}{Z\eta\eta_s}$$

$$A = \frac{Ki}{Z}\left(\frac{1}{G} + \frac{1}{G_v}\right), \qquad B = \frac{Ki}{ZG}$$

Now

$$\alpha = -\frac{\delta_0''}{\delta_0' - \delta_\infty'}, \qquad \beta = -\frac{\delta_\infty' \delta_0''}{\delta_0' - \delta_\infty'}$$

$$A = \delta_0 - \frac{(\delta_0' - \delta_\infty')^2}{\delta_0''}, \qquad B = -\frac{(\delta_0' - \delta_\infty')_2}{\delta_0''}$$

δ_0 being the instantaneous displacement of the ring due to instantaneous elasticity, δ_0' and δ_∞' the slope of $\delta(t)$ at $t = 0$ and $t \to \infty$, and δ_0'' the slope at $t = 0$ of $\delta'(t)$. All these quantities may be determined by experiment.

From them may be calculated the rheological parameters

$$G_l = \frac{Ki}{Z\delta_0}, \qquad G = \frac{Ki}{ZB}$$

$$\eta = \frac{Ki}{Z\delta'_\infty}, \qquad \eta_s = \frac{Ki}{Z(\delta'_0 - \delta'_\infty)}$$

Acknowledgment

I am greatly indebted to Professor F. C. Goodrich for the careful translation of the entire French manuscript.

Symbols

A	molecular area
C	torsion wire constant
E	surface Young's modulus
E_G	Gibbs elasticity
G	surface elastic or shear modulus
G^*	complex surface modulus
$\bar{G}$	absolute surface modulus
ΔG_0	free energy of adsorption
I	moment of inertia
J	surface compliance modulus
K	surface compressibility
k	Boltzmann's constant
P	damping constant
p_{ij}	stress component
$\mathscr{R}(t)$	creep recovery function
$\mathscr{S}$	strain tensor
$\mathscr{S}'$	rate of strain tensor
S	surface area
$\mathscr{T}$	stress tensor
$\mathscr{T}'$	rate of stress tensor
T	oscillation period
$\mathbf{u}$	displacement vector
u_α	displacement component
$\mathbf{v}$	velocity vector
v_α	velocity component
x_i	coordinate
Γ	surface excess concentration
γ	surface or interfacial tension
Δ	logarithmic decrement of damping
δ	angular deflection
ε_{ij}	stress tensor component
ε'_{ij}	rate of stress tensor component
ζ	surface dilational viscosity
ζ_M	Marangoni viscosity
η	surface shear viscosity

η_0 bulk viscosity of subphase
θ relaxation time
$\varkappa$ surface compression modulus
λ viscosity coefficient for shear normal to film plane
μ chemical potential
ξ surface flexibility
π surface pressure
ρ density
σ surface Poisson's ratio
τ retardation time
Φ surface loss angle or dissipation factor
$\Phi(t)$ creep function
χ elastic modulus for shear normal to film plane
$\psi(t)$ relaxation function
ω angular velocity

References

1. J. T. Davies and E. K. Rideal, *Interfacial Phenomena*, Academic Press, London, 1963.
2. G. L. Gaines, *Insoluble Monolayers at Liquid–Gas Interfaces*, Wiley-Interscience, New York, 1966.
3. J. A. F. Plateau, *Phil. Mag. Ser. 4*, **38**, 445 (1869).
4. J. A. F. Plateau, *Bull. Acad. Belg. Ser. 2*, **34**, 404 (1872).
5. J. A. F. Plateau, *Statique Expérimentale et Théorique des Liquides Soumis aux Seules Forces Moléculaires*, Gauthier-Villars, Paris, 1873.
6. J. A. F. Plateau, *Bull. Acad. Belg. Ser. 2*, **48**, 106 (1879).
7. C. G. M. Marangoni, *Ann. Phys. (Poggendorff)*, **142**, 337 (1871).
8. C. G. M. Marangoni, *Nuovo Cimento Ser. 2*, **5, 6**, 239 (1872).
9. C. G. M. Marangoni, *Nuovo Cimento Ser. 3*, **3**, 50, 97, 193 (1878).
10. C. G. M. Marangoni, *Beiblätter Ann. Phys. (Poggendorff)*, **3**, 842 (1879).
11. J. W. Gibbs, *Trans. Conn. Acad.*, **3**, 343 (1878).
12. J. W. Gibbs, *Collected Works*, Vol. I, Longmans, Green, New York, 1931, pp. 269, 300.
13. Rayleigh (J. W. S. Strutt), *Proc. Roy. Soc. (London)*, **47**, 281, 364 (1890).
14. Rayleigh (J. W. S. Strutt), *Proc. Roy. Soc. (London)*, **48**, 127 (1890).
15. Rayleigh (J. W. S. Strutt), *Phil. Mag. Ser. 5*, **30**, 386 (1890).
16. J. Boussinesq, *Ann. Chim. Phys. Ser. 8*, **29**, 349 (1913).
17. I. Langmuir, *Science*, **84**, 378 (1936).
18. I. Langmuir and V. J. Schaefer, *J. Am. Chem. Soc.*, **59**, 2400 (1937).
19. W. D. Harkins and R. J. Myers, *Nature*, **140**, 465 (1937).
20. W. D. Harkins and J. G. Kirkwood, *J. Chem. Phys.*, **6**, 53 (1938).
21. J. G. Fourt and W. D. Harkins, *J. Phys. Chem.*, **42**, 897 (1938).
22. E. Boyd and W. D. Harkins, *J. Am. Chem. Soc.*, **61**, 1188 (1939).
23. M. Joly, *J. Phys. Radium*, **8**, 471 (1937).
24. M. Joly, *J. Chim. Phys.*, **36**, 285 (1939).
25. M. Joly, *Kolloid-Z.*, **89**, 26 (1939).
26. M. Joly, *J. Physique*, **7**, 83, 112 (1946).
27. M. Joly, *J. Chim. Phys.*, **44**, 206, 213 (1947).
28. R. Chaminade, D. G. Dervichian, and M. Joly, *J. Chim. Phys.*, **47**, 883 (1950).
29. M. Joly, *J. Colloid Sci.*, **5**, 49 (1950).
30. M. Joly, *Kolloid-Z.*, **126**, 35 (1952).

31. W. J. Moore and H. Eyring, *J. Chem. Phys.*, **6**, 391 (1938).
32. A. A. Trapeznikov, *Acta Physicochim. USSR*, **10**, 65 (1939).
33. A. A. Trapeznikov, *Dokl. Akad. Nauk SSSR*, **30**, 321 (1941).
34. A. A. Trapeznikov, *Acta Physicochim. USSR*, **19**, 553 (1944).
35. A. A. Trapeznikov, *Acta Physicochim. USSR*, **20**, 589 (1945).
36. A. A. Trapeznikov, *Dokl. Akad. Nauk SSSR*, **63**, 57 (1948).
37. K. V. Zotova and A. A. Trapeznikov, *Dokl. Akad. Nauk SSSR*, **117**, 833 (1957).
38. A. A. Trapeznikov, *Vysokomolekul. Soedin.*, **3**, 1708 (1961).
39. A. A. Trapeznikov, *Kolloidn. Zh.*, **24**, 97 (1962).
40. A. A. Trapeznikov, *Kolloidn. Zh.*, **25**, 613 (1963).
41. A. A. Trapeznikov, *Kolloidn. Zh.*, **26**, 190 (1964).
42. T. Tachibana and K. Inokuchi, *J. Colloid Sci.*, **8**, 341 (1953).
43. K. Inokuchi, *Bull. Chem. Soc. Japan*, **26**, 500 (1953).
44. K. Inokuchi, *Bull. Chem. Soc. Japan*, **27**, 432 (1954).
45. K. Inokuchi, *Bull. Chem. Soc. Japan*, **28**, 453 (1955).
46. W. E. Ewers and R. A. Sack, *Australian J. Chem.*, **7**, 40 (1954).
47. L. De Bernard, *Mem. Serv. Chim. Etat*, **41**, 287 (1956).
48. L. De Bernard, *Proc. Intern. Congr. Surface Activity, 2nd, London, 1957*, **1**, 360.
49. J. T. Davies, *Proc. Intern. Congr. Surface Activity, 2nd, London, 1957*, **1**, 240.
50. J. T. Davies and G. R. A. Mayers, *Trans. Faraday Soc.*, **56**, 691 (1960).
51. J. Jaffe and J. M. Loutz, *J. Polymer Sci.*, **29**, 381 (1958).
52. J. Jaffe and C. Berliner, *J. Chim. Phys.*, **63**, 389 (1966).
53. J. Jaffe, C. Berliner, and M. Lambert, *J. Chim. Phys.*, **64**, 499 (1967).
54. T. Isemura and K. Fukuzuka, *Mem. Inst. Sci. Ind. Res. Osaka Univ.*, **14**, 169 (1957).
55. S. Ikeda and T. Isemura, *Bull. Chem. Soc. Japan*, **33**, 131, 137, 753 (1960).
56. S. Ikeda and T. Isemura, *Bull. Chem. Soc. Japan*, **34**, 416, 422 (1961).
57. K. Motomura and R. Matuura, *J. Colloid Sci.*, **18**, 295 (1963).
58. K. Motomura, *J. Phys. Chem.*, **68**, 2826 (1964).
59. A. N. Frumkin and V. G. Levich, *Zh. Fiz. Khim.*, **21**, 1183 (1947).
60. K. C. D. Hickman, *Ind. Eng. Chem.*, **44**, 1892 (1952).
61. J. B. Lewis and H. R. C. Pratt, *Nature*, **171**, 1155 (1953).
62. K. C. D. Hickman and W. A. Torpey, *Ind. Eng. Chem.*, **46**, 1446 (1954).
63. J. G. Oldroyd, *Proc. Roy. Soc. (London) Ser. A*, **232**, 567 (1955).
64. A. L. Fedosov, *Zh. Fiz. Khim.*, **30**, 223 (1956).
65. J. T. Davies and D. A. Haydon, *Proc. Intern. Congr. Surface Activity, 2nd, London, 1957*, **1**, 417.
66. M. Linton and K. L. Sutherland, *Proc. Intern. Congr. Surface Activity, 2nd, London, 1957*, **1**, 494.
67. M. A. Nawab and S. G. Mason, *Trans. Faraday Soc.*, **54**, 1712 (1958).
68. L. E. Scriven and D. L. Pigford, *A.I.Ch.E. J.*, **4**, 439 (1958).
69. L. E. Scriven and C. V. Sternling, *Nature*, **187**, 186 (1960).
70. D. G. Dervichian and M. Joly, *J. Phys. Radium*, **10**, 375 (1939).
71. D. J. Crisp, *J. Colloid Sci.*, **1**, 49, 161 (1946).
72. D. J. Crisp, in *Surface Phenomena in Chemistry and Biology*, J. F. Danielli, K. G. A. Pankhurst, and A. C. Riddiford, Eds., Pergamon Press, London, 1958, p. 23.
73. T. Tachibana, K. Inokuchi, and T. Inokuchi, *Kolloid-Z.*, **167**, 141 (1959).
74. T. Isemura and K. Fukuzuka, *Mem. Inst. Sci. Ind. Res. Osaka Univ.*, **13**, 137 (1956).
75. D. G. Dervichian and M. Joly, *Compt. Rend.*, **208**, 1488 (1939).
76. E. J. Burcik, J. R. Sears, and A. Tillotson, *J. Colloid Sci.*, **9**, 281 (1954).
77. E. J. Burcik and R. C. Newman, *J. Colloid Sci.*, **12**, 10 (1957).
78. J. Ross, *J. Phys. Chem.*, **62**, 531 (1958).

79. T. Isemura and K. Hamaguchi, *Mem. Inst. Sci. Ind. Res. Osaka Univ.*, **9**, 134 (1952).
80. T. Isemura and K. Hamaguchi, *Bull. Chem. Soc. Japan*, **27**, 125, 339 (1954).
81. M. Joly, *Biorheology*, **4**, 11 (1966).
82. M. Joly, *Cah. Groupe Fr. Rheol.*, **1**, 217 (1967).
83. I. Langmuir, *J. Am. Chem. Soc.*, **38**, 221 (1916).
84. I. Langmuir, *J. Am. Chem. Soc.* **39**, 1848 (1917).
85. F. C. Goodrich, "The Thermodynamics of Fluid Interfaces," in *Surface and Colloid Science*, Vol. 1, Wiley-Interscience, New York, 1969, p. 1.
86. D. G. Dervichian, *J. Chim. Phys.*, **30**, 468 (1933).
87. Lord Rayleigh, *Phil. Mag.*, **48**, 337 (1899).
88. A. Cary and E. K. Rideal, *Proc. Roy. Soc. (London) Ser. A*, **109**, 318 (1925).
89. W. D. Harkins, T. F. Young, and G. E. Boyd, *J. Chem. Phys.*, **8**, 954 (1940).
90. G. E. Boyd and J. Schubert, *J. Phys. Chem.*, **61**, 1271 (1957).
91. G. E. Boyd, *J. Phys. Chem.*, **62**, 536 (1958).
92. J. H. Brooks and A. E. Alexander, *J. Phys. Chem.*, **66**, 1851 (1962).
93. A. E. Alexander and F. C. Goodrich, *J. Colloid Sci.*, **19**, 473 (1964).
94. L. Ter-Minassian-Saraga, *J. Chim. Phys.*, **52**, 80, 99, 181 (1955).
95. N. K. Adam, *The Physics and Chemistry of Surface*, Oxford University Press, 1941.
96. A. E. Alexander and T. Teorell, *Trans. Faraday Soc.*, **35**, 727 (1939).
97. J. T. Davies, *Trans. Faraday Soc.*, **48**, 1052 (1952).
98. T. Isemura, H. Hotta, and S. Otsuka, *Bull. Chem. Soc. Japan*, **27**, 93 (1954).
99. H. Hotta, *Bull. Chem. Soc. Japan*, **27**, 80, 412 (1954).
100. A. F. H. Ward and L. Tordai, *Trans. Faraday Soc.*, **42**, 399, 408, 413 (1946).
101. A. F. H. Ward, *Surface Chemistry*, Butterworths, London, 1949, p. 65.
102. B. A. Pethica, *Trans. Faraday Soc.*, **50**, 413 (1954).
103. B. A. Pethica, *Trans. Faraday Soc.*, **51**, 1402 (1955).
104. J. J. Betts and B. A. Pethica, *Proc. Intern. Congr. Surface Activity*, 2nd, London, **1**, 393.
105. R. Merigoux, *Compt. Rend.*, **202**, 2049 (1936).
106. R. Merigoux, *Compt. Rend.*, **203**, 848 (1936).
107. R. Merigoux, Thesis, Paris, 1938 (ed. by *Revue d'Optique théorique et expérimentale*).
108. J. H. Schulman and T. Teorell, *Trans. Faraday Soc.*, **34**, 1337 (1938).
109. J. Frenkel, *Kinetic Theory of Liquids*, Clarendon Press, Oxford, 1946, p. 5.
110. D. G. Dervichian, *J. Chem. Phys.*, **7**, 931 (1939).
111. D. G. Dervichian, in *Changements de Phases*, Editions de la Société de Chimie-Physique, Paris, 1952.
112. W. D. Harkins, *The Physical Chemistry of Surface Films*, Reinhold, New York, 1952.
113. M. Joly, *Surface Chemistry*, Butterworths, London, 1949, p. 37.
114. J. B. Bateman and L. A. Chambers, *J. Chem. Phys.*, **7**, 244 (1939).
115. M. Reiner, *Rhéologie Théorique*, Dunod, Paris, 1955.
116. J. W. Gibbs, *Collected Works* Vol. I, Yale University Press, New Haven, 1948, p. 301.
117. W. E. Ewers and K. L. Sutherland, *Australian J. Sci. Res. Ser. A, Phys.*, **5**, 697 (1952).
118. F. Van Voorst Vader, T. F. Erkens, and M. Van Den Tempel, *Trans. Faraday Soc.*, **60**, 1170 (1964).
119. S. J. Singer, *J. Chem. Phys.*, **16**, 872 (1948).
120. J. T. Davies, *Biochim. Biophys. Acta*, **11**, 165 (1953).
121. J. T. Davies, *J. Colloid Sci. Suppl*, **1**, 9 (1954).
122. H. Hotta, *J. Colloid Sci.*, **9**, 504 (1954).
123. K. J. Mysels, *J. Phys. Chem.*, **68**, 3441 (1964).
124. J. A. Kitchener, in *Recent Progress in Surface Science*, Vol. I, J. F. Danielli, K. G. A. Pankhurst, and A. C. Riddiford, Eds., Academic Press, New York, 1964, p. 51.

125. N. W. Tschoegl, *J. Colloid Sci.*, **13**, 500 (1958).
126. N. W. Tschoegl and A. E. Alexander, *J. Colloid Sci.*, **15**, 168 (1960).
127. B. Persoz, *Introduction à l'Etude de la Rhéologie*, Dunod, Paris, 1960.
128. J. Mandel, *Cours de Mécanique des Milieux Continus*, Gauthier-Villars, Paris, 1966.
129. T. Tachibana, K. Inokuchi, and T. Inokuchi, *Biochim. Biophys. Acta*, **24**, 174 (1957).
130. T. Alfrey, *Mechanical Behavior of High Polymers*, Interscience, New York, 1948, p. 105.
131. B. Biswas and D. A. Haydon, *Proc. Roy. Soc. (London) Ser. A*, **271**, 296 (1963).
132. B. Biswas and D. A. Haydon, *Proc. Roy. Soc. (London) Ser. A*, **271**, 317 (1963).
133. F. C. Goodrich, *Proc. Roy. Soc. (London) Ser. A*, **260**, 480, 490, 503 (1961).
134. J. R. Van Wazer, *J. Colloid Sci.*, **2**, 223 (1947).
135. D. F. Cheesman and O. Sten-Knudsen, *Biochim. Biophys. Acta*, **33**, 158 (1959).
136. N. W. Tschoegl, *J. Colloid Sci.*, **16**, 89 (1961).
137. H. Mouquin and E. K. Rideal, *Proc. Roy. Soc. (London) Ser. A*, **114**, 690 (1927).
138. C. W. N. Cumper and A. E. Alexander, *Australian J. Sci. Res. Ser. A*, **5**, 189 (1952).
139. L. Fourt, *J. Phys. Chem.*, **43**, 887 (1939).
140. J. A. Kitchener, *Nature*, **194**, 676 (1962).
141. J. A. Kitchener, *Nature*, **195**, 1094 (1962).
142. J. A. Kitchener, *Quart. Rev. (London)*, **13**, 71 (1959).
143. H. Lemonde, *J. Physique*, **9**, 505 (1958).
144. J. Thibaud and H. Lemonde, *J. Physique*, **11**, 36 (1940).
145. R. Matalon, *Mem. Serv. Chim. Etat*, **32**, 361 (1945).
146. R. Matalon, in *Surface Chemistry*, Butterworths, London, 1949, p. 195.
147. K. J. Mysels, M. C. Cox, and J. D. Skewis, *J. Phys. Chem.*, **65**, 1107 (1961).
148. K. J. Mysels and M. C. Cox, *J. Colloid Sci.*, **17**, 136 (1962).
149. R. J. Grabenstetter and J. M. Corkill, *J. Colloid Sci.*, **18**, 401 (1963).
150. W. Schwindt and B. Stuke, *Proc. Intern. Congr. Surface Activity, 2nd, London, 1957*, **1**, 487.
151. M. Kalousek and V. Vyšin, *Collection Czech. Chem. Commun.*, **20**, 777 (1955).
152. Z. Knor, M. Kalousek, and V. Boháčkova, *Collection Czech. Chem. Commun.*, **24**, 1373 (1959).
153. O. H. Faxén, *Proc. Roy. Scand. Acad. Eng. Sci.*, **187**, 1946.
154. R. J. Myers and W. D. Harkins, *J. Chem. Phys.*, **5**, 601 (1937).
155. I. Langmuir and V. J. Schaeffer, *Chem. Rev.*, **24**, 181 (1939).
156. J. Pouradier, *J. Chim. Phys.*, **46**, 627 (1949).
157. C. W. N. Cumper and A. E. Alexander, *Trans. Faraday Soc.*, **46**, 235 (1950).
158. M. Kalousek and V. Vyšin, *Chem. Listy*, **48**, 486 (1954).
159. G. E. Boyd and F. Vaslow, *J. Colloid Sci.*, **13**, 275 (1958).
160. N. L. Jarvis, *J. Phys. Chem.*, **70**, 3027 (1966).
161. N. L. Gershfeld and C. Y. C. Pak, *J. Colloid Interface Sci.*, **23**, 215 (1967).
162. N. W. Tschoegl, *Kolloid-Z.*, **181**, 19 (1962).
163. B. C. Blakey and A. S. C. Lawrence, *Discussions Faraday Soc.*, **18**, 268 (1954).
164. R. Bulas and C. A. Kumins, *J. Colloid Sci.*, **13**, 429 (1958).
165. P. E. Rouse and K. Sittel, *J. Appl. Phys.*, **24**, 690 (1953).
166. S. C. Ellis, A. F. Lanham, and K. G. A. Pankhurst, *J. Sci. Instr.*, **32**, 70 (1955).
167. A. G. Brown, W. C. Thuman, and J. W. Mac Bain, *J. Colloid Sci.*, **8**, 491 (1953).
168. M. Joly, *J. Phys. Radium*, **9**, 345 (1938).
169. W. D. Harkins and J. G. Kirwood, *J. Chem. Phys.*, **6**, 298 (1938).
170. G. C. Nutting and W. D. Harkins, *J. Am. Chem. Soc.*, **62**, 3155 (1940).
171. W. E. Ewers and R. A. Sack, *Nature*, **168**, 964 (1951).
172. H. J. Trurnit and W. E. Lauer, *Rev. Sci. Instr.*, **30**, 975 (1959).

173. R. A. Burton and R. J. Mannheimer, American Chemical Society Symposium on Ordered Fluids and Liquid Crystals, Atlantic City, N.J., September 14, 1965.
174. J. J. Hermans, *Physica*, **6**, 313 (1939).
175. S. E. Bressler, B. Talmud, and D. Talmud, *Phys. Zh. SSSR*, **4**, 864 (1933).
176. R. S. Hansen, *J. Phys. Chem.*, **63**, 637 (1959).
177. E. J. Burcik and R. C. Newman, *J. Colloid Sci.*, **15**, 383 (1960).
178. D. W. Criddle and A. L. Meader, *J. Appl. Phys.*, **26**, 838 (1955).
179. L. E. Nielsen, R. Wall, and G. J. Adams, *J. Colloid Sci.*, **13**, 441 (1958).
180. L. E. Nielsen, *Rev. Sci. Instr.*, **22**, 690 (1951).
181. K. Motomura and R. Matuura, *Bull. Chem. Soc. Japan*, **35**, 289 (1962).
182. S. Oka and Y. Sato, *Bull. Kobayashi Inst. Phys. Res.*, **5**, 96 (1955).
183. A. G. Thomas, *Nature*, **179**, 776 (1957).
184. C. W. N. Cumper, *J. Colloid Interface Sci.*, **23**, 154 (1967).
185. K. Inokuchi, *Bull. Chem. Soc. Japan*, **27**, 203 (1954).

Rheological Properties of Monomolecular Films: Part II: Experimental Results. Theoretical Interpretation. Applications

M. JOLY

Service de Biophysique, Institut Pasteur, Paris, France

I. THE RHEOLOGICAL PROPERTIES OF VARIOUS TYPES OF MONOMOLECULAR FILMS

We shall now review the principal experimental results bearing on the rheological behavior of various types of monomolecular films.

An examination of the literature immediately brings to light a difficulty which makes this a delicate task. The fact is that while there is general agreement as to the overall rheological behavior of films of a given substance, large discrepancies appear when the numerical values are compared. For example if cetyl alcohol is spread at a water surface under a surface pressure of 10 dyne/cm, values of the surface viscosity ranging from 1.4×10^{-2} to 3.90×10^{-1} g/sec have been measured by various authors (1–4). Our discussion in the preceding sections easily explains the reason. Not only are certain experimental methods inaccurate, but sometimes the method chosen by the investigator is not the most appropriate for the type of film studied. Furthermore, to the extent that the system studied displays neither pure instantaneous elasticity nor pure Newtonian viscosity, the several methods do not measure exactly the same thing; and it follows that a critical discussion of the results would be necessary in order to make a valid comparison. Most frequently authors do not carry out a systematic rheological investigation because it is not their principal objective, and they are content with the determination of an apparent surface viscosity which for non-Newtonian systems depends heavily upon the experimental apparatus used together with its mode of operation. Moreover, as has been discussed elsewhere (5) in numerous publications, the experimental conditions are imprecisely described. The result is that the systems studied are often insufficiently defined, as much with respect to their physicochemical state as to their mechanical characterization. Thus too frequently, the temperature, the nature of the substrate, and the specification of the stress distribution are not given with sufficient exactness. It is recognized, moreover, that the mechanical properties of a body depend upon its purity. It thus may well be that the observed differences between the results could be consequences of the fact that the samples used by different authors were not the same, or that the spreading solvents used were not always the same. The detection of solvent retention in the monolayer is a matter of some difficulty.

Despite these reservations, numerous experimental results seem to be well established, and from these we shall examine some that allow the broad outline of the rheological behavior of monomolecular films of different types of substances to be described. For the purposes of this review, we shall take up successively insoluble films of small amphiphilic molecules, insoluble films of macromolecules, and soluble films adsorbed at the surfaces of solutions. This classification should not be interpreted to imply the absence of common behavior among these types of film.

A. Insoluble Films of Small Amphiphilic Molecules

The members of this family that have been the most studied are aliphatic compounds. Because of the extensive research which has been lavished on the determination of isotherms $\pi = f(A)$, it is possible to calculate many of the compression moduli of the different physical states of the films.

Moreover, it is the shear viscosity that has been the objective of the most systematic research.

1. The Compression Modulus

As has been indicated above, two-dimensional systems are generally much more compressible than three-dimensional systems.   Thus for a solid film of trimyristin on water at 19.2°C and with a molecular area of 57 Å^2, $\varkappa$ is 475 g/sec^2 (6).   For a stearic acid film on 0.01 M HCl at 20°C and molecular area 19 Å^2, one finds $\varkappa = 750$ g/sec^2.

For a given substance the compression modulus depends upon the physical state of the film and upon the molecular packing.   Thus at the mesomorphic–solid transition point of behenic acid on 0.001 M HCl at 26°C, in the neighborhood of $A = 18.9$ Å^2 one finds $\varkappa = 627$ g/sec^2 for the solid film and $\varkappa = 93.5$ g/sec^2 for the mesomorphic film (7).   For the stearic acid film mentioned immediately above, the value $\varkappa = 750$ g/sec^2 at $A = 19$ Å^2 falls for the mesomorphic film at $A = 20$ Å^2 to $\varkappa = 140$ g/sec^2 (6).   Table I lists values of compression moduli found for the long-chain alcohols (8, 9).   In a corresponding way, for ethylene glycol monooctadecyl ether spread on water (9) we have in the solid state $\varkappa = 700$ g/sec^2 and in the mesomorphic state $\varkappa = 139$–145 g/sec^2.   For $C_{22}H_{45}OC_2H_4OH$ in the solid state $\varkappa = 1070$ g/sec^2 and in the mesomorphic state $\varkappa = 168$–207 g/sec^2.

If an isotherm $\pi = f(A)$ exhibits a transition region, for example, between solid and mesomorphic phases, the compression modulus falls to a minimum in this region.   This behavior (10) is demonstrated by a film of octadecyl-acetamide $C_{18}H_{37}NHCOCH_3$ spread on 0.001 N H_2SO_4 at 20.2°C:

$$A \text{ (Å}^2) \quad = 19 \quad 21 \quad 23$$
$$\varkappa \text{ (g/sec}^2) = 70.5 \quad 14.4 \quad 70.7$$

For a film in a single surface phase, whatever the nature of the phase, $\varkappa$ is always a decreasing function of A.   This is readily observable with aliphatic compounds (6) as shown in Table II.

As a general rule for aliphatic compounds compared at the same molecular area and with all other conditions the same, $\varkappa$ increases with the length of the

TABLE I
Compression Moduli of Primary Aliphatic Alcohols, G (g/sec^2)

Alcohol	Solid state	Liquid condensed
$C_{16}H_{33}OH$	757	183
$C_{18}H_{37}OH$	1150–1470	175–198
$C_{20}H_{41}OH$	1410	218
$C_{22}H_{45}OH$	1095–1440	228–519

TABLE II
Compression Modulus as a Function of Molecular Area

State	Film	T (°C)	A (Å²)	$\varkappa$ (g/sec²)
Solid	Trimyristin on water	19.2	57	475
			60	345
Mesomorphic	Stearic acid on 0.01 N HCl	20	20	150
			21	125
			23	95.5
Liquid	Triolein on water	20	100	65
			120	40.7
—	Triricinolein on water	20	90	31.5
			130	29.2
			170	21.4
—	Oleic acid on 0.01 N HCl	17	35	57
			40	37.4
			45	26
Gaseous	Ethyl 11-hydroxystearate on water	20	100	60
			140	9.2
			180	2.85
—	Methyl 11-oxostearate on water	20	120	20
			180	3.53
—	Tricaproin on water	20	70	30
			90	24
			110	15.3
			130	8
			150	5.7
			170	4.3

chain. The compression modulus also obviously depends upon the nature of the polar group. Thus for example (11) the compression modulus of sodium n-octadecylsulfate spread at the 0.1 M NaCl/n-heptane interface at 20°C at a molecular area of 66.5 Å² is $\varkappa = 31.8$/sec², whereas for n-octadecyltrimethylammonium bromide the modulus is $\varkappa = 43.3$ g/sec². On water at 25°C, the rectilinear portion of the isotherm in the mesomorphic phase of stearic acid shows $\varkappa = 527$ g/sec², whereas for octadecylphosphoric acid the result is $\varkappa = 285$ g/sec² (12).

So long as phase changes in the surface do not occur, the compression moduli are relatively insensitive to changes in temperature. Thus for a film of dimyristylpiperazine

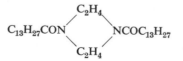

on 0.01 N HCl at a molecular area of $A = 110$ Å^2, one finds (13)

$$T \ (^\circ C) \quad = \ 2 \quad 20 \quad 27 \quad 30 \quad 35$$
$$\varkappa \ (g/sec^2) = 41.3 \quad 44.5 \quad 45.5 \quad 43 \quad 43$$

For a film of hexadecyldicarboxylic acid spread on a sulfuric acid solution of pH 2 and compressed at the rate of 21.8 Å^2/molecule/min, at an area of $A = 100$ Å^2 the data are (14)

$$T \ (^\circ C) \quad = 11.7 \quad 13.2 \quad 16.2 \quad 21.5$$
$$\varkappa \ (g/sec^2) = 20.6 \quad 22.3 \quad 25.3 \quad 26.8$$

Tetradecyldicarboxylic acid spread on concentrated ammonium sulfate solution at pH 2 and compressed at a rate 10.9 Å^2/molecule/min shows at $A = 100$ Å^2 a compression modulus $\varkappa = 32.4 \ g/sec^2$ at 15°C and $\varkappa = 35.3 \ g/sec^2$ at 65°C. Monooctadecylphosphoric acid (15) spread on 0.1 M NaCl at pH 5.6 and a molecular area $A = 25$ Å^2 shows $\varkappa = 10 \ g/sec^2$ at 13.5°C; $\varkappa = 97 \ g/sec^2$ at 20°C; and $\varkappa = 88 \ g/sec^2$ at 25°C. For diethylene glycol monodocosyl ether at a molecular area $A = 24$ Å^2, the compression modulus as a function of the temperature is (9)

$$T \ (^\circ C) \quad = \ 15 \quad 20 \quad 25 \quad 30$$
$$\varkappa \ (g/sec^2) = 133.5 \quad 129.5 \quad 125.5 \quad 118$$

It is to be remarked that the trend of $\varkappa$ as a function of temperature is not the same for all substances and depends upon the temperature range studied.

It is equally true that the composition of the substrate influences the compression modulus. Thus for dimyristylpiperazine at $A = 110$ Å^2 and 25°C, $\varkappa$ decreases gradually as the hydrochloric acid concentration increases (13):

$$[HCl] \ (N) = \ 0.01 \quad 0.1 \quad 1 \quad 5.3 \quad 10.6$$
$$\varkappa \ (g/sec^2) \ = 44.1 \quad 44 \quad 42.2 \quad 39.4 \quad 39.2$$

For pentadecylcarboxylic acid spread on 0.01 M NaCl solution at $A = 25$ Å^2, the compression modulus decreases significantly with increasing pH (16):

$$pH \quad = \ 2 \quad 3.2 \quad 4.4 \quad 6.3 \quad 7.2$$
$$\varkappa \ (g/sec^2) = 20.2 \quad 19.6 \quad 17 \quad 6 \quad 4.8$$

The influence of the pH also reveals itself with relatively complex molecules such as chlorophyll a. For this molecule at an area $A = 80$ Å^2, alteration of the pH from 8 to 4 increases $\varkappa$ from 54.5 to 60 g/sec^2. This change corresponds to the conversion of chlorophyll a into pheophytine (17).

TABLE III
Compression Moduli of the 18-Carbon Unsaturated, Carboxylic Acids

Acid	Conformation	$\varkappa$ (g/sec²)
Oleic	cis	39.6
Linoleic	cis–cis	33
Linolenic	cis–cis–cis	25.5
Arachidonic	cis–cis–cis–cis	37.3
Elaidic	trans	21.8
Linolelaidic	trans–trans	12
Elaidolinolenic	trans–trans–trans	13.6

The ionic strength of the substrate is also a factor which can influence the compression modulus. Thus for sodium octadecylsulfate at an area $A = 75$ Å² at 9.5°C, $\varkappa$ increases from 3.55 to 4.57 g/sec² when the concentration of NaCl in the substrate is increased from 0.01 to 0.1 M.

We have seen that for fixed molecular area, temperature, and substrate composition, the compression modulus for aliphatic compounds depends upon the length of the chain and the nature of the polar group. It is necessary also to remark that $\varkappa$ also varies with the number and the location of double bonds (18). Table III gives supporting data for carboxylic acids containing 18 carbon atoms spread on 0.01 N H₂SO₄ plus 0.12% hydroquinone at 24.5°C and $A = 45$ Å². If the double bonds are conjugated, there are notable differences in the compression modulus between the cis and trans configurations. Thus at $A = 29$ Å² and 22°C, $\varkappa$ is 37.4 g/sec² for β eleostearic acid (*trans,trans,trans*-9,11,13-octadecatrienoic acid), while under the same conditions, $\varkappa = 58.2$ g/sec² for α eleostearic acid (*cis,cis,cis*-9,11,13-octadecatrienoic acid).

The differences in $\varkappa$ between phospholipids are probably of the same origin. Table IV summarizes data (19) calculated from compression isotherms at 20°C on 0.5 M NaCl at pH 5.3 and $A = 75$ Å².

TABLE IV
Compression Moduli of the Phospholipids

Phospholipid	$\varkappa$ (g/sec²)
2,3-dielaidoyl-1-phosphatidylethanolamine	35.1
2,3-dioleoyl-DL-phosphatidylethanolamine	44.5
2-stearoyl-3-elaidoyl-DL-phosphatidylethanolamine	3.3
2-oleoyl-3-elaidoyl-DL-phosphatidylethanolamine	45
2-oleoyl-3-stearoyl-DL-phosphatidylethanolamine	35
2,3-dielaidoyl-DL-phosphatidylcholine	56.5
2-elaidoyl-3-stearoyl-DL-phosphatidylcholine	28.4

TABLE V

Compression Moduli of Monomethylpalmitic Acids

Position of the methyl group	$\varkappa$ (g/sec^2) $\pm 3\%$	Position of the methyl group	$\varkappa$ (g/sec^2) $\pm 3\%$
2	62.7	9	94.5
3	69.5	10	103.5
4	87	11	104.5
5	77	12	96
6	86.5	13	101
7	83.5	14	66.5
8	91.5	15	$\simeq 0$

At constant molecular area, substitutions also have an important influence on the compression modulus. This is particularly obvious for the ω monohalogen derivatives (20). Thus for octadecanol spread on sulfuric acid at pH 2.2 at 20°C and a molecular area $A = 20$ Å^2, the measured modulus is $\varkappa = 1320$ g/sec^2 while under the same conditions, 18-fluoro-octadecanol shows $\varkappa = 317$ g/sec^2. When octadecanoic acid is spread on 0.01 M CaCl$_2$ at pH 3.9 and 20°C, at $A = 24$ Å^2 one finds $\varkappa = 55.7$ g/sec^2, while for 18-bromooctadecanoic acid under the same conditions, $\varkappa = 24.3$ g/sec^2. For phytol and isophytol (21) on distilled water at 20°C and $A = 42$ Å^2, the values of $\varkappa$ are 65 and 76 g/sec^2, respectively. In a similar way, the isotherms of 3-methyl- and 10-methylhexadecanol on water at $A = 34$ Å^2 and 20°C lead to $\varkappa = 45.3$ and $\varkappa = 70$ g/sec^2 respectively. The influence of the position of substitution has been systematically studied for the monomethylpalmitic and monomethylstearic acids (22, 23). Tables V and VI list values of $\varkappa$ derived from compression isotherms at 10°C on water

TABLE VI

Compression Moduli of the Monomethylstearic acids

Position of the methyl group	$\varkappa$ (g/sec^2) $\pm 3\%$	Position of the methyl group	$\varkappa$ (g/sec^2) $\pm 3\%$
2	172	10	Collapse
3	159.5	11	Collapse
4	147.5	12	143.5
5	105	13	138.5
6	125.5	14	115.5
7	130.5	15	123.5
8	134.5	16	161
9	Collapse	17	172

at $A = 32$ Å^2 for the monomethylpalmitic acids and at $A = 28$ Å^2 for the monomethylstearic acids.

2. Dilational Viscosity

It does not appear that direct measurements of the dilational viscosity have been made for insoluble films of small, amphiphilic molecules.

This is the more remarkable because the possible influence of the rate of compression upon the form of the isotherms $\pi = f(A)$ has been known for a long time (24, 25). Thus for stearic acid spread on 0.01 N HCl at 25°C, it has been shown (26) that the compressibility is practically independent of the rate of compression between molecular areas of $A = 24.5$ and $A = 21$ Å^2. For $A < 21$ Å^2, however, large differences appear. In particular the two-dimensional solid phase can be obtained only at high rates of compression, of the order of 2.43 Å^2/molecule/min. At a compression rate of the order 0.213 Å^2/molecule/min, it is a region of high compressibility which appears at areas less than 21 Å^2. Finally, for exceedingly small compression rates, even this range disappears, and the film collapses at 21 Å^2. It is to be remarked that a series of six or seven successive rapid compressions and expansions leads gradually to isotherms $\pi = f(A)$ comparable to those obtained in a single, very slow compression. It will be recalled that isotherms traced rapidly show a higher-order transition point at $A = 21$ Å^2.

The influence of the compression rate on the measured value of the compression modulus is particularly noticeable in the α,ω-dicarboxylic acids (14). For example, the C_{16} diacid spread on sulfuric acid at pH 2 at 22°C and $A = 100$ Å^2 exhibits the following changes in $\varkappa$ as a function of the compression rate v (Å^2/molecule/min):

$$v \quad = \quad 0.242 \quad 0.727 \quad 2.91 \quad 7.27 \quad 10.9 \quad 21.8$$

$$\varkappa \text{ (g/sec}^2) = 13.4 \quad \quad 13.9 \quad \quad 15.7 \quad 22.7 \quad 26 \quad \quad 27$$

From these changes in the isotherms $\pi = f(A)$ as a function of the compression rate can be estimated the pressure relaxation which is observed after the rapid compression of certain monomolecular films. Stearic acid appears to have been most thoroughly studied from this point of view (26–29). Thus for stearic acid films spread on 0.01 N HCl at 21°C, after rapid compression of the film to A the total pressure loss after 5 min has been found to be 0.3 dyne/cm for $A = 22$ Å^2, 1.2 dyne/cm for $A = 19.8$ Å^2, and 4.8 dyne/cm for $A = 19.3$ Å^2. At 25°C the effect is even more marked, the drop in surface pressure being already 0.3 dyne/cm after 15 min at $A = 24$ Å^2. For $A = 21$ Å^2 the drop was 1.65 dyne/cm after 13 min and 5.5 dyne/cm after 120 min. Twelve seconds after a direct compression to 19.2 Å^2 the pressure dropped by 25 dyne/cm. The reverse effect of a buildup of the surface pressure after rapid expansion to A can also be observed.   Thus for stearic acid at 25°C, after a rapid expansion to $A = 23$ Å^2, the pressure after 19 minutes increased by 1.3 dyne/cm, and for $A = 22$ Å^2, the increase was 2.7 dyne/cm after 53 min.

3. Viscoelasticity

The systematic study of the viscoelastic behavior of surface films of small molecules has up to the present time been little developed.   Measurements have nevertheless been carried out upon saponin regarded as a Voigt body (30).   Spread at the air/water interface at pH 5.5 and 24°C, the rheological parameters* of the film are $G = 18.9$ g/sec^2 and $\eta_s = 17$ g/sec.   At the water/styrene interface the measured values are $G = 0.03$ g/sec^2 and $\eta_s = 1.07$ g/sec.   At the air interface of a solution of 0.1 M KCNS and pH 5.4, the parameters become $G = 44.5$ g/sec^2 and $\eta_s = 18.2$ g/sec; at the solution/styrene interface $G = 1.88$ g/sec^2 and $\eta_s = 9.3$ g/sec.   When the solution is replaced by 0.1 M CaCl$_2$ at pH 4.8, the parameters at the air interface are $G = 56$ g/sec^2 and $\eta_s = 13.7$ g/sec, while at the styrene interface they are $G = 16$ g/sec^2 and $\eta_c = 14.2$ g/sec.

Using the deflection method, a rather complete study of the aluminum salts of stearic acid has been carried out (31).   At a molecular area of 81.8 Å^2, a film of aluminum distearate spread on water at pH 5.5 and 25°C exhibits deflection data which can be interpreted using a four-parameter model.   Using the notation of Figure 8 in Part I, the measured values of the Burger's body were $G = 25.3$ g/sec^2, $G_l = 18.1$ g/sec^2, $\eta = 5650$ g/sec, and $\eta_s = 2870$ g/sec.   The values of these four parameters increase as the molecular area is diminished.   For $A = 60$ Å^2, they are approximately doubled.   The same type of behavior is shown by a film of stearic acid spread on a solution of aluminum chloride at 25°C, but the four parameters change rapidly with the molecular area.   Near $A = 45$ Å^2, η and η_s are of the order of 300–400 g/sec, and G and G_l of the order of 2 or 3 g/sec^2.   If A is approximately 33 Å^2, η and η_s are of the order of 5×10^5 g/sec^1; G is near 500 g/sec^2 and G_l near 100 g/sec^2.   By comparing the two preceding films at equal areas per chain, it appears that at large areas, films of the distearate spread on water are more rigid than those of stearic acid spread on aluminum chloride solution.   At small areas the reverse is true.   When aluminum distearate is spread on aluminum chloride solution, the rheological behavior of the surface can be interpreted by means of a three-parameter model.   The values of these parameters (for notation, see Figure 6 in Part I) are sensitive functions of the molecular area.   At $A = 100$ Å^2, G_1 is of the order of 20 g/sec^2,

---

* For notations see Figure 4 in Part I.

G_2 is about 10 g/sec², and η_s is approximately 3000 g/sec. When $A = 80$ Å², G_1 and G_2 are close to 50 g/sec², while η_s is of the order of 10,000 g/sec. If the film is compressed to $A = 75.6$ Å² it becomes purely elastic.

4. Shear Viscosity

Surface shear viscosity has been most thoroughly studied for films of small, amphiphilic molecules, and among these it has been the aliphatic compounds that have received the greatest attention. Before we take up examples of the various chemical species, it will be useful to make a number of remarks concerning the general behavior of these films, behavior which at first sight seems surprising.

When the films are dilute (gaseous, liquid, or expanded mesomorphic), which is to say when the area per chain for aliphatic compounds is relatively large, the surface viscosity is in general small, and can be measured precisely only by the method of the floating canal. It has been found that at low surface concentrations, the surface viscosity decreases as the film is compressed, while for condensed or highly viscous films, the surface viscosity increases with further compression. Tables VII and VIII furnish examples of the decrease in surface viscosity with molecular area (3). As we shall see in greater detail in Section II, this behavior is due to the structure of the kinetic units in the film, which, as has been indicated in Part I (Sections

TABLE VII
Surface Viscosity of Slightly Condensed Films of Fatty Acids

Film	Temperature (°C)	Molecular area (Å²)	$\eta \times 10^4$ (g/sec†)
Myristic acid			
on 0.01 N HCl	22	43.9	1.52
		39	1.18
		35.8	1.01
		33.4	0.81
		31.1	0.50
		29.6	0.17
Palmitic acid			
on 0.01 N HCl	25.3	29	2.55
		28.5	1.8
		28.1	1.32
		27.7	1.16
		27.3	1.12
Oleic acid			
on 0.01 N HCl	17	47.7	1.68
		39.9	1.43
		34.9	0.38

TABLE VIII

Surface Viscosity of Slightly Condensed Films of Triglycerides

Film	Temperature (°C)	Molecular area (Å^2)	$\eta \times 10^4$ (g/sec)
Tricaproin on water	20	600	3.6
		300	2.75
		138	1.75
		120	0.65
		110	0.335
		83	0.19
Tricaprylin on water	20	270	8.1
		170	2.75
		142	1.38
		120	0.82
		90	0.68
Tricaprin on water	19.5	130.5	1.28
		115	0.99
		105	0.82
		88.4	0.78
		68.6	0.73
Trilaurin on water	22	111	1.4
		102.4	1.18
		95.2	0.96
Triolein on water	20	132	1.43
		125	1.38
		115.5	1.21
		107	0.63
		100.5	0.31
Triricinolein on water	20	188	1.11
		156	0.91
		141	0.44
		124	0.22

II.C.1 and II.C.2), are the ensemble of an amphiphilic molecule together with those molecules of the substrate with which it is associated. For a given length of chain and molecular spacing, the contribution to the surface viscosity of the chain–chain interactions increases less rapidly with compression than does the decrease in the contribution from the associated substrate molecules. It follows that $\partial \eta / \partial A$ is positive for such a domain of surface concentration. If one could imagine the surface viscosity to be due exclusively to the amphiphilic molecules, meaning a hypothetical quantity η_c which would be observed if the molecules were not firmly bound to those of the substrate and could move without friction on the substrate, then $\partial \eta_c / \partial A < 0$ in the majority of cases. Table IX presents several examples of this phenomenon calculated by a method to be discussed in Section IV.

TABLE IX

Hypothetical Surface Viscosities η_c of Slightly Condensed Films

Film	Temperature (°C)	Molecular area (Å²)	$\eta_c \times 10^6$ (g/sec)
Palmitic acid			
on 0.01 N HCl	25.3	27.3	1.43
		24.5	3.48
		22	7.75
Stearic acid			
on 0.01 N HCl	20	22	7.21
		21	14.4
Tricaproin on water	20	89.5	0.007
		83	0.012
Tricaprylin on water	20	89.5	0.02
		83	0.036
Tricaprin on water	20	89.5	0.023
		83	0.049
Trilaurin on water	16.25	89.5	0.04
		83	0.08

Authors frequently use surface pressure as the independent variable rather than the molecular area. This is convenient, for the surface pressure is easily measured. It does not, however, lend itself to easy interpretation of the results; for unlike the molecular area, it varies only indirectly with intermolecular distances, which are the important parameters in influencing intermolecular interactions and through them the surface viscosity. Very frequently, moreover, measurements are carried out using apparatus insufficiently sensitive to detect variations in the surface viscosity as a function of the state of condensation of the film.

a. Fatty Acids

Long-chain, saturated, monobasic acids spread on a slightly acidified substrate generally yield fluid films when the molecular area exceeds 19 Å². The viscosity of such films is relatively small compared to other aliphatic compounds with the same chain length. Carboxylic acids containing 14–20 carbon atoms have been the most thoroughly studied (32–34). Their behavior up to $A = 20.5$ Å² is Newtonian. For A less than 19 Å², the films are solid. Over the entire Newtonian region, even though the films are relatively condensed (mesomorphic or liquid condensed: $A < 23.5$ Å²), the logarithm of the surface viscosity varies almost linearly with the surface pressure. Table X gives several values of η as a function of π for different acids spread on a substrate of pH 2. The often considerable variations of

TABLE X

Surface Viscosities of Saturated Monocarboxylic Acids as a Function of Temperature and Surface Pressure

Acid	T (°C)	π (dyne/cm)				
		2	5	10	15	20
		$\eta \times 10^3$ (g/sec)				
C_{14}	20		0.2 ± 0.04	0.2		
C_{15}	25					1.9
C_{16}	20		0.22			0.4
	25			0.6	1.5	4.4
C_{17}	25		0.4	1.1	2.2	5.2
C_{18}	20	0.3				1
	25	1.2	1.5	2.1	3	4.2
	28		0.28			0.44
C_{20}	25	10	12.3	17.8	25.3	35.8

the data with temperature are most probably due less to the temperature itself than to the fact that the experimental methods were different: oscillatory (32) for the data at 25°C, and flow along a deep canal (34, 35) for the measurements at 20 and 28°C.   The effect of raising the temperature at constant surface pressure, moreover, is for fatty acids generally to decrease the surface viscosity.   For example, arachidic acid on a substrate of pH 2 at a surface pressure 10 dyne/cm has been determined by the oscillation method (32) to have viscosities $\eta = 9.1 \times 10^{-2}$ g/sec at 10°C; $\eta = 1.78 \times 10^{-2}$ g/sec at 22°C; and $\eta = 1.47 \times 10^{-2}$ g/sec at 31.5°C.   For palmitic acid under the same conditions, the floating canal method has been used (3) to find $\eta = 2.45 \times 10^{-4}$ g/sec at 17°C, $\eta = 2.6 \times 10^{-4}$ g/sec at 22°C, and $\eta = 1.75 \times 10^{-4}$ g/sec at 25.3°C.   In comparing these data it should be kept in mind that the shear rates $\dot{\gamma}$ generated in the oscillation and in the flow methods are very different.   It is not impossible that the surface viscosities of the long-chain acids are only apparently Newtonian and that they are actually larger for the low shear rates used in the oscillation method than for the relatively larger values of $\dot{\gamma}$ which are generated by flow along a canal.

For a given temperature and surface pressure, the nature of the substrate plays a role in the value of η.   Stearic acid between 26 and 28°C at a surface pressure of 5 dyne/cm for flow through a deep canal (35) shows $\eta = 2.78 \times 10^{-4}$ g/sec on 0.02 M HCl, $\eta = 3.59 \times 10^{-4}$ g/sec on water, and $\eta = 5.28 \times 10^{-4}$ g/sec on 1.0 M NaCl.   When the surface pressure is increased to $\pi = 20$ dyne/cm, the corresponding values of η are 4.37×10^{-4}, 8.81×10^{-4}, and 4.36×10^{-3} g/sec, respectively.   If heavy water is substituted for ordinary water (36), the surface viscosity of stearic acid measured by the canal method at 25°C on 0.01 N HCl shows no perceptible modification:

$$\pi \text{ (dyne/cm)} \quad\quad = 4 \quad\quad 6 \quad\quad 8 \quad\quad 10 \quad\quad 12$$

$$\eta_{H_2O} \times 10^4 \text{ (g/sec)} = 1.01 \quad 1.06 \quad 1.28 \quad 1.72 \quad 2.16$$

$$\eta_{D_2O} \times 10^4 \text{ (g/sec)} = 1.08 \quad 1.08 \quad 1.23 \quad 1.64 \quad 2.14$$

It was shown early in the systematic investigation of surface viscosity (6) that when the measurements are sufficiently precise, variations in η as a function of A are a convenient way of detecting higher-order transitions within the films, for such transitions appear as abrupt changes of slope in the plots of η versus A. Figure 1 shows results of this type for the fatty acids (3, 37, 38). This phenomenon will be examined in greater detail in Sections II and IV.

b. Alcohols

Fatty alcohols have also been the subject of several surface rheological investigations. An early result was the discovery that for a given surface pressure and length of chain, alcohols are much more viscous than acids (1, 32, 33, 35). As an example, at $T = 25°C$, $\pi = 4$ dyne/cm, and using the oscillation method (1, 32, 33), one finds for cetyl alcohol $\eta = 6.6 \times 10^{-3}$ g/sec while for palmitic acid $\eta = 2 \times 10^{-4}$ g/sec. For 17 carbon atoms in the chains, the results are $\eta = 10^{-2}$ g/sec for the alcohol and $\eta = 3 \times 10^{-4}$ g/sec for the acid. For octadecanol $\eta = 2.3 \times 10^{-2}$ g/sec, while for stearic acid $\eta = 1.4 \times 10^{-3}$ g/sec. These latter two compounds have also been studied by the deep canal method (35), for which films spread on water at $T = 26–28°C$ and $\pi = 5$ and 20 dyne/cm show respectively $\eta = 1.29 \times 10^{-3}$ and 2.14×10^{-3} g/sec for the alcohol, and $\eta = 3.6 \times 10^{-4}$ and 8.8×10^{-4} g/sec for the acid.

Another notable feature of the alcohol films is their non-Newtonian behavior (1, 34). It is this property that accounts in large part for the large scatter in published values of η. Using the method of continuous rotation, a precise study has been carried out of this behavior (37–39). For cetyl alcohol on water at 19.8°C and $\pi = 2$ dyne/cm the data are

$$\dot{\gamma} \text{ (sec}^{-1}) \quad\quad = 1 \quad\quad 2 \quad 3 \quad\quad 4 \quad\quad 5$$

$$\eta \times 10^3 \text{ (g/sec)} = 2.5 \quad 2 \quad 1.51 \quad 1.33 \quad 1.25$$

If $\pi = 20$ dyne/cm and $T = 16.9°C$ the data are

$$\dot{\gamma} \text{ (sec}^{-1}) \quad\quad = 0.25 \quad 0.5 \quad\quad 1 \quad\quad 1.5 \quad\quad 1.75$$

$$\eta \times 10^2 \text{ (g/sec)} = 7.5 \quad\quad 6.95 \quad 6.07 \quad 5.45 \quad 5.2$$

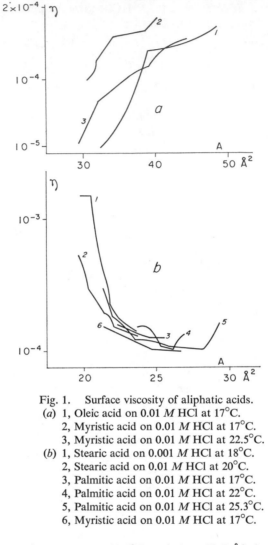

Fig. 1.   Surface viscosity of aliphatic acids.
(a) 1, Oleic acid on 0.01 M HCl at 17°C.
    2, Myristic acid on 0.01 M HCl at 17°C.
    3, Myristic acid on 0.01 M HCl at 22.5°C.
(b) 1, Stearic acid on 0.001 M HCl at 18°C.
    2, Stearic acid on 0.01 M HCl at 20°C.
    3, Palmitic acid on 0.01 M HCl at 17°C.
    4, Palmitic acid on 0.01 M HCl at 22°C.
    5, Palmitic acid on 0.01 M HCl at 25.3°C.
    6, Myristic acid on 0.01 M HCl at 17°C.

For tetradecanol on water at 18.1°C and $A = 20.5$ Å² there results

$$\dot{\gamma} \ (\text{sec}^{-1}) \qquad = 0.57 \quad 0.89 \quad 1.25 \quad 5.07$$
$$\eta \times 10^3 \ (\text{g/sec}) = 2 \qquad 1.5 \quad\ \ 1.2 \quad\ \ 0.4$$

For dodecanol on water at 20.5°C and $A = 37$ Å², one finds

$$\dot{\gamma} \ (\text{sec}^{-1}) \qquad = 0.6 \quad 2.7 \quad 6.5$$
$$\eta \times 10^3 \ (\text{g/sec}) = 2 \qquad 1 \qquad 0.4$$

TABLE XI
Non-Newtonian Surface Viscosity

Compound	T (°C)	π (dyne/cm)	A (Å^2)	η_0 (g/sec)	η_∞ (g/sec)
$C_{14}H_{29}OH$	24.8	7.1	19.24	0.313	0.060
$C_{16}H_{33}OH$	24.9	10.9	20.22	0.322	0.075
$C_{18}H_{37}OH$	25.0	13.5	19.75	0.094	0.005
$C_{20}H_{41}OH$	25.1	15.8	19.47	0.020	0.0017
$C_{14}H_{29}OC_2H_4OH$	25.0	23.4	18.37	0.390	0.055
$C_{16}H_{33}OC_2H_4OH$	25.1	24.8	19.92	0.260	0.038
$C_{18}H_{37}OC_2H_4OH$	24.9	26.5	19.64	0.050	0.005
$C_{20}H_{41}OC_2H_4OH$	25.1	31.8	18.63	0.231	0.014

Using the same method, the non-Newtonian behavior of a series of normal, long-chain alcohols and the corresponding alkoxyethanols has been investigated in the neighborhood of the transition point between mesomorphic and solid films. Table XI presents values of η_0 and η_∞, which are the limits of η as $\dot\gamma \to 0$ and $\dot\gamma \to \infty$. Of the eight substances studied, a rapid fall in η is observed to occur between $\dot\gamma = 0.1$ and $\dot\gamma = 0.6$/sec (40).

Long-chain alcohols also exhibit antithixotropic behavior, which is to say that their surface viscosities increase with the duration of a continuously applied shear stress. Octadecanol spread on water at 19.1°C and a surface pressure of 13 dyne/cm shows within 10 min an increase of surface viscosity from $\eta = 4 \times 10^{-3}$ to $\eta = 1.15 \times 10^{-2}$ g/sec when the turning couple is maintained constant at 25.7 erg. The phenomenon is the result of a change in phase induced by the flow (38), and is accompanied by a progressive diminution of the molecular area (see Section II).

The change in the surface viscosity of the aliphatic alcohols as a function of surface pressure or of molecular area is a matter of controversy. This results from the non-Newtonian character of the viscosity and from the variety of experimental methods employed (1, 3, 34, 41, 42). A linear relation between log η and π has been proposed (1, 33) as a result of experiments using the oscillation method. For cetyl alcohol spread on water at 17°C the data are (3)

$$\pi \text{ (dyne/cm)} = 1 \quad 2 \quad 3 \quad 5 \quad 7$$
$$\eta \times 10^3 \text{ (g/sec)} = 4.5 \quad 4.6 \quad 5.1 \quad 6.1 \quad 8.3$$

On the other hand the viscosity of octadecanol under the same conditions decreases with increasing pressure over a certain span:

$$\pi \text{ (dyne/cm)} = 1 \quad 2 \quad 6 \quad 10 \quad 20 \quad 26 \quad 32 \quad 40$$
$$\eta \times 10^3 \text{ (g/sec)} = 26 \quad 21 \quad 16 \quad 10 \quad 14 \quad 13 \quad 11 \quad 9.7$$

If the experimental method is altered to flow along a deep canal with the flux maintained constant (34), a plot of η against π at 20°C exhibits a lower plateau in the neighborhood of $\pi = 2$ dyne/cm and an upper plateau near $\pi = 14$ dyne/cm. The change in η as a function of chain length was inverted on these two plateaus. For $\pi = 2$ dyne/cm the surface viscosities are 4×10^{-4} g/sec for tetradecanol, 1×10^{-3} g/sec for hexadecanol, and 1.3×10^{-2} g/sec for octadecanol. If π is increased to 14 dyne/cm, the results respectively are 7×10^{-2}, 3×10^{-2}, and 2.2×10^{-2} g/sec. Using the method of steady rotation at constant shear rate (37), the surface viscosity of myristic alcohol at 18.1°C has been found to be essentially independent of π from 1 to 5 dyne/cm: $\eta \simeq 2 \times 10^{-3}$ g/sec for $\dot{\gamma} \simeq 0.6$ sec^{-1} and $\eta \simeq 4 \times 10^{-4}$ g/sec for $\dot{\gamma} \simeq 5.9$ sec^{-1}.

At room temperature the surface viscosities of the aliphatic alcohols uniformly increase with temperature (3). Data for octadecanol spread on water at $\pi = 4$ dyne/cm are $\eta = 1.9 \times 10^{-2}$ g/sec at 17°C and $\eta = 3.6 \times 10^{-2}$ g/sec at 18.6°C. If the surface pressure is increased to $\pi = 12$ dyne/cm these values change to $\eta = 1.1 \times 10^{-2}$ g/sec at 17°C and $\eta = 4.2 \times 10^{-2}$ g/sec at 18.6°C. For dodecanol on water at $A = 30.8$ Å^2 some results are $\eta = 1.3 \times 10^{-3}$ g/sec at 17°C and $\eta = 3.9 \times 10^{-3}$ g/sec at 18.9°C. Experimental work over large temperature intervals has been carried out for condensed films in equilibrium with a crystal (43). Using tetradecanol spread on 0.01 M NaCl, a sharp maximum in η has been observed in the neighborhood of 41°C:

T (°C) =	17.5	29	38	39.8	40.5	40.9
η (g/sec) =	0.332	0.54	1.03	1.34	2.31	3.7

T (°C) =	41.6	42	51	54	55	56.8
η (g/sec) =	1.665	0.844	0.557	0.448	0.367	2×10^{-4}

Analogous work with hexacosanol reveals a transition near 50°C.

T (°C) =	46	48	55	65	75
η (g/sec) =	200	44	130	500	500

c. Amides

The behavior of the aliphatic amides is analogous to that of the alcohols (34, 37–39). The strongly non-Newtonian character of their surface viscosities at very low shear rates has the paradoxical result that the surface viscosity can appear to be small and Newtonian if it is measured by flow along a canal (34). Thus for hexadecylamide on 0.01 N H_2SO_4 at 20°C the viscosity appears to be of the order of 2×10^{-2} g/sec and constant between $\pi = 2$ and $\pi = 20$ dyne/cm. For octadecylamide under the same conditions the viscosity has been measured to be 8×10^{-3} g/sec at $\pi = 4$ dyne/cm and 4.6×10^{-3} g/sec for all surface pressures between 16 and 20 dyne/cm. By contrast the surface viscosity changes rapidly with shear rate when measured by the rotation method. Data for stearic amide on water at 19.1°C and $\pi = 11$ dyne/cm are

$\dot{\gamma}$ (sec^{-1})	=	0.2	0.5	1	2	3
$\eta \times 10^3$ (g/sec)	= 25		11	7.8	4.6	2.96

The non-Newtonian behavior is accompanied by a decided antithixotropy.

Octadecylamide spread on water at 20.1°C, $\pi = 8$ dyne/cm, and subjected to a constant turning couple of 31.6 erg displays a rise in surface viscosity from 0.01 to 1.5 g/sec after the passage of 130 min. This is accompanied by a 6% diminution of the apparent molecular area.

The value of η determined from the initial period of flow under constant $\dot{\gamma}$ increases with surface pressure. Octadecylamide, for instance, spread on water at 21°C and sheared at a rate $\dot{\gamma} = 0.24$ sec^{-1} gives $\eta = 1.4 \times 10^{-2}$ g/sec when $A = 24.5$ Å^2 and $\eta = 4.4 \times 10^{-2}$ g/sec when $A = 21.5$ Å^2. The behavior of octadecylacetamide spread on 0.001 N H_2SO_4 at 20.3°C is the same (10). At successive molecular areas $A = 23$, 21, and 19 Å^2 the respective surface viscosities are $\eta = 1.11 \times 10^{-3}$, 3.32×10^{-3}, and 4.22×10^{-2} g/sec.

d. Amines

Unlike the amides, the aliphatic amines exhibit surface viscosities which are very sensitive to the pH of the substrate (34). On the acidic side, the viscosity is very small (order of 2×10^{-4} g/sec) and Newtonian, while on alkaline substrates the viscosity is large (higher than 10^{-1} g/sec) and non-Newtonian even at low surface pressure.

e. Quaternary Ammonium Salts

The surface viscosity of aliphatic quaternary amines depends upon the salt concentration in the substrate (44). This behavior is illustrated by the octadecyltrimethylammonium ion $C_{18}H_{37}N(CH_3)_3^+$ at an area $A = 85$ Å^2. Table XII shows values of the surface viscosity as a function of sodium halide concentration in the substrate. Measurements made by flow along a floating canal pass through a minimum.

TABLE XII

Surface Viscosity of the Octadecyltrimethylammonium Ion

Concentration of the sodium halide	$\eta \times 10^4$ (g/sec)		
	NaCl	NaI	NaF
0.01 M	2.8	2.33	
0.0625 M	1.66	1.6	1.73
0.25 M	2	2.26	1.46
1 M	3.95	2.96	3.38

f. Phosphates

Rheological properties of phosphate films are sensitive to the pH of the substrate (45).   For monooctadecylphosphate [I] the surface viscosity may

$$C_{18}H_{33}\!-\!O\!-\!\overset{\displaystyle O}{\underset{\displaystyle OH}{\overset{\|}{P}}}\!-\!OH \qquad [I]$$

be demonstrated, moreover, to increase linearly with the time of aging of the film.   At constant surface pressure and temperature, $\partial\eta/\partial t$ falls with increasing pH.   At 22°C, $\pi = 12$ dyne/cm, and pH $= 5.8$ the viscosity is Newtonian and the temporal behavior is

$$t \text{ (min)} \qquad\quad = 10 \quad 20 \quad 80 \quad 160$$
$$\eta \times 10^2 \text{ (g/sec)} = \quad 3.2 \quad 4.! \quad 9.3 \quad 16$$

At pH $= 4.1$ the viscosity is still Newtonian, and for surface ages of 10, 20, and 80 min the respective values of η are 0.086, 0.114, and 0.27 g/sec.   At pH $= 3.1$, $\eta = 0.1$ g/sec after 10 min and $\eta = 0.207$ g/sec after 20 min. Viscosities higher than 0.2 g/sec are no longer Newtonian.   This feature has been interpreted as due to the progressive formation of hydrogen bonds between the phosphate groups.

g. Dibasic Acids

Dibasic carboxylic acids yields gaseous films (3, 38) which are stable only at very low surface pressures and which exhibit very low surface viscosity. Data for the C_{16} dibasic acid spread on 0.01 N HCl at 22.5°C are $\eta = 7.4 \times 10^{-5}$ g/sec when $A = 131.5$ Å^2 ($\pi = 1$ dyne/cm), and $\eta = 1.5 \times 10^{-5}$ g/sec when $A = 106.5$ Å^2 ($\pi = 2$ dyne/cm).   This rapid decrease in η is a result of the dominant contribution to the surface viscosity of the molecules of water bound to the two carboxylate groups.   For the C_{20} dibasic acid on the same substrate at 20.5°C, corresponding data are $\eta = 1.54 \times 10^{-4}$ g/sec at $A = 107.5$ Å^2 ($\pi = 1$ dyne/cm), and $\eta = 6.6 \times 10^{-5}$ g/sec when $A = 91.5$ Å^2 ($\pi = 3$ dyne/cm).

h. Esters

Esters such as methyl 11-oxostearate or ethyl 11-hydroxystearate spread on water at 20°C show a behavior analogous to that of the dibasic acids (3, 37). Data for the first compound are

π (dyne/cm) =	1	2	4
A (Å^2) = 262		175	128
η (g/sec) =	8.2×10^{-4}	1.05×10^{-4}	2.7×10^{-5}

and for the second

π (dyne/cm) =	1	2	4	8
A (Å^2) = 186		150	130	112
η (g/sec) =	5×10^{-4}	1.6×10^{-4}	4.95×10^{-5}	3.1×10^{-5}

i. Triglycerides

Table VIII summarizes data on the surface viscosity of triglycerides as a function of molecular area (3, 37, 38). For these compounds η decreases with increasing temperature. Sample values for trilaurin spread on water at $A = 90$ Å^2 are $\eta = 1.55 \times 10^{-4}$ g/sec at 16°C and $\eta = 8 \times 10^{-5}$ g/sec at 22°C. When $A = 100$ Å^2 the viscosities at the same temperatures are respectively 1.7×10^{-4} g/sec and 1.1×10^{-4} g/sec. For $A = 110$ Å^2 they increase to 1.8×10^{-4} and 1.35×10^{-4} g/sec. Saturated triglycerides whose chains exceed 14 carbon atoms generally yield solid films at ordinary temperatures.

j. Diglycerides

Saturated long-chain diglycerides form relatively viscous films whose fluidity increases with temperature (35). Typical behavior is that of 1,3-dipalmitine spread on water. At $\pi = 5$ dyne/cm the data are

T (°C) = 20	26	32
η (g/sec) = 5.25×10^{-3}	3.16×10^{-3}	3.83×10^{-4}

Data for 1,3-distearine under the same conditions are

T (°C) = 26	30	40
η (g/sec) = 6.38×10^{-2}	4.52×10^{-2}	3.16×10^{-3}

If $\pi = 20$ dyne/cm and $T = 28$°C, $\eta = 1.78 \times 10^{-2}$ g/sec for the dipalmitine and $\eta = 9.45 \times 10^{-2}$ g/sec for the distearine.

k. Phospholipids

The phospholipids have also been investigated (35). At room temperatures and $\pi = 5$ dyne/cm on water some representative results are $\eta = 2.8–3.0 \times 10^{-4}$ g/sec for the phosphatidylcholines, $\eta = 2.9–3.1 \times 10^{-4}$ g/sec for the hydrogenated phosphatidylcholines (the hydrolecithins), and $\eta = 0.8–1.4 \times 10^{-4}$ g/sec for the phosphatidylserines. For the sake of comparison, $\eta = 2.0 - 2.8 \times 10^{-4}$ g/sec for the phosphatidic acids.

l. Peptides

A few measurements of the surface viscosity of cyclic peptides have been carried out (46). For these molecules which have multiple attachments to the water surface through several polar groups, η increases rather rapidly as the area per residue A_r decreases. A representative example is fungisporine, the octapeptide cyclo-(D-Phe-L-Phe-D-Val-L-Val)$_2$, for which at 14°C on 0.01 M KCl:

A_r (Å^2)	=	25	30	35	40	50
$\eta \times 10^3$ (g/sec)	=	174	28	10.5	6.5	4.2

On the same substrate at 15°C data for the heptapeptide gramicidin J, cyclo-(D-Orn-L-Val-L-Orn-D-Phe-D-Leu-L-Phe-L-Pro) are

A_r (Å^2)	=	18.5	19.5	20
$\eta \times 10^3$ (g/sec)	=	167	31	3.9

B. Insoluble Films of Macromolecular Substances

Surface films of macromolecular substances have been extensively investigated, as much for naturally occurring biopolymers as for synthetics; and indeed the mechanical properties of such films have received more attention than those of small molecules. As was pointed out in Part I, Section II.C.3, it is for macromolecular films that the surface flexibility parameter ξ was introduced. In Table XIII are listed values of ξ calculated by different authors from the compression isotherms (47–52). It is readily observable that the flexibility is much greater at the oil/water interface than at the air/water interface, a phenomenon due to the greater solubility in the oil phase of the nonpolar moiety of the polymeric chains. It is also noteworthy that the proteins have very low flexibilities, indicative of a highly structural organization.

1. The Compression Modulus

A large amount of data exists concerning the isotherms $\pi = f(A)$ of diverse series of macromolecular substances, and as a result a good deal is

TABLE XIII

Surface Flexibilities, ξ

Substance	Air/water interface	Oil/water interface
Nylon on 0.01 N HCl	0.1	
Nylon on 3 N HCl	0.6	
Nylon on 5.5 N HCl	1.3	
Poly ε-caproamide		1.75
Polyvinyl alcohol	0.5	
Polyvinyl acetate	0.20	1.60
Polyvinyl stearate	0.02	1.60
Poly-N-vinylpyrrolidone		1.60
Polyacrylonitrile		1.05
Polymethacrylic acid at pH 1.6		1.75
Polymethyl methacrylate		1.75
Poly-n-butyl acrylate	2.0	2.0
Poly-n-butyl methacrylate	1.3	
Poly-β-ethoxyethyl methacrylate	1.3	
Polyethylene terephthalate		0.02
Cellulose triacetate	0.20	2.0
Poly-DL-leucine	0.12	1.33
Poly-DL-alanine		1.33
Copoly 1:2:1 of glutamic acid, leucine, lysine at pH 7	0.008	0.19
Human methemoglobine	0.015	0.12
Bovine serum albumin	0.034	
N-acetyl bovine serum albumin	0.038	
O-N-acetylated serum albumin	0.04	

known about their compression moduli. As is the case for films of small molecules, the compression moduli of macromolecular films are small, even in condensed states. Let us review successively the principal types of macromolecules.

a. Nonionic Polymers

In Section I.A we established in a general way the fact that $\varkappa$ is a decreasing function of A for films of small molecules, always providing that the change in molecular area does not involve a phase change within the film. In a similar way for nonionic, linear polymers, $\varkappa$ increases as the area per residue A_r diminishes. Typical is the behavior of polyvinyl acetate spread on water at 35°C, for which from the compression isotherm (53) may be calculated $\varkappa = 3.6$ g/sec^2 at $A_r = 40$ Å^2 and $\varkappa = 10.8$ g/sec^2 at $A_r = 30$ Å^2. For polymethyl acrylate under the same conditions $\varkappa = 2.86$ g/sec^2 at $A_r = 35$ Å^2 and $\varkappa = 9.75$ g/sec^2 at $A_r = 25$ Å^2, while for polymethyl methacrylate $\varkappa = 6.6$ g/sec^2 when $A_r = 21$ Å^2, and $\varkappa = 33$ g/sec^2 for $A_r = 17$ Å^2.

The compression modulus is little influenced by the molecular weight. The compressibility of polymethyl acrylate (54) is practically invariant for M varying from 2.6×10^4 to 4.75×10^6. The behavior of oligomeric compounds is analogous. Thus compounds obtained by attaching a molecule of n-dodecanol to a polyethylene oxide chain (55) show no more than a 10% variation in $\varkappa$ when the number of ethylene oxide residues is changed from 7 to 30.

For A constant, $\varkappa$ generally increases with temperature. A sample of polymethyl acrylate (56) of molecular weight 140,000, for example, when spread into a film of 0.2 mg/m² ($A = 115,500$ Å²) shows $\varkappa = 0.407, 0.645$, and 1.248 g/sec², respectively, for $T = 20, 35$, and 50°C. From work on dilute films of polymethyl methacrylate (57) of molecular weight $M = 85,000$, values of $\varkappa$ have been calculated. For the atactic polymer at a surface concentration of 0.4 mg/m² ($A = 35,000$ Å²),

T (°C)	= 25	30	35	40	45
$\varkappa \times 10^2$ (g/sec²) =	3.65	3.96	4.68	6.5	8.65

For the isotactic polymer at 0.1 mg/m² ($A = 140,000$ Å²),

T (°C)	= 25	30	35	40	45
$\varkappa \times 10^2$ (g/sec²) =	4.26	4.8	5.79	7.46	8.44

The great influence of stereoregularity upon the compressibility of the dilute films should be noted.

It is to be expected that the nature of the interface will have a considerable influence upon the compression modulus. For polyethylene terephthalate (58) at 15°C and $A_r = 60$ Å², $\varkappa$ at the air/water interface is 18 g/sec², while at the water/petroleum ether interface $\varkappa = 0.435$ g/sec². Another example is poly-N-vinylpyrrolidone (58) of molecular weight 13,400. At 19°C, pH 11, and $A_r = 30$ Å², one finds at the air/water interface $\varkappa = 11.55$ g/sec², while at the air/petroleum ether interface, $\varkappa = 2.42$ g/sec².

b. Polyelectrolytes

At constant molecular area, the compression moduli of linear polyelectrolytes also increases with temperature and depends upon the stereoconfiguration. An atactic polymethacrylic acid, for example, of molecular weight 65,000 spread as a dilute film on 0.01 M HCl at 0.4 mg/m² ($A = 26,750$ Å²) shows compression moduli (59)

T (°C)	= 25	30	35	40	45
$\varkappa \times 10^2$ (g/sec²) =	1.74	2.15	4	5.74	8.93

The isotactic polymer at 0.1 mg/m^2 ($A = 107{,}000$ Å^2) exhibits the behavior

T (°C)	= 25	30	35	40	45
$\varkappa \times 10^2$ (g/sec^2) =	4.89	6.09	7.05	8.45	9.37

The properties of films of polyelectrolytes are profoundly dependent upon the pH. Data tracing the change of the compression modulus with pH are given below (60) for a vinyl acetate–maleic acid copolymer spread at the air/petroleum ether interface at 20°C and $A_r = 40$ Å^2.

pH	= 1.6–2.8	3.2	4.0	4.8	5.6
$\varkappa$ (g/sec^2) = 15.6		11.5	7.35	4.75	0.7

A 69% methacrylic acid–31% diethylaminoethyl vinyl ether copolymer has been studied both at the air/water interface and at the air/petroleum ether interface (61, 62). For $T = 10$–15°C and $A_r = 15$ Å^2, values of the compression modulus at the former interface are

pH	= 1.4	2.4	3.9	4.4
$\varkappa$ (g/sec^2) =	3.83	3.27	1.58	0.435

while at the latter interface for $T = 17$–22°C and $A_r = 25$ Å^2,

pH	= 1.2–3.2	3.5	4.0	4.8	5.7
$\varkappa$ (g/sec^2) = 5.15		3.78	2.57	2.18	1.8

The specific chemical nature of salts contained in the substrate plays a role in determining the compression modulus. As an example, polymethacrylic acid of molecular weight $M = 23{,}000$ spread at 20°C at a surface concentration 0.4 mg/m^2 ($A = 9500$ Å^2), on a substrate of pII 4.2 and ionic strength 0.0022 mole/l, exhibits a compression modulus which decreases with increasing charge of the metal ion. Using metal chlorides, the successive values of $\varkappa$ for K^+, Ba^{2+}, Cu^{2+}, and Cr^{3+} in the substrate are 0.0313, 0.0231, 0.02, and 0.0105 g/sec^2 (63).

c. Polypeptides

Synthetic polypeptides are among those macromolecular substances whose surface films have been most copiously studied, for they provide a simple model for the behavior of proteins.

As with other polymers, outside of regions in which phase changes are taking place, the compression modulus increases with decreasing area per residue. Typical data are those for poly-L-alanine of polymerization number approximately 250 spread on water at 9°C (64).

A_r (Å^2)	= 14	18	22	26
$\varkappa$ (g/sec^2) =	23.6	3	0.915	0.39

From compression isotherms of the copolymer 1:1:1 (L-proline, L-leucine, DL-alanine) spread on water at 16.7°C one finds (64):

$$A_r \, (\text{Å}^2) \quad = \quad 5 \qquad 10 \qquad 15 \qquad 20$$

$$\varkappa \, (\text{g/sec}^2) = 18.75 \quad 14.3 \quad 8.82 \quad 3.68$$

A phase change must necessarily introduce a discontinuity into $\varkappa$. This behavior is exhibited by poly-L-propyl-L-leucylglycine spread on water at 16.7°C (64):

$$A_r \, (\text{Å}^2) \quad = \quad 6 \qquad 10 \qquad 15 \quad 20$$

$$\varkappa \, (\text{g/sec}^2) = 10.05 \quad 7.57 \quad 31 \quad 10$$

It is frequently the case after a transition point in the isotherm $\pi = f(A)$ that the compression modulus is smaller in the condensed than in the more dilute phase. An example is poly-γ-benzyl-L-glutamate spread at the air/water interface at 9°C (65) for which $\varkappa \simeq 11.7$ g/sec^2 for A_r between 11.4 and 20.3 Å^2, but $\varkappa \simeq 79.5$ g/sec^2 for A_r between 20.3 and 22.8 Å^2. Another example is poly-β-benzyl-L-aspartate at 10.8°C. Here one finds $\varkappa \simeq 7.75$ g/sec^2 for A_r between 14 and 17 Å^2; $\varkappa \simeq 30.4$ g/sec^2 for A_r between 17 and 20.3 Å^2; and $\varkappa \simeq 45$ g/sec^2 for A_r between 20.3 and 21.5 Å^2. In a similar way, data for the copolymer 1:1 (γ-benzyl-L-glutamate, β-benzyl-L-aspartate) at 12.3°C are $\varkappa \simeq 0.825$ g/sec^2 for A_r in the range 12–18.3 Å^2 and $\varkappa \simeq 51.3$ g/sec^2 for A_r between 18.3 and 23 Å^2.

Unlike the behavior of other linear polymers, the compression modulus of certain synthetic polypeptides decreases with rising temperature. For example, for the polypeptide obtained from the polymerization of α-aminolauric acid (66), there is found below and above the phase transition

$$T \, (°\text{C}) \qquad\qquad\qquad = \quad 8.8 \quad 16.6 \quad 20.5 \quad 25.4 \quad 27.8$$

$$A_r = 14 \, \text{Å}^2; \, \varkappa \, (\text{g/sec}^2) = 17.4 \quad 5.55 \quad 5.92 \quad 4.49 \quad 3.34$$

$$A_r = 23 \, \text{Å}^2; \, \varkappa \, (\text{g/sec}^2) = 68.2 \quad 63.7 \quad 60 \quad 44.2 \quad 39.2$$

For polypeptides that are polyelectrolytes, $\varkappa$ depends upon the pH, but the changes are irregular. Thus for poly-L-glutamic acid (67) spread on water at 10°C and $A_r = 14$ Å^2, for pH values 1.6–4.6, 5.1, and 5.6 the respective values of $\varkappa$ are 18.85, 20.4, and 16.75 g/sec^2. If the copolymer 1:2:1 (L-lysine, L-leucine, L-glutamic acid) is spread on water at 8°C and $A_r = 14$ Å^2 (67), the change in $\varkappa$ with pH is

$$\text{pH} \qquad = \quad 1.6 \quad 3 \quad 4.4 \quad 5.8 \quad 7 \quad 9.4 \quad 12.3$$

$$\varkappa \, (\text{g/sec}^2) = 18 \quad 17.3 \quad 4.15 \quad 5.15 \quad 51.6 \quad 26.2 \quad 45.6$$

The salt content of the aqueous substrate also influences the compression modulus. An example is polycarbobenzoxylysine (68) at an area of 0.5 m²/mg. On substrates which are 1.1, 2.6, and 3.8 M in $(NH_4)_2SO_4$ the respective compression moduli are $\varkappa = 4.18$, 3.36, and 4.45 g/sec². Spread on 2.4 and 6.0 M solutions of LiCl, the compression moduli are $\varkappa = 2.55$ and 3.67 g/sec², respectively.

The structural changes which occur when proteins denature have prompted studies of the action of urea on films of polypeptides. Such studies (69) on poly-γ-benzyl-L-glutamate at a fixed area of $A_r = 23$ Å² have yielded values $\varkappa = 2.65$, 17.1, and 37.9 g/sec² when the polymer is spread on aqueous solutions containing 0, 0.10, and 30% of urea, respectively.

Another set of results for poly-DL-leucine (70) spread at 25°C, $A_r = 20$ Å², and pH = 10.5 is

Molar conc. of urea = 0		0.5	1.7	3.6	7.2
π (dyne/cm)	= 0.95	2.25	5.35	7.1	10.25
$\varkappa$ (g/sec²)	= 8.15	33.7	76.5	66.5	57.3

The $\alpha \rightarrow \beta$ transition which occurs upon breaking the intramolecular hydrogen bonds has also been studied in surface films of synthetic polypeptides. An example is poly-γ-methylglutamate (71) at a constant surface pressure of 10 dyne/cm. When spread on water at 23.4°C it takes the α conformation with $\varkappa = 116.5$ g/sec² and $A_r = 7.8$ Å². Spread on 0.02 M formic acid at 17.4°C it assumes the β conformation with $\varkappa = 121$ g/sec and $A_r = 10.8$ Å².

On the other hand, the polypeptide obtained from the polymerization of α-aminocapric acid (72) is always in the β form on either side of the phase transition plateau. On water at 21°C, $\varkappa = 9.55$ g/sec² when $A_r = 11$ Å², and $\varkappa = 34.8$ g/sec² when $A_r = 21$ Å². For the same areas per residue but spread on 0.2 M formic acid, $\varkappa = 13.05$ and 53.7 g/sec², respectively.

d. Proteins

Studies of monomolecular films of proteins are very numerous, and many of their isotherms $\pi = f(A)$ exhibit an inflection point. At surface pressures exceeding that at the inflection point, the compression isotherm is in general no longer reproducible. At surface pressures lower than that at the inflection point $\varkappa$ decreases as the molecular area increases, but the indications are that this behavior is reversed for surface areas lower than the critical area. In Table XIV examples of this behavior are given (73–76). From the table the influence of the nature of the interface upon the compressibility of protein films may be deduced.

TABLE XIV

Compression Moduli of Protein Films; The Effect of Surface Concentration

Protein	Interface	T (°C)	pH	S (m²/mg)	$\varkappa$ (g/sec²)
Ovalbumin	Air/water		1	0.86	86
				0.90	83
				0.94	69
			3	0.76	29.8
				0.78	25.7
Bovine hemoglobin	20% (NH₄)₂SO₄/air	31		0.7	37.7
				0.9	21
				1	8.25
				1.1	3.95
Wheat gluten	0.1 M phosphate buffer/air	25	6.8	0.25	7.95
				0.5	13.2
				1	18.4
				1.5	7.95
				1.75	1.4
	0.1 M phosphate buffer/CCl₄	—	—	0.25	6.27
				0.5	10.8
				1	18.4
				2	8.53
				3	3.07
				4	1.99
				5	1.15
Bovine β globulin	Water/petroleum ether	25		0.5	7.05
				0.7	9.85
				1	9.02
				1.3	6.1
Pepsin	—		—	0.5	12
				0.75	18
				1	6.6
Insulin	—		—	0.5	16.1
				0.75	18
				1	18.7

Whenever $\varkappa$ has been determined as a function of temperature, it has been confirmed that at constant area $\varkappa(T)$ exhibits a maximum while at constant surface pressure, $\varkappa(T)$ displays a minimum. Thus for lysozyme (77) spread on 0.001 N HCl at $\pi = 6$ dyne/cm,

$$T \ (°C) \quad = 15 \quad\quad 22 \quad\quad 24 \quad\quad 27 \quad\quad 29.5 \quad 30.5$$
$$\varkappa \ (\text{g/sec}^2) = 28.6 \quad 22.2 \quad 26.1 \quad 28.3 \quad 32.1 \quad 32.2$$

while for the same film at $A_r = 8$ Å²

$$T \ (°C) \quad = 15 \quad\quad\quad 22 \quad\quad 24 \quad\quad 27 \quad 29.5 \quad 30.5$$
$$\varkappa \ (\text{g/sec}^2) = \quad 0.53 \quad\quad 3.9 \quad\quad 6.8 \quad 27 \quad 29.5 \quad 24.1$$

The influence upon $\varkappa$ of the salt concentration in the substrate depends very much upon the molecular area chosen.   Thus at 1.5 m²/mg, a monolayer of Taka-amylase A (78) spread on a substrate of pH 2 at 20°C shows $\varkappa =$ 1.41 g/sec² in the absence of KCl and $\varkappa = 1.44$ g/sec² when the KCl concentration is 0.5 M.   The same monolayer at 1.25 m²/mg under the same conditions shows $\varkappa = 2.86$ g/sec² and $\varkappa = 10.25$ g/sec², respectively.

As with the majority of polyelectrolytes, one of the principal experimental parameters to which the compression modulus is sensitive is the pH of the substrate.   This sensitivity, however, is also dependent upon the salt concentration in the substrate.   As an example, gelatin (78) spread on water at 20°C and $A_r = 10$ Å² displays $\varkappa = 0.735, 1.56$, and 0.75 g/sec² for successive pH values 2.0, 5.6, and 11.2.   On 1 M KCl, however, the same sequence of pH changes leads to $\varkappa = 3.87, 3.29$, and 3.87 g/sec², respectively.

Even taking account of the experimental error of $\pm 5\%$ inherent in the determination of $\varkappa$, the changes which occur when the pH is altered at constant molecular area appear to be less regular than those which occur when π is held constant.   Films of insulin (79, 80) spread on water at 0.8 m²/mg, $T = 18$–$20°C$, and ionic strength $\mu = 0.01$ mole/l exhibit the following changes in $\varkappa$ with pH:

pH $=$ 3.1   3.33   4.65   5.45   6.86   7.67   8.34   8.95   9.70
$\varkappa$ (g/sec²) $=$ 19.2 33.4   28.8   33.4   27.5   32   22.4   22.7   17.6

For the same film at a constant surface pressure of $\pi = 10$ dyne/cm, the changes in $\varkappa$ for pH readings of 2.2, 5.1, and 7.4 are $\varkappa = 17.7, 43$, and 40 g/sec², respectively.

As long as the pH values selected exclude the denaturation or the hydrolysis of the protein, it is a general rule that in the neighborhood of the isoelectric point the compression modulus assumes its maximum values.   An example is pig serum albumin (80).   At a surface pressure $\pi = 10$ dyne/cm, changes in $\varkappa$ with pH are

pH $=$ 2.2   5.1   7.4
$\varkappa$ (g/sec²) $=$ 36.8   50   35.6

For bovine serum albumin spread at the petroleum ether/water interface at 23°C and area 1 m²/mg, calculated values of $\varkappa$ are (81)

pH $=$ 2.2   6.3   12.5
$\varkappa$ (g/sec²) $=$ 7.55   13.45   6.37

Corresponding data for bovine γ-globulin (82) spread at the air/water interface at 23°C and an area 1 m²/mg are

pH $=$ 1.4   8.9   12.5
$\varkappa$ (g/sec²) $=$ 2.26   1.55   4.51

When the same film is spread at the petroleum ether/water interface these pH values lead to $\varkappa = 4.75$, 5.34, and 4.37 g/sec^2.

Proteins capable of self-aggregation such as the IgG globulins, which form pentamers (83), have compression moduli which are greater in the monomeric than in the polymeric state.   Thus spread on a substrate of pH 3 at a surface concentration 1.66 m^2/mg ($A = 16,000$ Å^2 for the monomer, 80,000 Å^2 for the pentamer), $\varkappa = 7.4$ g/sec^2 for the unassociated protein and $\varkappa = 5.6$ g/sec^2 for the aggregate.

The importance of denaturation in determining the compression modulus is greatly influenced by the way in which the denaturation is accomplished. Heating of horse serum albumin for 30 min at 100°C produces a decrease in $\varkappa$ (74).   Thus at $A = 9250$ Å^2, pH 3, $\varkappa = 17.3$ g/sec^2 for the native protein and 10.7 g/sec^2 for the denatured product.   At pH 5, these values are altered to $\varkappa = 6.4$ and 2.66 g/sec^2, respectively.   Contrasting behavior is that of lysozyme (84) denatured by 8 M urea.   At $A_r = 12$ Å^2 and $T = 14$°C, $\varkappa$ is increased from 11.15 g/sec^2 for the native protein to 45.7 g/sec^2 for its denatured product

2. Dilational Viscosity

Direct measurements of the dilational viscosity of polymeric films have apparently never been made.   On the other hand plots of compression isotherms $\pi = f(A)$ often show hysteresis once a certain stage of the compression has been exceeded.   The lack of reversibility of the isotherms of polymethyl methacrylate, of polyamides, and of polystyrene is particularly marked (85).   Thus with polystyrene at $A_r = 2.5$ Å^2, the surface pressure on the compression branch of the isotherm is 62.3 dyne/cm, while on the decompression branch it is 18.5 dyne/cm.   Films of ethylcellulose show large hysteresis loops whenever the area per residue is less than 18 Å^2 (86). Quite different is the behavior of polyvinyl acetate (87) of molecular weight $M \simeq 10^6$ spread at 25°C, for which no hysteresis has even been observed.

Hysteresis effects in protein films are often very pronounced.   An example is horse serum albumin (88) spread on water of pH 4.7.   At $A = 5450$ Å^2, the surface pressure upon compression is 20.5 dyne/cm, while upon decompression it is 10.2 dyne/cm.   For the same film at $\pi = 20$ dyne/cm A is 5670 Å^2 upon compression and 1690 Å^2 upon the expansion branch of the isotherm.   As might be expected, these films exhibit a relaxation of pressure with time.   Thus if the compression is halted at $A = 5450$ Å^2, the pressure drops spontaneously by 2.5 dyne/cm in 2 min.

Analogously, if a film of pepsin or of bovine serum albumin (89) spread on water at pH 5.5 is maintained at constant surface pressure after a rapid compression, the area occupied per molecule will be observed to decrease spontaneously.   This relaxation effect is the more pronounced, the higher the pressure and the lower the temperature. Thus for pepsin at $\pi = 15$ dyne/cm, $\Delta S/S_0 = 0.066$ when $T = 5°C$ and $\Delta S/S_0 = 0.047$ when $T = 20°C$. At the latter temperature and $\pi = 30$ dyne/cm, $\Delta S/S_0 = 0.33$. For bovine serum albumin at $\pi = 20$ dyne/cm, $\Delta S/S_0 = 0.29$ at 5°C, and $\Delta S/S_0 = 0.139$ at 20°C. Increasing the surface pressure to 25 dyne/cm at 20°C results in $\Delta S/S_0 = 0.562$. If the substrate beneath the albumin film is replaced by a 25% solution of ammonium sulfate, then at $T = 25°C$ and $\pi = 20$ dyne/cm, $\Delta S/S_0 = 0.033$; but compressing the film to 30 dyne/cm increases $\Delta S/S_0$ to 0.71. A film of polyalanine spread under the same conditions already exhibits $\Delta S/S_0 = 0.109$ when π is only 20 dyne/cm.

3. Elasticity and Viscoelasticity

Purely elastic behavior is relatively rare among macromolecular surface films, viscoelastic behavior being far more common. This type of behavior has been studied by oscillatory and by deflection methods; but because of the approximate nature of the oscillation method, its concordance with the results of the deflection method is not always very good.

a. Nonionic Polymers

The viscoelasticity of a film of polymethyl methacrylate at the air/water interface at 24°C has been interpreted by means of a Voigt model (90). Both the viscosity and the rigidity increase rapidly as the area per residue decreases:

A_r (Å^2) $=$	16	18	20	22
G (g/sec^2) $=$	1.14	0.25	0.11	0.055
η_s (g/sec) $=$	3390	44.2	8.9	3.24

At 35°C the deflection data require the use of three- or four-parameter models depending upon the area per residue (91). At $A_r = 25.4$ Å^2, the deflection curve is described by $\delta = 8.35 - 0.56 \exp(-0.0201t)$; and if the characteristics of the apparatus are taken into account, from this may be calculated $G_1 = 0.023$ g/sec^2, $G_2 = 0.009$ g/sec^2, and $\eta_s = 0.16$ g/sec. Upon compression of the film to $A_r = 22.3$ Å^2, these figures must be replaced by $\delta = 9.35 - 1.82 \exp(-0.00811t) - 1.3 \exp(-0.0345t)$; whence $G_1 = 0.0458$ g/sec^2, $G = 0.0427$ g/sec^2, $\eta_s = 1.72$ g/sec, and $\eta = 2.21$ g/sec. Finally at $A_r = 16.2$ Å^2, the deflection curve is fitted by $\delta = 4.93 + 0.00210t - 1.65 \exp(-0.0066t)$, from which $G_l = 0.856$ g/sec^2, $G = 1.46$ g/sec^2, $\eta_s = 230$ g/sec, and $\eta = 1080$ g/sec.

Nylon-6 prepared from the polymerization of ε-aminocaproic acid shows pure Hookean elasticity so long as the area per residue exceeds a certain lower value characteristic of the sample (92, 93). For a polymer of $M = 15,500$ spread on water at 31°C this lower value is near 25 Å². The elasticity modulus increases as A_r is reduced:

$$A_r \text{ (Å}^2) \qquad\qquad = 50 \quad 40 \quad 30 \quad 25$$

$$G \times 10^2 \text{ (g/sec}^2) = \quad 1.5 \quad 2 \quad 14 \quad 34$$

For a polymer of $M = 17,300$ between 10 and 40°C, the behavior is purely elastic at $A_r \geq 42$ Å². The elastic modulus decreases linearly with increasing temperature. Relevant data taken at $A_r = 41.8$ Å² are

$$T \text{ (°C)} \quad = 10 \qquad 20 \qquad 30 \qquad 40$$

$$G \text{ (g/sec}^2) = \quad 0.965 \quad 0.845 \quad 0.725 \quad 0.605$$

This linearity is observed also for the instantaneous elastic modulus of very condensed films. At $A_r = 7$ Å² some results are

$$T \text{ (°C)} \qquad = 10 \quad 20 \quad 30 \quad 40$$

$$G_l \text{ (g/sec}^2) = 145 \quad 123 \quad 99 \quad 78$$

It is also possible to generalize that both G and G_l increase with the molecular weight of the polymer. Supporting data for films spread at 20°C are to be found in Table XV.

For moderate values of the surface concentration, creep experiments can be satisfactorily described by a four-parameter model with a single retardation time t. Thus at $A_r = 25$ Å² and $T = 20$°C, one finds $G_l = 1.6$ g/sec², $G = 19.5$ g/sec², $\eta_s = 2200$ g/sec, $\eta = 7800$ g/sec, with $\tau = 113$ sec.   At higher surface concentrations, a six-parameter model is required embracing retardation times τ_1 and τ_2 related to the pairs of rheological coefficients G_1, η_1 and G_2, η_2. Measured values at $A_r = 12$ Å² are $G_l = 11.2$ g/sec², $\eta = 13,000$ g/sec, $G_1 = 109$ g/sec², $G_2 = 107$ g/sec², $\eta_1 = 1900$ g/sec, and $\eta_2 = 7700$ g/sec, from which $\tau_1 = 17$ sec and $\tau_2 = 72$ sec. At $A_r = 7$ Å², these values change to $G_l = 112.3$ g/sec², $\eta = 7 \times 10^5$ g/sec, $G_1 = 1590$ g/sec², $G_2 = 675$ g/sec², $\eta_1 = 4.3 \times 10^4$ g/sec, and $\eta_2 = 8.5 \times 10^4$ g/sec, whence $\tau_1 = 27$ sec and $\tau_2 = 126$ sec. After the achievement of steady

TABLE XV
Instantaneous Elasticity of Films of Nylon-6, G_1 (g/sec²)

A_r (Å²)	DP =	20	60	100	140
13	$G_l =$	5.33	12.65	14.8	14.8
33	$G_l =$	1.12	2	2	2
42	$G_l =$	0.125	0.435	0.787	1.34

flow, the variation of η as a function of temperature suggests an apparent activation energy of flow of the order of 6.4 kcal/mole.

Experiments on the relaxation of films of nylon-6 can be interpreted by assuming three relaxation times θ_1, θ_2, θ_3, of which the third is of the order of 10 sec. At $A_r = 7$ Å², θ_1 decreases with rising temperature while θ_2 is practically independent of temperature:

T (°C)	= 10	20	26	33
$\theta_1 \times 10^{-4}$ (sec) =	2.1	1.5	1.4	0.9
$\theta_2 \times 10^{-2}$ (sec) =	1.4	1.6	1.3	1.4

Data taken on a sample of nylon-5 studied by the oscillation method (73) at the water/petroleum ether interface at pH 6 and $T = 25°C$, have been described by the Voigt model:

A_r (Å²)	= 44	46	50	60
G (g/sec²) =	7	4	2.1	0.3
η_s (g/sec) =	3.62	1.87	1.44	0.81

b. Polyelectrolytes

The viscoelastic behavior of polymethacrylic acid has been studied by the oscillation method (73) at the water/petroleum ether interface. At $T = 25°C$, an ionic strength of 0.03 mole/l, and pH = 1 data are

A_r (Å²)	= 8	10	12	15	20
G (g/sec²) =	11	4.5	1.5	0.2	
η_s (g/sec) =	4.8	3.62	2.5	1	0.155

At pH 3 the film is more easily deformed:

A_r (Å²)	= 5	8	10	12
G (g/sec²) =	10.7	0.9	0.1	
η_s (g/sec) =	5	0.5	0.2	0.075

In either case, the deformability of the film increases with the area per residue.

c. Polypeptides

Polyalanine has been studied by the oscillation method at the water/petroleum ether interface at pH 6 and $T = 25°C$ (73). As the film is compressed its deformability rapidly decreases. Interpretation of the data by means of a Voigt model leads to

$$
\begin{array}{llll}
A_r \; (\text{Å}^2) & = 12 & 14 & 16 \\
G \; (\text{g/sec}^2) & = 16.8 & 0.96 & 0.16 \\
\eta_s \; (\text{g/sec}) & = 6 & 2 & 0.16
\end{array}
$$

A sample of poly-DL-alanine of molecular weight 6500 has been studied at 24°C using the deflection method (90). Its behavior may be described by a Burgers model, whence it is found that the rheological parameters are very sensitive to small changes in molecular area. Changing A_r from 14 to 15 Å^2, for example, causes changes in G_i from 6.4 to 2.9 g/sec^2, in G from 10.2 to 6.85 g/sec^2, in η_s from 2070 to 1180 g/sec, and in η from 12,600 to 7650 g/sec. Parallel behavior is noted at the water/benzene interface:

$$
\begin{array}{lllll}
A_r \; (\text{Å}^2) & = 17 & 19 & 21 & 23 \\
G_i \; (\text{g/sec}^2) & = 7.1 & 1.57 & 0.755 & 0.715 \\
G \; (\text{g/sec}^2) & = 19.5 & 3.18 & 1.11 & 0.57 \\
\eta_s \times 10^{-2} \; (\text{g/sec}) & = 22.9 & 7.08 & 2.08 & 1.32 \\
\eta \times 10^{-2} \; (\text{g/sec}) & = 100 & 14.8 & 5.37 & 3.63
\end{array}
$$

Using the oscillation method at the air/water interface, the rheological behavior of polyphenylalanine has been described by a two-parameter model (73):

$$
\begin{array}{llll}
A_r \; (\text{Å}^2) & = 10 & 12.5 & 15 \\
G \; (\text{g/sec}^2) & = 31 & 3.5 & 0.1 \\
\eta_s \; (\text{g/sec}) & = 5.13 & 1.87 & 0.44
\end{array}
$$

The fact that these two films have been studied by different experimental techniques makes a comparison of their behaviors difficult.

d. Proteins

At the air/petroleum ether interface, a concentrated film of β bovine globulin at 25°C behaves like a Voigt solid (73) whose deformability decreases rapidly as the film is compressed:

$$
\begin{array}{lll}
S \; (\text{m}^2/\text{mg}) & = 0.5 & 0.7 \\
G \; (\text{g/sec}^2) & = 10.6 & 0.32 \\
\eta_s \; (\text{g/sec}) & = 3 & 1
\end{array}
$$

For the same conditions, both pepsin and insulin behave in a similar way (73). For pepsin,

$$
\begin{array}{lll}
A \; (\text{Å}^2) & = 3000 & 4500 \\
S \; (\text{m}^2/\text{mg}) & = 0.5 & 0.75 \\
G \; (\text{g/sec}^2) & = 9.6 & 0.8 \\
\eta_s \; (\text{g/sec}) & = 3.6 & 0.8
\end{array}
$$

while for insulin

$$
\begin{array}{lcc}
A \ (\text{Å}^2) & = 1050 & 1500 \\
S \ (\text{m}^2/\text{mg}) = & 0.35 & 0.5 \\
G \ (\text{g}/\text{sec}^2) = & 1.6 & 0.6 \\
\eta_s \ (\text{g}/\text{sec}) = & 2.2 & 0.4
\end{array}
$$

At the air/water interface for pH 6 and $T = 25°C$, pepsin is considerably less deformable than at the water/petroleum ether interface (94). Compressing the film from $A = 6550 \ \text{Å}^2$ to $4950 \ \text{Å}^2$ causes a rise in G from 1 to 4 dyne/cm. If the substrate is a 60% solution by weight of saccharose in water the same compression changes G from 38 to 6.2 dyne/cm.

At the water/benzene interface, bovine serum albumin behaves like a Burger's body (90) whose deformability increases rapidly with A_r:

$$
\begin{array}{lccc}
A_r \ (\text{Å}^2) & = 16 & 18 & 20 \\
G_l \ (\text{g}/\text{sec}^2) = & 1.76 & 0.71 & 0.51 \\
G \ (\text{g}/\text{sec}^2) = & 1.19 & 0.27 & 0.11 \\
\eta_s \ (\text{g}/\text{sec}) & = 257 & 42.8 & 8.9 \\
\eta \ (\text{g}/\text{sec}) & = 710 & 90 & 14.8
\end{array}
$$

The modulus of instantaneous elasticity of a film of ovalbumin spread on $0.1 \ N$ HCl at 21°C increases monotonically with compression (92):

$$
\begin{array}{llcccc}
S \ (\text{m}^2/\text{mg}) & = 4 & 3 & 2 & 1.5 & 1.2 \\
G_l \times 10^{-2} \ (\text{g}/\text{sec}^2) = & 1 & 5 & 13 & 21.5 & 35
\end{array}
$$

For pH between 2 and 7, the viscoelastic behavior of films of ovalbumin can be described by a four-parameter model. If pH > 7, a three-parameter model is adequate, for the instantaneous elasticity disappears (95).

When spread at 18°C upon tanning solutions, gelatin behaves like a Burger's body (96). Data for various substrates are as follows:

	0.001% chestnut tannin plus 20% NaCl	0.01% chrome hydroxyl sulfate plus 20% NaCl	0.05% potassium alum plus 20% NaCl
$G_l \ (\text{g}/\text{sec}^2)$	758	14.6	10.1
$G \ (\text{g}/\text{sec}^2)$	565	58.2	9.8
$\eta_s \ (\text{g}/\text{sec})$	1090	110.6	117
$\eta \ (\text{g}/\text{sec})$	4.72×10^5	8300	1370

Spread upon a solution of chromium sulfate, gelatin shows purely elastic behavior between pH 3.5 and 6, with G_l passing through a maximum near pH 5.5.

Oscillation experiments on wheat gluten spread at 25°C on water of ionic strength 0.1 and pH 6.8 can be interpreted from the Voigt model (97).   At the air/water interface,

$$S \text{ (m}^2/\text{mg)} = 0.2 \quad 0.4$$
$$G \text{ (g/sec}^2) = 1.96 \quad 0.013$$
$$\eta_s \text{ (g/sec)} = 2.22 \quad 0.27$$

while at the water/carbon tetrachloride interface,

$$S \text{ (m}^2/\text{mg)} = 0.4 \quad 0.9$$
$$G \text{ (g/sec}^2) = 3.98 \quad 0.044$$
$$\eta_s \text{ (g/sec)} = 2.6 \quad 0.18$$

G and η_s vary with the pH and are maximum at the isoelectric point.   They also increase with time without corresponding changes in S or π, tending towards an asymptotic value.

4. Shear Viscosity

The study of the rheological properties of macromolecular fluid films has in a large number of cases been limited to the measurement of their apparent viscosities.   It is furthermore obvious that the sensitivity of the apparatus used does not always permit a distinction between purely viscous and visco-elastic behavior, particularly when the flow is non-Newtonian.   All that can be said for such experiments is that in first approximation the film can be represented as a Maxwell liquid whose elastic term is small compared to its viscous term.   It is, moreover, not always certain whenever the oscillation method is employed whether an apparently Newtonian behavior is rigorously Newtonian.   Despite these limitations, surface viscometry has played an important role in the study of macromolecular surface films.

a. Nonionic Polymers

In almost the entirety of the films studied, η increases as the surface area per residue is reduced.   Representative data for polyvinyl stearate of polymerization degree 226 spread on 0.01 N HCl at 25°C are (98)

$$A_r \text{ (Å}^2) = 27.5 \quad 50$$
$$\eta \text{ (g/sec)} = 0.0275 \quad 0.00125$$

For polymethyl acrylate spread on water at 35°C, viscosities have been determined by the deflection method (91):

$$A_r \text{ (Å}^2) = 17 \quad 23$$
$$\eta \text{ (g/sec)} = 0.0065 \quad 0.0043$$

This dependence of η upon A_r is particularly noteworthy in the series of nylons derived from the ω-aminocarboxylic acids. Data obtained by the oscillation method are listed in Table XVI (99). Applying the remarks of Section I.B.3.a to nylon-6, it is practically certain that viscosities measured by the oscillation method are no more than apparent viscosities, and that the real rheological behavior of these materials is viscoelastic. A comparison of polynonamethyleneurea to nylon-11 (which has the same monomer length) shows that it is more viscous at low A_r and slightly less viscous at higher A_r:

$$A_r \, (\text{Å}^2) \qquad = 32 \quad 40 \quad 50 \quad 60 \quad\quad 80$$
$$\eta \times 10^2 \, (\text{g/sec}) = 38 \quad 10 \quad 2 \quad 1.4 \quad 0.2$$

In addition to the area per monomer, the degree of polymerization plays a role in the determination of the surface shear viscosity, as can be seen from an examination of Table XVII summarizing experiments on polyvinyl alcohol and polyvinyl acetate (98) spread on water at 25°C. Over a wide range of surface pressures, the surface viscosity of polyvinyl acetate is a function of the molecular weight M:

$$\log \eta = 1.755 \times 10^{-3}\sqrt{M} + 0.1634\pi - 6.255$$

The Staudinger equation relating the molecular weight and the intrinsic surface viscosity (see Part I, Section II.C.4) has been confirmed for interfaces (57, 100). Examples are for polyvinyl acetate

$$[\eta] = 3.2 \times 10^{-5} \, M^{0.63}$$

TABLE XVI
Surface Viscosity of Nylons at the Air/Water Interface

Polymer	T (°C)		$\eta \times 10^2$ (g/sec)			
Nylon-6	22	$A_r \, (\text{Å}^2) = 20$	40	60	80	
		28	7.5	1.2	0.2	
Nylon-7	17	$A_r \, (\text{Å}^2) = 27$	30	34	38	
		25	4.6	2.1	0.7	
Nylon-8	21	$A_r \, (\text{Å}^2) = 40$	60	80		
		37	11.3	1.8		
Nylon-9	24	$A_r \, (\text{Å}^2) = 44$	50	60	80	100
		22	7.4	5.6	2	0.4
Nylon-10	21	$A_r \, (\text{Å}^2) = 26$	30	40	60	
		36	11	1.4	0.5	
Nylon-11	21	$A_r \, (\text{Å}^2) = 26$	30	40	60	80
		38	26	5	1.6	0.3
Nylon-12	17.5	$A_r \, (\text{Å}^2) = 24$	30	40	60	
		29	12	3	0.2	

and for cellulose acetate

$$[\eta] = 1.26 \times 10^{-7} M^{0.97}$$

For polymethyl methacrylate the intrinsic surface viscosity of the atactic form may be calculated from

$$[\eta] = 4 \times 10^{-9} M^{1.36}$$

while for the isotactic form

$$[\eta] = 1.6 \times 10^{-7} M^{1.16}$$

The corresponding apparent activation energies for flow for the two structures are 9 and 11.8 kcal/mole.

The surface viscosities of nonionic polymers are highly temperature sensitive.   For polyvinyl acetate the data fit the equation (101)

$$\log \eta = \alpha\sqrt{M} + \frac{\varepsilon}{T} + \zeta$$

in which α, ε, and ζ are independent of both M and T.   Despite the sensitivity of the surface viscosity to A_r, the energy of activation for flow is practically independent of A_r, being of the order 12.6 kcal/mole.   In Table XVIII are listed values of η measured for a sample of polymerization degree 2540 spread on water.

It is remarkable that some polymers form extremely fluid films at the air/water interface.   This occurs for the polydimethylsiloxanes (102) of general formula

$$C_2H_5O[Si(CH_3)_2O]_nC_2H_5$$

and for

$$(CH_3)_3Si[OSi(CH_3)_2]_nOSi(CH_3)_2$$

The viscosities of these compounds, determined by the canal method, are less than 10^{-5} g/sec even for molecular weights as high as 1.05×10^5.

TABLE XVII

Effect of the Degree of Polymerization on the Surface Shear Viscosity $\eta \times 10^3$ (g/sec)

Polymer	DP	A_r (Å^2) = 10	12	14	16
Polyvinyl alcohol on water at 25°C	1560	5.5		0.8	
	2510	12.2		1.25	
Polyvinyl acetate on water at 25°C	467		1.85	0.532	0.162
	2540		5.2	1.49	0.34
	16000		6.98	2	0.807

TABLE XVIII

Effect of Temperature on the Surface Viscosity of Polyvinyl
Acetate $\eta \times 10^3$ (g/sec)

A_r (Å²)	T (°C) = 8.6	13.7	21.5	25
12	68	19.3	4.68	5.2
14	11	4.1	1.46	1.49
16	3.22	0.77	0.255	0.34

b. Polyelectrolytes

Aside from the polypeptides, comparatively little research has been directed at the surface viscometry of polyelectrolytes. Among the results, however, are measurements of the intrinsic viscosity of polyacrylic acid (100):

$$[\eta] = 10^{-7} M^{1.2}$$

A sample of polymethacrylic acid of molecular weight 23,000 spread at 20°C on a substrate of pH 4.2 and ionic strength 0.0022 mole/l has shown itself to possess a reduced surface viscosity which is an increasing function of the concentration of Cu^{2+} ions in the substrate. At a surface concentration of 0.7 mg/m² ($A = 5400$ Å²), the reduced surface viscosity is 0.9 at $(Cu^{2+}) = 0.0011$ mole/l^{-1} and 0.40 at $(Cu^{2+}) = 0.0044$ mole/l.

c. Polypeptides

Synthetic polypeptides display a rheological behavior analogous to that of other linear polymers. Investigations have been reported for homopolymers as well as for copolymers.

For nonionic homopolymers, surface viscosity is a sensitive function of the area per residue. Data for poly-γ-benzyl-L-glutamate (65) spread on water at 9°C are

$$A_r \text{ (Å}^2) \quad\quad = \quad 22 \quad 24 \quad 26 \quad 28 \quad 30$$
$$\eta \times 10^3 \text{ (g/sec)} = 130 \quad 35 \quad 10 \quad 5 \quad 1.5$$

For poly-β-benzyl-L-aspartate at 10.8°C,

$$A_r \text{ (Å}^2) \quad\quad = 14 \quad 16 \quad 18 \quad 20$$
$$\eta \times 10^3 \text{ (g/sec)} = 70 \quad 18 \quad 6 \quad 1$$

When studied by the oscillation method, poly-L-leucine spread on water at 16°C yields data (103)

$$A_r \text{ (Å}^2) \quad\quad = 16 \quad 17 \quad 20 \quad 25$$
$$\eta \times 10^2 \text{ (g/sec)} = 26 \quad 8.4 \quad 1.8 \quad 0.6$$

With poly-DL-alanine (104–105), η depends both upon A_r and upon the molecular weight. For a sample of polymerization degree 40,

$$A_r \ (\text{Å}^2) \qquad\qquad = 15 \quad 20 \quad 25 \quad 30$$
$$\eta \times 10^2 \ (\text{g/sec}) = 28 \quad 4.6 \quad 1.5 \quad 0.2$$

while if the degree of polymerization is 300,

$$A_r \ (\text{Å}^2) \qquad\qquad = 22 \quad 26 \quad 30 \quad 34$$
$$\eta \times 10^2 \ (\text{g/sec}) = 17 \quad 4.46 \quad 1.48 \quad 0.556$$

For a given A_r, the surface viscosity is observed to increase markedly with the degree of polymerization. It has been established for this polypeptide that the surface viscosity varies with the surface pressure according to

$$\log \eta = -3.2 + 9.24\pi$$

which is independent of the temperature.

The polypeptide obtained from the polymerization of α-aminoisobutyric acid has been investigated by the oscillation method (105). At 17°C on distilled water,

$$A_r \ (\text{Å}^2) \qquad\qquad = \ \ 6.5 \quad 7.5 \quad 9 \qquad 11$$
$$\eta \times 10^2 \ (\text{g/sec}) = 25.8 \quad 7.4 \quad 3.05 \quad 0.61$$

For a fixed area per residue, this type of polypeptide exhibits an increasing surface viscosity with increasing length of the molecular side chains (106). Data relevant to several derivatives are listed in Table XIX.

The configuration of polypeptides plays a role in their surface viscosities (106). Thus on water at 10°C with $A_r = 23 \ \text{Å}^2$, the surface viscosity of poly-γ-benzyl-L-glutamate is 0.266 g/sec, while for poly-γ-benzyl-DL-glutamate it is 0.125 g/sec. This difference disappears at higher surface dilutions: $\eta = 0.021$ g/sec for both polypeptides at $A_r = 28 \ \text{Å}^2$.

The $\alpha \rightarrow \beta$ transition can be easily detected by the study of surface viscosity (106). Data taken at 10°C may be compared for poly-γ-methyl-L-glutamate (see Table XX). Changes in surface viscosity which are induced in polypeptide films by the presence of urea in the substrate are probably due to

TABLE XIX

Effect of Side Chain Length on Surface Viscosity of Poly-α-aminocarboxylic Acids

Aminocaproic		Aminocaprylic		Aminocapric		Aminolauric	
$A_r \ (\text{Å}^2)$	η (g/sec)	$A_r \ (\text{Å}^2)$	η (g/sec)	$A_r \ (\text{Å}^2)$	η (g/sec)	$A_r \ (\text{Å}^2)$	η (g/sec)
14	0.15	18	0.18	22	0.33	28	0.245
		20	0.078	24	0.105	30	0.09

TABLE XX

Effect of Conformation on Surface Viscosity of
Poly-γ-methyl-L-glutamate

α form (on water)		β form (on 0.02 M formic acid)	
A_r (Å^2)	η (g/sec)	A_r (Å^2)	η (g/sec)
11	0.065	11	0.225
15	0.042	15	0.0025

changes in the conformation of the polymer. For a film of poly-γ-benzyl-L-glutamate at $A_r = 35$ Å^2 (69):

$$\% \text{ urea} = 0.5 \quad 5 \quad 10$$
$$\eta \text{ (g/sec)} = 0.028 \quad 0.0329 \quad 0.0452$$

The surface viscosity of polypeptides is a sensitive function of temperature (65). For a film of poly-γ-benzyl-L-glutamate at $A_r = 25$ Å^2

$$T \text{ (°C)} \qquad = 5.6 \quad 9 \quad 16.2 \quad 24$$
$$\eta \times 10^3 \text{ (g/sec)} = 13 \quad 13 \quad 38 \quad 120$$

and at $A_r = 28$ Å^2:

$$T \text{ (°C)} \qquad = 5.6 \quad 9 \quad 16.2 \quad 24$$
$$\eta \times 10^3 \text{ (g/sec)} = 1 \quad 4.3 \quad 7.7 \quad 40$$

Data for poly-β-benzyl-L-aspartate at $A_r = 18$ Å^2 are

$$T \text{ (°C)} \qquad = 10.8 \quad 17.9 \quad 24.5$$
$$\eta \times 10^3 \text{ (g/sec)} = 6.6 \quad 24 \quad 77$$

As might be expected, the surface viscosities of ionic polypeptides are pH dependent. For poly-L-glutamic acid (67) spread on water at 22°C and $A_r = 26$ Å^2,

$$\text{pH} \qquad = 1.6 \quad 4.4 \quad 4.8$$
$$\eta \times 10^2 \text{ (g/sec)} = 7.23 \quad 5.45 \quad 1.89$$

The biological importance of proteins has stimulated research on simple models which are polypeptides synthesized by the copolymerization of various amino acids. Their rheological properties are not essentially different from those of homopolymers.

Two-component copolymers always exhibit an increasing surface viscosity with decreasing A_r. Typical is the behavior of a glycine–alanine copolymer (106) spread on water at 22°C:

$$A_r \text{ (Å}^2\text{)} = 10 \quad 14$$
$$\eta \text{ (g/sec)} = 0.18 \quad 0.065$$

A series of copolymers of leucine and sarcosine (103) spread on water at 16°C at a fixed surface area A_r shows a diminishing surface viscosity as the proportion of sarcosine is increased. At a L-leucine/sarcosine ratio of 1:3, the surface viscosity is undetectable by the oscillation method. The 1:1 copolymer is palpably viscous only for highly condensed films:

$$A_r \text{ (Å}^2) \ = \ 3.8 \qquad 5$$
$$\eta \text{ (g/sec)} = \ 0.215 \qquad 0.006$$

while for the 3:1 copolymer,

$$A_r \text{ (Å}^2) \ = 12 \qquad 14$$
$$\eta \text{ (g/sec)} = \ 0.2 \qquad 0.115$$

For equivalent values of A_r, the 1:1 copolymer (γ-benzyl-L-glutamate, β-benzyl-L-aspartate) has a higher surface viscosity than the corresponding homopolymers (65) (see above). At $T = 12.3°C$

$$A_r \text{ (Å}^2) \qquad\quad = 24 \quad 26 \quad 28 \quad 30 \quad 32$$
$$\eta \times 10^3 \text{ (g/sec)} = 70 \quad 39 \quad 19 \quad\ \ 7 \quad\ \ 3$$

Among copolymers of three components, the polypeptide 1:3:1 (L-lysine, L-phenylalanine, L-glutamic acid) has been studied in detail (107). As with other polypeptides, η is a decreasing function of A_r. At pH 5.6 on 0.07 M KCl,

$$A_r \text{ (Å}^2) \qquad\quad = 15 \qquad 16 \qquad 18 \qquad 20 \qquad 22$$
$$\eta \times 10^3 \text{ (g/sec)} = \ 6.05 \quad\ 3.51 \quad\ 2.15 \quad\ 0.87 \quad\ 0.31$$

and at pH 6.8 on 0.28 M KCl,

$$A_r \text{ (Å}^2) \qquad\quad = 15 \quad\ \ 16 \quad\ \ 18 \quad\ \ 20 \quad\ \ 22 \quad\ \ 24 \quad\ \ 26$$
$$\eta \times 10^3 \text{ (g/sec)} = 12.2 \quad 4.37 \quad 2.76 \quad 2.07 \quad 1.61 \quad 1.14 \quad 0.88$$

Because it is a polyelectrolyte, the surface viscosity of this copolymer is a function of pH and of the ionic strength. At fixed $A_r = 17$ Å^2 and pH 5.6, the variation of η with the concentration of KCl in the substrate is

$$C_{KCl} \text{ (mole/l)} \ \ = 0.07 \quad 0.14 \quad 0.28 \quad 0.42 \quad 0.56$$
$$\eta \times 10^3 \text{ (g/sec)} = 2.81 \quad\ 2.23 \quad\ 1.68 \quad\ 1.32 \quad\ 1.08$$

Still at fixed $A_r = 17$ Å^2 and with $C_{KCl} = 0.28$ mole/l, the dependence of η on pH is

$$\text{pH} \qquad\qquad\quad = 3 \qquad\ 4 \qquad\ \ 5 \qquad\ 6 \qquad 7 \qquad 8$$
$$\eta \times 10^3 \text{ (g/sec)} = 0.53 \quad 0.945 \quad 1.35 \quad 2.24 \quad 2.7 \quad 1.06$$

TABLE XXI

Surface Viscosity of Copoly 1:2:1 (L-Lysine, L-Leucine, L-Glutamic Acid) on Water at 7°C

pH 7		pH 8.3		pH 9.2	
A_r (Å²)	η (g/sec)	A_r (Å²)	η (g/sec)	A_r (Å²)	η (g/sec)
21	0.2	19	0.142	15	0.312
26	0.0078	21	0.01	16	0.0755

If phenylalanine is replaced by leucine as in the copolymer 1:2:1 (L-leucine, L-lysine, L-glutamic acid), η is still a decreasing function of A_r, but it is appreciably larger than in the example above (67), as shown in Table XXI. On the other hand, the variation of η with pH is different (see Table XXII). For this copolymer the way in which η changes with temperature depends upon A_r as seen also on Table XXII.

A nonionic copolymer such as 1:1:1 (L-proline, L-leucine, DL-alanine) of polymerization degree 129 exhibits a surface viscosity which varies smoothly with A_r and T. Supporting data for films spread on distilled water are tabulated in Table XXIII (104). They may be represented as a function of surface pressure by

$$\log \eta = -17.3 + 0.33\pi + \frac{3370}{T}$$

in which T is the absolute temperature.

For all the preceding copolymers, the distribution of residues along the chain is random. It is interesting to compare their properties with those of a homopolymer whose monomer is a holigopeptide. For a poly-L-prolyl-L-leucylglycine of polymerization degree 13 spread on distilled water (104) the surface viscosity varies with the area per monomer A_m (as distinct from

TABLE XXII

Influence of pH on Surface Viscosity of Copoly 1:2:1 (L-Lysine, L-Leucine, L-Glutamic Acid) Spread on Water

$A_r = 14$ Å²			$A_r = 15$ Å²			$A_r = 21$ Å²			$A_r = 26$ Å²		
T (°C)	pH	η (g/sec)	T (°C)	pH	η (g/sec)	T (°C)	pH	η (g/sec)	T (°C)	pH	η (g/sec)
7	1.6	0.069	7	1.6	0.027	7	7	0.2	7	7	0.0078
—	5.8	0.0445	—	5.8	0.0045	14	—	0.12	14	—	0.0367

TABLE XXIII
Surface Viscosity of the Synthetic Polypeptide Copoly 1:1:1
(L-Proline, L-Leucine, DL-Alanine) $\eta \times 10^2$ (g/sec)

T (°C)	A_r (Å²) = 6	7	8	9
4.7		13.8	2.68	0.815
16.7		6.75	1.045	
20.5	15.6	3.49	0.745	
29.9	9.4	1.58	0.186	

the area per amino acid residue A_r) and with the temperature in a manner entirely analogous to that of the random copolymers (see Table XXIV). The data are summarized by

$$\log \eta = 22.5 + 0.46\pi + \frac{3560}{T}$$

with T the absolute temperature.

d. Proteins

The surface viscosity of a large number of protein films has been determined with the data tabulated as a function of surface pressure.   At low surface pressures the surface viscosity of proteins is almost always Newtonian.   It is often possible to define with rather good precision a critical surface pressure π_n above which the viscosity ceases to be Newtonian and another critical pressure π_r above which the film exhibits rigidity (108, 109).   Typical data for films spread on 0.01 N HCl at 17°C are listed below:

Protein	π_n (dyne/cm)	π_r (dyne/cm)
Bovine serum albumin	4	8
Horse serum albumin	10	
Horse pseudoglobulin	2	2
Ovalbumin	4	7
Bovine hemoglobin	3	6
Gliadin	16	

TABLE XXIV
Surface Viscosity of the Polypeptide Poly-L-prolyl-L-leucylglycine, η (g/sec)

T (°C)	A_m (Å²) = 17	19	20	21	22	23	25
6.9					13.45	4.06	1.32
16.7			14.2		2.79		0.303
21.5		13.25			2.79	0.698	
30.4		16.9	2.8			0.698	

Generally η increases with surface pressure (108–110) (see Table XXV), which is to say that it increases as the molecular area decreases. Data for bovine γ-globulin (111) spread at 24°C on a substrate whose pH lies between 2.2 and 11.9 and whose ionic strength is 0.01 mole/l are

$$A_r \text{ (Å}^2) = 12 \quad 16 \quad 24$$

$$\eta \text{ (g/sec)} = 0.275 \quad 0.0269 \quad 1.25 \times 10^{-4}$$

For ovalbumin of molecular weight 42,000 on a substrate of pH 1 viscosity data are

$$A \text{ (Å}^2) = 5680 \quad 5960 \quad 6230 \quad 6520$$

$$\eta \times 10^2 \text{ (g/sec)} = 12 \quad 3 \quad 1.65 \quad 1$$

whereas at pH 3,

$$A \text{ (Å}^2) = 5270 \quad 5400 \quad 5680 \quad 6230$$

$$\eta \times 10^2 \text{ (g/sec)} = 5.85 \quad 3.2 \quad 1.2 \quad 0.7$$

Sometimes compression of the film is accompanied by its partial solution in the substrate. This is suggested, for example, by the abnormally small areas per residue found with gelatin at high pressures spread at 20°C on 1 M KCl of pH 5.6 (78, 112):

$$A_r \text{ (Å}^2) = 1 \quad 2.5 \quad 5 \quad 7.5$$

$$\eta \times 10^3 \text{ (g/sec)} = 75 \quad 30 \quad 5 \quad 1$$

These results have been explained by supposing that the cis portions of the L-prolyl-L-hydroxyprolyl chain remain on the surface while the trans portions are submerged beneath it.

Whatever the interface, η always decreases with increasing area per molecule in the film. Table XXVI lists viscosity data obtained by the method of forced flow in a circular canal (see Part I, Section III.C.2.d) for films of bovine serum albumin and bovine γ-globulin taken on substrates of varying pH and temperature (113).

Because proteins are polyelectrolytes, the pH and the ionic strength have pronounced influence upon the surface viscosity. Data for bovine serum albumin (111) spread at 24°C on an aqueous substrate of ionic strength 0.01 and varying pH are listed in Table XXVII. Similar variation of the surface viscosity of Taka-amylase A with the KCl concentration in the substrate is exhibited in Table XXVIII for a fixed temperature $T = 20°C$ and pH 2.

Quite independently of the ionic strength, the composition of the substrate plays a role in the surface viscosity of protein films. The influence of saccharose has in particular been studied (94). Pepsin of molecular weight 36,000 spread on water at pH 6 and $A = 8250$ Å^2 shows an increase in η

TABLE XXV

Surface Viscosity of Proteins as a Function of Surface Pressure[a]

Protein	T (°C)	pH	π (dyne/cm) =	1	2	3	4	5	6	7	8	10	12	16
			$\eta \times 10^3$ (g/sec) =	18										
Gelatin	20	4.7					78		164		250			
Gliadin	17	2		1.5	1.4		1.9		3.3		5.3	9.6	16	45
Bovine hemoglobin	17	2		1.9	1.7	(11)								
Ovalbumin	17	2		2.3	15	23		(29)	(22)	(38)		(30)		
Bovine serum albumin	17	2		1.2	3.1	11	18	(30)	(34)	(39)		(200)		
Horse — serum albumin	17	2		1.3	1.4		2.5		9.3		33	(76)		

[a] The values in parentheses refer to non-Newtonian films whose apparent viscosity was determined by the oscillation method.

124

TABLE XXVI
Surface Viscosity of Bovine Serum Proteins

Protein	Interface	T (°C)	pH	S (m²/mg)	$\eta \times 10^3$ (g/sec)
Bovine serum albumin	air/water		2	0.75	0.84
				0.8	0.182
	benzene/water		—	0.75	6.2
				0.8	0.505
	—		6.5	1.3	3.26
				1.4	0.708
				1.6	0.174
	ethyl acetate/water		—	0.475	28.2
				0.5	0.818
	—		7.7	0.675	30.4
				0.7	4.9
				0.75	0.316
Bovine γ-globulin	benzene/water	18	6.5	1.3	51.3
				1.4	1.74
				1.5	0.527
	—	20.5	—	1.25	3.96
				1.3	0.598
				1.4	0.129
	—	24	—	0.8	55
				0.9	2.16

from 1 to 5 g/sec when the substrate is replaced by a 60% by weight solution of saccharose, and η does not fall to 1 on this substrate until A is increased to 11,200 Å². Under the same conditions data for insulin ($M = 18,000$) are

Substrate	=	Water	50% saccharose	60% saccharose
$\eta = 1$ g/sec when		$A = 2040$ Å² 2960		4680
$\eta = 3$ g/sec when		$A = 1170$ 2750		3140

Similarly for bovine serum albumin ($M = 66,000$),

Substrate	=	Water	50% saccharose	60% saccharose
$\eta = 1$ g/sec when	$A = 11,260$ Å²	15,350		18,950
$\eta = 4$ g/sec when	$A = 10,200$	11,500		15,050

For human serum albumin,

Substrate	=	Water	60% saccharose
$\eta = 1$ g/sec when	$A = 12,850$ Å²	16,900	
$\eta = 4$ g/sec when	$A = 11,200$	14,000	

TABLE XXVII

Effect of pH on the Surface Viscosity of Bovine Serum Albumin,
$\eta \times 10^2$ (g/sec)

pH	A_r (Å²) = 12.7	16	24
2.2	36	0.0845	
5.7		36	0.244
11.9	16.5	5.43	0.241

We have remarked that the surface viscosity of protein films is frequently non-Newtonian.   Representative data for horse serum albumin (114) on water at pH 3.2 for two different shear rates are

π (dyne/cm)   = 3   6   10
η (g/sec) (for $\dot{\gamma} = 0.3$ sec⁻¹) = 0.0221   0.107   0.402
η (g/sec) (for $\dot{\gamma} = 0.75$ sec⁻¹) = 0.019   0.0735   0.168

When proteins are denatured, their surface viscosity is observed to increase markedly.   Viscosity data for the native protein lysozyme (84) spread on 0.01 M K_2CO_3 solution at pH 10.5 are

A (Å²)   = 2190   2320   2580
$\eta \times 10^3$ (g/sec) =   15   2.7   0.4

whereas if the protein is denatured by 8 M urea plus 40% isopropyl alcohol,

A (Å²)   = 2580   2710   2840
$\eta \times 10^3$ (g/sec) =   18   7.2   1.2

Further denaturation data are presented in Table XXIX for the surface viscosity of ovalbumin as a function of molecular area and pH at 19°C.   By comparing η for the denatured with that for the native protein, the reader will observe that the same surface viscosities are achieved for the denatured product only at much higher molecular areas.

TABLE XXVIII

Effect of Ionic Strength on the Surface Viscosity of Taka-amylase A, $\eta \times 10^2$ (g/sec)

S (m²/mg)	Molarity of KCl = 0	0.01	0.025	0.1	0.5
1	11.4	7.9	14		
1.2	4.5	1.6	5.6	9.2	10.5
1.5	1.9	0.9	3.4	4.5	5.8
1.7	0.7	0.7	2.5	3.4	5.2
1.9	0.2	0.45	0.8	2.8	5

TABLE XXIX
Surface Viscosity of Ovalbumin Denatured by Urea, $\eta \times 10^3$ (g/sec)

A (Å^2)	pH	$\eta \times 10^3$	A (Å^2)	pH	$\eta \times 10^3$
8330	10.5	22.8	11350	7.6	0.6
9100	7.6	12.2	12000	4.6	24
—	10.5	6.8	12850	—	13
9850	7.6	5	13650	—	7.2
—	10.5	2.2	14400	—	2.6
10600	7.6	1.88			
—	10.5	0.4			

C. Adsorbed Films of Soluble Substances

So far as their rheological properties are concerned, interfacial films of soluble materials have been less studied than have insoluble films. We have remarked in Part I, Section III that the rigorous determination of the rheological coefficients of such films encounter great difficulties. Despite this fact, reasonably accurate order of magnitude investigations have been made for a wide variety of soluble films.

1. Dilational Strains

It is obvious that for soluble films the measured values of Young's and the compression modulus can be no more than apparent values. Despite this fact they have in certain cases been determined, and it has been shown, for example, that for adsorbed films of capric acid, $\varkappa$ decreases progressively as the rate of compression is increased (115). The Young's modulus of films of saponin has been determined as a function of the concentration of the solution and of the age of the surface (116). Data are listed in Table XXX, where the reader may readily confirm that with the exception of very dilute solutions, the results are badly scattered.

TABLE XXX
Young's Modulus of Saponin Films Adsorbed at the Air/Water Interface

c (%)	t (min)	E (g/sec^2)	c (%)	t (min)	E (g/sec^2)
0.001	15	117	0.01	210	240–250
	65	220		1200	240
	125	270	0.1	5	72–110
0.005	6	100		78	110
	76	180		150	110–160
	200	210–240	0.2	3–4	60–110
0.01	5	110–140		56–81	140–160
	90	190		115–140	110–230

Gibbs's elasticity has been measured for several adsorption films of small molecules (117, 118). For a 0.001% solution of lauryl alcohol, $E_G = 26 \pm 3$ g/sec². For films of lauryl sulfate it has been shown that E_G depends not only upon the concentration but also upon the initial thickness d of the stretched film, as shown in Table XXXI. Direct measurements of the dilational viscosity ζ have been carried out for adsorbed films of small molecules (119). Values lying between 795 and 2000 g/sec have been measured for a solution of 4.66×10^{-5} M 1,2-dodecanediol at 21°C with expansion rate $(1/S)(\partial S/\partial t) \leq 0.15$ sec⁻¹. Similarly, values of ζ between 585 and 1370 g/sec are found for a compound synthesized from five residues of ethylene oxide plus lauryl alcohol with concentrations ranging from 1.85×10^{-5} to 2.62×10^{-5} mole/l.

Dilational viscosity is exhibited indirectly in the important hysteresis observed in the laminometer during the extension and retraction of stretched films. For a 0.1% solution of ovalbumin (120),

$$\begin{aligned}
\text{pH} &= 7.7 \quad 7.7 \quad 4.5 \\
\text{Ionic strength (mole/l)} &= 0.1 \quad 0.02 \quad 0.1 \\
\text{Hysteresis (dyne/cm)} &= 1.5 \quad 2.3 \quad 5
\end{aligned}$$

Corresponding to this hysteresis there is relaxation in surface pressure when the film is strained by either compression or extension. It can attain 2 dyne/cm/min at pH 5.1.

2. Shear Strains

Shear strains in adsorbed films have been studied for a rather large number of substances.

a. Small Molecules

The known fact that the surface tensions of dilute solutions of inorganic electrolytes exhibit a maximum when plotted against the concentration has led to the search for a corresponding behavior in the surface viscosity (121). Using the oscillation method, KCl, KI, RbCl, and LiF all show a minimum in η in the neighborhood of $c \simeq 10^{-3}$ mole/l at which point $\eta_{min}/\eta_0 \simeq 0.8$.

TABLE XXXI
Gibbs's Elasticity of Lauryl Sulfate Films

c = 0.008 M		c = 0.01 M	
d (μ)	E_G (g/sec²)	d (μ)	E_G (g/sec²)
2	9	2	0.8
1	14	1	1.2
0.2	37	0.2	33

In general, however, it has been the aliphatic compounds which have been studied. The viscosities of fatty acids at the xylene/mercury interface have been studied by the rotation method (122). The surface viscosity of stearic acid, for example, passes through a maximum with increasing concentration:

$$c \times 10^3 \text{ (mole/l)} = 0.01 \quad 0.1 \quad 0.5 \quad 1 \quad 2.5 \quad 5 \quad 7.5$$

$$\eta \times 10^3 \text{ (g/sec)} = 1.1 \quad 7.2 \quad 94 \quad 110 \quad 87 \quad 28 \quad 20$$

With oleic acid, η exhibits first a maximum and then a minimum as c increases:

$$c \times 10^3 \text{ (mole/l)} = 0.05 \quad 0.1 \quad 0.15 \quad 0.5 \quad 0.7 \quad 10$$

$$\eta \times 10^3 \text{ (g/sec)} = 1.1 \quad 9.4 \quad 72 \quad 10 \quad 11 \quad 200$$

As a counter example, the surface viscosity of films of hexadecylamine at 25°C increases monotonically with concentration:

$$c \times 10^3 \text{ (mole/l)} = \quad 0.01 \quad 1.1 \quad 1 \quad 5 \quad 10$$

$$\eta \times 10^3 \text{ (g/sec)} = \simeq 10^{-1} \quad \simeq 10^{-1} \quad \simeq 0.2 \quad \simeq 0.7 \quad 3$$

Application of the method of constant volume efflux from a canal (123) to solutions of octanol at the air/water interface has yielded

$$c \text{ (mole/l)} = \quad 3.8 \times 10^{-4} \quad 7.7 \times 10^{-4}$$

$$\eta \text{ (g/sec)} = 10^{-5} \quad\quad 1.3 \times 10^{-4}$$

At the xylene/mercury interface the surface viscosity of hexadecanol passes through a maximum as a function of the concentration (122):

$$c \times 10^3 \text{ (mole/l)} = 0.1 \quad 1 \quad 5 \quad 20 \quad 30 \quad 50 \quad 100$$

$$\eta \times 10^3 \text{ (g/sec)} = 1.4 \quad 2.9 \quad 4.5 \quad 33 \quad 34 \quad 25 \quad 12$$

Solutions of sodium dodecylsulfate studied by the canal method at the air/water interface reveal an increasing surface viscosity with concentration (123):

$$c \times 10^3 \text{ (mole/l)} = 0.17 \quad 0.35 \quad 3.5$$

$$\eta \times 10^5 \text{ (g/sec)} = 4 \quad 9\text{--}11 \quad 14\text{--}36$$

If the concentration of sodium dodecylsulfate is maintained constant at $c = 4 \times 10^{-3}\ M$, the surface viscosity of the water/benzene interface declines with rising temperature (113):

$$T \text{ (°C)} \quad\quad = 18 \quad 20 \quad 22$$

$$\eta \times 10^4 \text{ (g/sec)} = 1.7 \quad 1.5 \quad \simeq 1$$

TABLE XXXII

Viscoelastic Behavior of Mixed Adsorbed Films of Sodium Lauryl Sulfate and Lauryl Alcohol

$c_{sulfate}$ (g/l)	$c_{alcohol}$ (g/l)	$\eta \times 10^3$ (g/sec)	$f_s \times 10^3$ (g/sec^2)	$c_{sulfate}$ (g/l)	$c_{alcohol}$ (g/l)	$\eta \times 10^3$ (g/sec)	$f_s \times 10^3$ (g/sec^2)
1	0	2	$\simeq 0$	5	0	4	$\simeq 0$
—	0.01	2	$\simeq 0$	—	0.05	3	$\simeq 0$
—	0.03	37	$\simeq 0$	—	0.15	3	$\simeq 0$
—	0.05	32	54	—	0.25	24	29
—	0.08	32	62	—	0.40	31	47

Using the rotation method (124), mixed adsorbed films of sodium lauryl sulfate and lauryl alcohol exhibit a viscoplastic behavior. Plastic yield values f_s and surface viscosities at 25°C are tabulated in Table XXXII.

Under the same conditions, a 1% solution of potassium laurate yields values $\eta = 0.039$ g/sec and $f_s = 0.059$ g/sec^2 while a 1% solution of sodium laurate at pH 10 and 20°C has $\eta < 10^{-4}$ g/sec (125). The addition of dodecanol to the latter solution increases its surface viscosity:

Concentration of dodecanol (%) = 0.001   0.005   0.01   0.015

$\eta \times 10^4$ (g/sec)   = 2   3.75   30   34

The same increase is observed with the addition of isopropanol amide:

Concentration of amide (%) = 0.001   0.003   0.006

$\eta \times 10^4$ (g/sec)   = 2.5   10   13.5

Among those slightly more complex molecules whose surface viscosities have been determined, we may single out sorbitan monooleate at the oil/water interface (126). After the surface was aged for an hour, a 1% solution exhibited $\eta = 0.15$ g/sec and a 2% solution $\eta = 0.8$ g/sec. In Table XXXIII are values of the elastic modulus of saponin solutions of different

TABLE XXXIII

Surface Elasticity of Adsorbed Films of Saponin

c (%)	t	G (g/sec^2)	c (%)	t	G (g/sec^2)
0.005	2 min	68	0.1	52 min	198
0.01	2 min	80	—	5 hr	320
—	27 min	150	1	1 min	154
—	5 hr	304	—	30 min	242
0.1	30 sec	122	—	3 hr	262
—	3 min	127	—	4 hr	304

concentrations and surface ages (116). Whatever the origin of the saponin, aging appears to have an important influence upon the mechanical properties of the interface (127). G and η_s are smaller for saponin films adsorbed at the water/toluene interface than at the water/air interface (128).

b. Macromolecules

Adsorption films of synthetic, nonionic polymers have attracted little attention. It has been reported that films of polyvinyl alcohol are more viscous at the water/styrene interface than they are at the air/water interface (30). Studies of surface viscosity as a function of time have been described for the alkylphenylpolyglycol ethers, for the alkylpolyglycol ethers, and for the polyglycol esters of fatty acids (129).

For polyelectrolytes other than proteins, the effect of the nature of the interface is clear for films of polymethacrylic acid (30). Data for a 0.25% solution at 24°C are summarized in Table XXXIV. The surface viscosity against air of a 0.1% solution of carboxymethylcellulose at 24°C drops from 0.4 g/sec at pH 2.95 to 0.035 g/sec at pH 4.3. At the water/styrene interface, however, the film is viscoelastic with $G = 0.004$ g/sec² and $\eta_s = 0.122$ g/sec. A 0.1% solution of pectin in 0.1 M KCl measured against petroleum ether produces a film from whose creep curves $G_l = 18$ g/sec², but for which the oscillation method yields $G_l = 20$ g/sec² at pH 5 and $T = 20$°C (130). The adsorption film of sodium arabinate under the same conditions but pH 3.8 yields $G_l = 38$ g/sec² and $\eta = 3.2 \times 10^4$ g/sec under a constant stress of 0.291 dyne/cm. For this polyelectrolyte, it has been shown by the oscillation method that G_l decreases with rising pH:

$$\text{pH} \quad = \quad 2 \quad 3.8 \quad 6 \quad 8$$
$$G_l \text{ (g/sec}^2) = 67 \quad 44 \quad 24.7 \quad 22.3$$

The relaxation curves of this film can be interpreted in terms of a continuous distribution of Maxwell bodies coupled in parallel (131). If the relaxation function is written

$$\Psi(t) = \int_{-\infty}^{+\infty} H(\log \theta) \exp\left(-\frac{t}{\theta}\right) d(\log \theta)$$

in which $H(\log \theta)$ is the relaxation spectrum, then numerical values of H for sodium arabinate at pH 8 are

$$\log_{10} \theta \quad = -4 \quad -2 \quad 0 \quad 1 \quad 2 \quad 3$$
$$H \times 10^3 = \quad 2 \quad 55 \quad 180 \quad 325 \quad 190 \quad 12$$

In a similar way, the relaxation spectrum of a film of poly-L-lysine of polymerization degree DP $= 15$ at the water/petroleum ether interface at

TABLE XXXIV

Influence of the Nature of the Interface on the Rheological Behavior
of Films of Polymethacrylic Acid ($c = 0.25\%$; $T = 24°C$)

Interface =	Water/Air	Water/Air	Water/Styrene
pH =	1.6	4.15	1.6
G (g/sec²) =	0.076	0.031	0.69
η (g/sec) =	0.164	0.013	1.19

pH 9.9 and 20°C takes values

$$\log_{10}\theta \quad = -2 \quad 0 \quad\quad 2 \quad\;\; 3$$
$$H \times 10^3 = \quad 6 \quad 84.8 \quad 391 \quad 12$$

These data are fitted empirically by

$$H = (4.18 \times 10^{-2})\theta^{½}\exp(-2.12 \times 10^{-3}\theta)$$

Under the same conditions, but under a constant stress of 0.582 dyne/cm,
the creep curve yields $\eta = 10^5$ g/sec.   As a function of pH, creep experiments
lead to

$$pH \quad\quad\quad = \;\; 7.9 \quad 8.2 \quad\;\; 9$$
$$G_i \text{ (g/sec}^2) = 17 \quad\;\; 39 \quad\; 150$$

but the oscillation method yields much larger values:

$$pH \quad\quad\; = 7 \quad 7.9 \quad 8.2 \quad\;\; 9 \quad\; 10 \quad\;\; 11 \quad\;\; 12 \;\; 13$$
$$G_i \text{ (g/sec}^2) = 6 \quad 50 \quad\;\; 84 \quad\;\; 235 \;\; 282 \;\; 236 \;\; 152 \quad 3$$

An analogous comparison can be made with a 0.1 % solution of bovine serum
albumin in 0.1 M KCl at the petroleum ether interface.   Data for 20°C are

$$pH \quad\quad\quad\quad\quad\quad = 2.3 \quad\; 5.2 \quad\;\; 6.9 \quad 10.7$$
$$G_i \text{ (g/sec}^2)\text{ (creep)} \quad\;\, = 1.1 \quad 10.3 \quad 6.9 \quad\;\; 3.3$$
$$G_i \text{ (g/sec}^2)\text{ (oscillation)} = 1.0 \quad 19.5 \quad 14.2 \quad\;\; 4.0$$

At pH 5.2 and a constant stress of 0.116 dyne/cm, the interfacial viscosity is
7.6×10^3 g/sec.   It has been observed that log η is a nearly linear function
of the stress:

$$\mathscr{T} \text{ (dyne/cm)} = 0.1 \quad 0.25$$
$$\log_{10}\eta \quad\quad\; = 4 \quad\;\; 2.56$$

The elastic modulus decreases with rising temperature:

$$T \text{ (°C)} \quad\quad\quad\quad\quad = 20 \quad\;\; 30 \quad\;\; 40 \quad\;\; 50$$
$$G_i \text{ (g/sec}^2)\text{ (pH 5.7)} = 18.3 \quad 7.6 \quad\; 2.1 \quad\;\; 1.2$$
$$G_i \text{ (g/sec}^2)\text{ (pH 2.3)} = \;\; 1.14 \quad 0.585 \quad 0.37 \quad 0.32$$

The relaxation spectrum at 20°C and pH 5.2 is summarized by (131)

$$\log_{10} \theta \ = -4 \quad -2 \quad 0 \quad 2 \quad 4$$

$$H \times 10^2 = \quad 1.8 \ \ 14 \ \ 19 \ \ 13 \ \ 3$$

The elastic modulus is very sensitive to the composition of the bulk phases bounding the interface. Thus a 0.1% solution of bovine serum albumin in 0.01 M KCl equilibrated against petroleum ether and studied by the oscillation method exhibits a G_l which decreases as n-decanol is added to the oil phase, becoming zero in the neighborhood of 0.1 M n-decanol (132). The addition of t-butylphenol, 3,5-xylenol, o-cresol, and phenol have the same effect, as does also the addition to the aqueous phase of tetradecyltrimethylammonium bromide. For the latter compound, $G_l = 18$ g/sec^2 for a 0.001% solution of the serum albumin at pH 5.7 in the absence of the quaternary salt, and $G_l = 0.214$ g/sec^2 after the addition of 10^{-5} M of cationic soap.

At the water/petroleum ether interface of a pepsin solution at 20°C, data determined by the oscillation method are (130):

$$pH \qquad = 2 \qquad 2.7 \quad 3$$

$$G_l \ (g/sec^2) = 8.15 \quad 4.1 \quad 11.3$$

Under a steady stress of 0.116 dyne/cm, the surface viscosity at pH 2.7 is 4.5×10^3 g/sec. As for the relaxation spectrum, data for pH 2.5 are

$$\log_{10} \theta \ = -4 \quad -2 \quad 0 \quad 1 \quad 2 \quad 4$$

$$H \times 10^3 = \quad 6 \quad 85 \ \ 220 \ \ 255 \ \ 200 \ \ 20$$

but if to the oil phase is added 5% of oleyl alcohol, the pH dependence of rheological parameters becomes (73)

pH	= 1	2	2.5	3	3.5	4	4.5
G (g/sec^2) =		0.05	0.84	18	6.5	0.96	0.05
$\eta_s \times 10^3$ (g/sec) =	3	18	43.5	244	270	129	33

Data for bovine gamma globulin taken under the same conditions are

pH	= 2	3	4	5	6	7	8
G (g/sec^2) =	5.6	12.8	8.8	4.7	1.2	0.08	0.06
$\eta_s \times 10^2$ (g/sec) =	148	195	140	105	76	49	1

The elasticity of adsorbed films of ovalbumin at the water interface was described long ago (133). Gelatin, however, exhibits no rigidity whatever the pH (30).   For a 0.25% solution at 24°C,

pH		=	2.10	4.75	6.0	8.7
$\eta \times 10^2$ (g/sec) (air/water interface)		=	<0.1	14	21	1.2
$\eta \times 10^2$ (g/sec) (styrene/water interface)		=	<0.1	19	5	2.7

II. THEORETICAL INTERPRETATION OF THE RHEOLOGICAL PROPERTIES OF MONOMOLECULAR FILMS

Up to the present time there has been little theoretical work done on the molecular interpretation of rheological processes in monomolecular films. In this section we shall review the principal attempts in this direction.

A. Dilational Strains

1. Gibbs Elasticity

A rigorous thermodynamic treatment of the Gibbs elasticity $E_G = 2 \, \partial\gamma/\partial \ln S$ has been proposed (134).

The variation in the surface tension $d\gamma = -d\pi$ is related to the surface concentration Γ_i and to the bulk phase concentrations c_i of surfactant molecules i by the Gibbs adsorption theorem,

$$d\pi = RT \sum_{i=2}^{n} \Gamma_i \, d \ln \gamma_i c_i$$

in which γ_i is the activity coefficient of component i, and where by convention $i = 1$ for the solvent.   If the volume of film element and the total mass of each component in a soap film are presumed constant, then, h being the thickness of the film,

$$E_G = 4RT \sum_{i=2}^{n} \frac{\Gamma_i^2}{c_i} \frac{1 + (d \ln \gamma_i/d \ln c_i)}{h + 2(d\Gamma_i/dc_i)}$$

with

$$\frac{d\Gamma_i}{dc_i} = \frac{\partial\Gamma_i}{\partial c_i} + \sum_{i \neq j} \frac{\partial\Gamma_i}{\partial c_j} \times \frac{dc_j}{dc_i}$$

These equations exhibit the influence of the thickness of the film and of the concentration of the surface-active materials.   Further information can be obtained only through a knowledge of the equation of state of the system.

In the bulk phase α the chemical potential of a component is

$$\mu_i^\alpha = (\mu_i^\alpha)_0 + RT \ln \gamma_i^\alpha c_i$$

in which $(\mu_i^\alpha)_0$ is the chemical potential in the standard state, here chosen in such a way that $\gamma_i \to 1$ as $c_i \to 0$. In the surface

$$\mu_i^s = (\mu_i^s)_0 + RT \ln\left(\gamma_i^s \frac{\Gamma_i}{\Gamma^\infty}\right) - \frac{\gamma}{\Gamma^\infty}$$

in which $(\mu_i^s)_0$ characterizes the standard state in the adsorbed layer. Γ^∞ is the total adsorption at saturation, whence it follows that Γ_i/Γ^∞ is the mole fraction in the interface. If a_i is the ratio of surface mole fraction to bulk phase mole fraction at infinite dilution, then

$$RT \ln a_i = (\mu_i^s)_0 - (\mu_i^\alpha)_0 - \frac{\gamma^0}{\Gamma^\infty} = -\lambda_{i0}^\alpha$$

in which γ^0 is the surface tension at infinite dilution and λ_{i0}^α is the molar free enthalpy of adsorption at infinite dilution.

If all the components are assumed to behave ideally, then

$$\Gamma^\infty = -\frac{1}{RT} \lim\left[\frac{d\gamma}{d \ln \gamma_i^\alpha c_i}\right]_{K_{ij}}$$

where

$$K_{ij} = \frac{\gamma_i^\alpha c_i}{\gamma_j^\alpha c_j} \qquad (i = 1, 2, \ldots, n; j = 2, 3, \ldots, n)$$

A generalization of the Szyszkowski-Langmuir equation may be written

$$\gamma^0 - \gamma = RT\Gamma^\infty \ln\left[\sum_{i=2}^{n} \frac{\gamma_i^\alpha c_i}{a_i} + 1\right]$$

so that

$$\Gamma_i = \Gamma^\infty \frac{\dfrac{\gamma_i^\alpha c_i}{a_i}}{\sum_{j=2}^{n} \dfrac{\gamma_j^\alpha c_j}{a_j} + 1}$$

in good agreement with the experimental results (135).

At concentrations less than the critical micelle concentration, $\gamma_2^\alpha = \gamma_3^\alpha = 1$. Taking a_i as a unit, the concentration of i may be written $x_i = c_i/a_i$, and the total quantity of i per unit volume of film is $g_i = x_i + 2\Gamma_i/a_i h$. Define y_i by

$$y_i = \frac{a_i h}{2\Gamma^\infty} = \frac{x_i}{(g_i - x_i)(1 + \sum_{i=2}^{n} x_i)}$$

Then in the special case of a single surface-active component, the surface elasticity of Gibbs becomes

$$E_G = 2RT\Gamma^\infty \frac{x_2}{1 + y_2(1 + x_2)^2} = 2RT\Gamma^\infty \frac{x_2(g_2 - x_2)}{g_2 + x_2^2}$$

It follows that at constant film thickness, the Gibbs elasticity varies linearly with the concentration so long as the latter is small.

At higher concentrations E_G achieves a maximum $E_{G,m}$ for which

$$x_{2,m} = \sqrt{1 + \frac{1}{y_2}} = \sqrt{g_{2,m}}$$

and we have

$$E_{G,m} = RT\Gamma^\infty(\sqrt{g_{2,m}} - 1)$$

Above the critical micelle concentration, $y_2{}^2 \neq 1$, and E_G drops rapidly to zero.

These predictions are in good agreement with experimentally determined values of the Gibbs elasticity (117).

If there is a second surface-active constituent

$$E_G = 2RT\Gamma^\infty \left(\frac{1 + x_2 + x_3}{1 + (x_2{}^2/g_2) + (x_3{}^2/g_3)} - 1 \right)$$

It follows that the Gibbs elasticity of a multicomponent solution is always greater than that of the weakest of its constituents, but less than the sum of the Gibbs elasticities of the components studied separately. For x_3 small, there is a critical value β of a_3/a_2 for which the addition of the second surfactant is without effect upon the Gibbs elasticity. If $a_3 < \beta a_2$, meaning a high degree of surface activity, E_G increases. Alternatively for $a_3 > \beta a_2$ (low surface activity), E_G decreases. Addition of 3 holding g_2 constant means that

$$\beta = \frac{g_2(g_2 - x_2{}^2)}{2x_2{}^3} + 1$$

whereas if x_2 is held constant,

$$\beta = \frac{g_2(g_2 - x_2{}^2)}{x_2{}^2(g_2 + x_2)} + 1$$

B. Shear Strains

1. Instantaneous Elasticity and Relaxation

Several attempts have been made to interpret the rheological behavior under shear of films of macromolecular substances (130, 131).

The fact that the modulus of instantaneous elasticity G decreases with rising temperature indicates that the stored elastic free energy consists principally of its enthalpic term (130). In sum,

$$G = \left(\frac{\partial \Delta H}{\partial(\tfrac{1}{2}\delta^2)} \right)_{T,\pi} - T \left(\frac{\partial \Delta S}{\partial(\tfrac{1}{2}\delta^2)} \right)_{T,\pi}$$

where δ is the deformation in radians and

$$\left(\frac{\partial G}{\partial T}\right)_{\delta,\pi} = -\left(\frac{\partial \Delta S}{\partial(\frac{1}{2}\delta^2)}\right)_{T,\pi} - T\left(\frac{\partial^2 \Delta S}{\partial T\, \partial(\frac{1}{2}\delta^2)}\right)_{T,\pi}$$

in which it has been assumed that ΔH is independent of temperature.

The rigidity of films of polypeptides, proteins, and polysaccharides is principally due to their hydrogen bonds. dG/dT increases with temperature and vanishes in the neighborhood of 50°C. As a consequence the entropy of deformation $\partial \Delta S/\partial(\frac{1}{2}\delta^2)$ decreases and can become negative, and at a sufficiently high temperature under pH conditions such that intermolecular interactions are weak, the major contribution to the elastic free energy is entropic.

Relaxation experiments suggest that the strain energy of a film is stored in the form of distorted intermolecular bonds. Under constant strain, internal flow takes place accompanied by the rupture and reformation of these bonds. The activation energy E for this process is less than the energy E_H of a bond, being given by $E = E_H - E_D$, where E_D is the strain energy (131).

If a distribution of activation energies E_i is assumed and n_i is the number of bonds possessing an activation energy E_i, the relaxation function is

$$\psi(t) = \frac{\mathcal{T}(t)}{\mathcal{T}_0} = \frac{\sum_i n_i(t)\bar{g}_i}{\sum_i n_i^0 \bar{g}_i}$$

in which n_i^0 is the number of bonds strained at time C and $\bar{g}_i$ is the average contribution of a bond of type i to the shear modulus. We suppose here that the shear modulus is independent of the strain.

For a uniform bond distribution, all the $\bar{g}_i$ are equal, and

$$\psi(t) = \frac{\sum_i n_i(t)}{\sum_i n_i^0}$$

Writing k_i for the unimolecular rate constant for breaking a bond of type i, then

$$n_i = n_i^0 e^{-k_i t}$$

and if k_i varies continuously

$$\psi(t) = \frac{\int n_i(t)\, dk_i}{\int n_i^0\, dk_i} = \int_0^\infty \frac{n^0(k)}{N_0} e^{-kt}\, dk$$

where $N_0 = \sum n_i^0$ is the total number of bonds initially present in the film. If this expression is compared with the phenomenological formula

$$\psi(t) = \int_0^\infty G(\theta)e^{-t/\theta}\, d\left(\frac{1}{\theta}\right)$$

given in Section II.D.3 of Part I, we may identify $\theta = 1/k$, so that the viscous relaxation time is identical with the kinetic relaxation time of the postulated reaction.   Now according to absolute reaction rate theory,

$$k = \varkappa \frac{RT}{Nh} e^{(\Delta S_+^+/R)} e^{-(E/RT)}$$

where $\varkappa$ is the transmission coefficient and ΔS_+^+ the entropy of activation.
    We may therefore write

$$\ln \theta = -\ln k = C + \frac{E}{RT}$$

and then

$$E = \frac{\ln(\theta_2/\theta_1)}{(1/T_1) - (1/T_2)}$$

θ_1 and θ_2 being the relaxation times corresponding to relaxation maxima at absolute temperatures T_1 and T_2.

    This equation has been applied to polylysine, sodium arabinate, and bovine serum albumin, for which the respective results are $E = 2.4$, 3, and 20 kcal/mole.   We conclude from this that E_D is less than 5% of E_H.

2. Viscosity

    Several attempts have been made to interpret the viscosity of monomolecular films.

    Because aside from highly condensed films, adsorbed amphiphilic molecules are in states less compact than is the case for three-dimensional liquids, it is reasonable to inquire if the viscosity of surface films cannot be understood in the same way as is the viscosity of gases, which is to say from the standpoint of fluctuation theory.   We are thus led to study momentum transfer by intermolecular collisions, taking account only of those forces of intermolecular interaction which contribute to the force–area isotherm $\pi = f(A)$ and neglecting interaction between the film and its substrate.

    Making use of these hypotheses, an accurate analysis (136) has led to an expression for the surface viscosity

$$\eta = \pi \sqrt{\frac{m}{2U}}$$

in which m is the mass of a molecule in the film, π is the surface pressure, and U is the surface energy per unit area.   Numerically this expression proves to be of the order 10^{-1} g/sec, and hence too small by a factor of roughly 10^8. It is obvious that this model is incapable of accounting for surface viscosity and thus that in addition to intermolecular interaction between the film molecules, the interaction with the substrate plays a fundamental role in the mechanism of surface rheology.

a. Eyring's Theory

Interpretations of surface rheology derived from the theory of liquids have been much more fruitful. We imagine that in a liquid each molecule resides in a potential well, each well corresponding to one of the possible equilibrium positions of the molecule. In such a model thermal agitation can be considered as consisting of oscillations around equilibrium positions which are themselves subject to disordered translations (137).

The mean lifetime of a molecule in one of its equilibrium positions is $\tau = \tau_0 \exp(U/kT)$ where τ_0 is the period of oscillation (of the order 10^{-13} sec) and U is the activation energy for a transition from one equilibrium position to another (of the order of several kcal/mole). Let δ be the mean amplitude of a random translation. The self-diffusion coefficient is

$$D = \frac{\delta^2}{\sigma\tau} = \frac{\delta^2}{\sigma\tau_0} e^{-U/kT}$$

and the viscosity is

$$\eta = \frac{kT\tau_0}{\pi\delta^2 r} e^{U/kT}$$

In the calculations it has been assumed that the molecular radius r is the same order of magnitude as δ, and that Stokes's law is valid even on a molecular scale. When this method is applied to a two-dimensional liquid, the surface viscosity becomes

$$\eta = C \exp\left(\frac{\Delta F}{kT}\right)$$

in which C and ΔF are practically independent of temperature. ΔF should be regarded as a free energy of activation.

The basic idea of this model is that during flow, the relative motion of the kinetic units does not take place in an arbitrary manner. They are able to pass from one potential well to the next only by leaping potential barriers, so that the mechanism of flow requires an activation process to which may be applied the theory of absolute reaction rates (138–140).

For surface flow of the Couette type, let λ_1 and λ_2 be the distances between kinetic units measured respectively perpendicular and parallel to the stream lines. For f the shear force per centimeter, Δu the increment of velocity between stream lines, $\dot{\gamma}$ the shear rate, and η the coefficient of surface shear viscosity

$$\eta = \frac{f}{\dot{\gamma}} = \frac{f\lambda_1}{\Delta u}$$

If we set λ equal to the distance between two potential wells and assume that the barrier is symmetric on each side of its maximum, then this maximum occurs at a distance $\lambda/2$ from each well.   The shear force acting on a kinetic unit is $f\lambda_2$, and the energy acquired by the kinetic unit in its motion through the distance $\frac{1}{2}\lambda$ is $\frac{1}{2}f\lambda\lambda_2$.   The effect of the force producing the flow is thus to reduce the height of the barrier by $\frac{1}{2}f\lambda\lambda_2$ in the direction of flow and to increase it by $\frac{1}{2}f\lambda\lambda_2$ in the opposite direction.

If E is the activation energy for transport over the potential barrier, then in the absence of shear stresses the number of kinetic units transported per second in either direction is

$$K = \frac{kT}{h} \frac{Q_+^{+}}{Q} e^{-E/kT}$$

in which Q and Q_+^{+} are the partition functions of the kinetic units in the initial and in the activated states, respectively, and h the Planck's constant. The transmission coefficient has been set equal to 1, which is to say that the tunnel effect has been neglected.   Under the action of a shear stress, the rate of transport over the barrier in the direction of the force is

$$K_1 = K e^{f\lambda\lambda_2/2kT}$$

and the rate in the opposite direction is

$$K_2 = K e^{-f\lambda\lambda_2/2kT}$$

But $\Delta u = \lambda \, (K_1 - K_2)$ whence

$$\Delta u = 2\lambda K \sinh \frac{f\lambda\lambda_2}{2kT}$$

and

$$\eta = \frac{f\lambda_1}{2\lambda K \sinh \dfrac{f\lambda\lambda_2}{2kT}}$$

Writing ΔF for the activation free energy for flow,

$$\frac{Q_+^{+}}{Q} e^{-E/kT} = e^{-\Delta F/kT}$$

whence

$$\eta = \frac{f\lambda_1 h e^{\Delta F/kT}}{e\lambda kT \sinh \dfrac{f\lambda\lambda_2}{2kT}}$$

Replacing f by $\eta\dot{\gamma}$

$$2\lambda kT \sinh \frac{\eta\dot{\gamma}\lambda\lambda_2}{2kT} = \dot{\gamma}\lambda_1 h e^{\Delta F/kT}$$

In addition $\lambda \simeq \lambda_1$, and $\lambda\lambda_2 \simeq A$, the area occupied by a kinetic unit. The final result is thus

$$\sinh \frac{\eta\dot{\gamma}A}{2kT} = \frac{\dot{\gamma}h e^{\Delta F/kT}}{2kT}$$

which if $\eta\dot{\gamma}A \ll 2kT$ reduces to $\eta = (h/A)\exp(\Delta F/kT)$.

For monomolecular layers $Q_+^{\ddagger}/Q \simeq A_+^{\ddagger}/A$, and in addition for sufficiently condensed states of the film $A_+^{\ddagger}/A \simeq 1$. In first approximation this means $\eta \simeq (h/A)\exp(\Delta E/kT)$.

The meaning of the energy of activation for flow in surface films has been the subject of a detailed study (37, 38, 141).

b. Calculation of the Activation Energy for Flow

The fact that the water molecules in immediate contact with the polar groups of the amphiphilic molecules in the film are bound to them and are transported with the same velocity (see Section II.B in Part I) permits the decomposition of the energy of activation for flow for the kinetic units into two terms

$$\Delta E = \Delta E_c + \Delta E_s$$

the first of which is characteristic of the amphiphilic molecule and the second of the bound water.

Eyring's equation now becomes

$$\ln \eta = \frac{\Delta E_c + \Delta E_s}{kT} - \ln A + \ln h$$

Without the participation of the water in the substrate we would have $\Delta E = \Delta E_c$ and the viscous contribution of the film would be

$$\ln \eta_c = \frac{\Delta E_c}{kT} - \ln A + \ln h$$

The contribution due exclusively to the film may be calculated from the measured surface viscosity η by

$$\ln \eta_c = \ln \eta - \frac{\Delta E_s}{kT}$$

Writing η_0 for the contribution to the surface viscosity of the water bound to the polar groups in the film, we have for the substrate contribution

$$\ln \eta_0 = \frac{\Delta E_s}{kT} - \ln A + \ln h$$

It is η_0 which enters into the definition of the specific, reduced, and intrinsic surface viscosities (see Section III.C.4 in Part I).

The calculation of ΔE_c and ΔE_s is possible through the use of a simple model for the molecular mechanism of laminar flow in surface films.

If we presume that the monomolecular film is sufficiently concentrated so that in first approximation the molecules are distributed in a quasihexagonal array, then ΔE_c can be calculated from the interaction energy W between a molecule and its immediate neighbors.   This approach amounts to estimating the activation energy for flow by the energy necessary to transport a film molecule from an initial equilibrium position to a neighboring one.

We decompose the latter energy into two parts: (1) the energy E_0 needed to create a hole in the monomolecular film into which the flowing molecule may pass; and (2) the height ΔE_p of the potential barrier which needs to be surmounted by the flowing molecule during its passage.

Roughly $\Delta E_0 = W$.   If we neglect conformational changes in the molecule during the course of its displacement, then ΔE_p is the sum of the strain energy ΔE_d of the quasihexagonal network plus the translational energy ΔE_t of the molecule.   Generally the order of magnitude of ΔE_p is about $0.15W$, whence

$$\Delta E_c \simeq 1.15W$$

For relatively weak variations in A (10–30%), the change in $\ln A$ is usually negligible.   We shall see furthermore that ΔE_s varies only slowly with A.   It follows that if we assume a reference area A_1 to which corresponds an interaction energy W_1, then

$$\ln\left(\frac{\eta}{\eta_1}\right) = \frac{1.15(W - W_1)}{kT}$$

If A is chosen in such a way that the compression isotherm over the region of areas considered is approximated by $(\pi - \pi_1)(A - A_1) = kT$, then the approximations $W_1 \simeq \pi_1 A_1$, $W \simeq \pi A$, and $A \simeq A_1$ yield

$$\log\left(\frac{\eta}{\eta_1}\right) = \alpha + \beta\pi$$

which is the empirical relation discovered by different authors (32, 104).

Such relations may also be shown to be valid for noncondensed states of the film.   By writing

$$\Delta F = \Delta E + \pi A_+^+ - T\,\Delta S_+^+$$

in which ΔS_+^+ is the entropy of activation and ΔA_+^+ the difference in area between the activated and the equilibrium states, the general formula for the surface viscosity becomes

$$\ln \eta = \ln \frac{h}{A} - \frac{\Delta S_+^+}{k} + \frac{\Delta A_+^+}{kT}\pi + \frac{\Delta E}{kT}$$

which has the form

$$\log \eta = \log a + b\pi + \frac{c}{T}$$

found empirically for synthetic polypeptides (104).   It should not be forgotten, however, that these empirical formulas are valid over only relatively narrow portions of the compression isotherms, and that our approximation for ΔE_c is very crude.

A more exact calculation of ΔE_c requires a consideration of molecular conformation changes which accompany the deformation of the quasi-network and molecular transport.   More explicitly, we need to consider changes in intermolecular distance.

It has been suggested (142, 143) that the molecules of a monomolecular film can exist in only a finite number of equilibrium states $\dots, i-1, i,$ $i+1, \dots$ to each of which corresponds a discrete molecular area $\dots, A_{i-1}, A_i, A_{i+1}, \dots$ and intermolecular distance $r_{i-1}, r_i, r_{i+1}, \dots .$ We recall that the values A_i are associated with the higher-order transitions exhibited by the compression isotherms and deduce the following result. During the flow of a film (all of whose molecules are at rest in the state i) some of the intermolecular distances fall below r_i (down to $0.94r_i$ in a hexagonal array) and leap abruptly into the state $i-1$ whose stable intermolecular distance lies immediately below the smallest intermolecular distance attained during the transition (less than $0.94r_i$, for example).   The activated state thus becomes the state $i-l$, for which we define an activation energy ΔE_f.   Explicitly (37, 141),

$$\Delta E_0 = W_i(r_i)$$

$$\Delta E_t = 0.7W_{i-l}(r_i)$$

$$\Delta E_d = -0.5W_{i-l}(r_i)$$

$$\Delta E_f = 6[W_i(r_i) - W_{i-l}(r_i)]$$

whence

$$\Delta E_{c,i} \simeq 7W_i(r_i) - 5.8W_{i-l}(r_i)$$

in which $W_i(r_i)$ is the energy of interaction between a molecule and its neighbors in the state i with lattice spacing r_i, and similarly for $W_{i-i}(r_i)$. $W(r)$ embraces ionic, dipole, dispersion, polarization, etc., effects and may thus be calculated from a knowledge of the lattice and molecular geometry.

Analogous reasoning (141) permits the calculation of ΔE_s as a function of the area occupied by a kinetic unit.   The model used requires a spacing of 3.84 Å between the water molecules in contact with the insoluble film.   A tetrahedral lattice is assumed for the water molecules in bulk with 2.8 Å for the distance of the four nearest neighbors and 4.2 for the distance of the 12 next nearest.   The calculation depends upon the value 538 cal/g for the heat of vaporization of water at 100°C.

For condensed films at low area ($A < 3 \times 10^{-15}$ cm²) the result is

$$\Delta E_s = 1.115 \times 10^{18} A^2 (B - 3.84)^{-1} [6.77 \times 10^{-2} - (2B - 3.84)^{-2}]$$

with $B = 1.24 \times 10^{18} \sqrt{A}$.

For condensed films at larger molecular areas ($A > 6 \times 10^{-15}$ cm²), the formula for ΔE_s is more complicated.   Let z number a sequence of concentric shells of water surrounding the polar part of an amphiphilic molecule; then

$$\Delta E_s = 6.2 \times 10^{-13} \sum_{z=1}^{Z} (B - 6.64z + 2.8)$$
$$\times \{(6.64z - 2.8)^{-2} - (2B - 6.64z + 2.8)^{-2}$$
$$+ \sum_{y(\neq z)=1}^{Z} (B - 6.64y + 2.8)[B - 3.32(y+z) + 2.8]^{-1}$$
$$\times ([3.32(y+z) - 2.8]^{-2} - [2B - 3.32(y+z) + 2.8]^{-2})\}$$

in which $Z = (B + 2.8)/6.64$.   For values of A between 3 and 6×10^{-15} cm², ΔE_s should be calculated by interpolating between the last two formulas.

If A is very large, it is a sufficient approximation to restrict z to its first three integer values, whence

$$\Delta E_s = 6.2 \times 10^{-13} C [6.8 \times 10^{-2} - (2B - 3.84)^{-2}]$$
$$+ 6.2 \times 10^{-13} D \{9.15 \times 10^{-3} - E + C(B - 2.15)^{-1}$$
$$\times [1.94 \times 10^{-2} - (2B - 2.16)^{-2}]\} + 6.2 \times 10^{-13}(B - 17.12)$$
$$\times \{3.41 \times 10^{-3} - (2B - 17.12)^{-2} + CD^{-1}(9.15 \times 10^{-3} - E)$$
$$+ D(B - 13.8)^{-1}[5.26 \times 10^{-3} - (2B - 13.8)^{-2}]\}$$

with $C = B - 3.84$, $D = B - 10.48$, and $E = (2B - 10.48)^{-2}$.

In practice, it is sufficient for molecular areas between 10^{-13} and 10^{-14} cm² to use the simplified formula

$$\Delta E_s = 9 \times 10^{-14} + 31A$$

and for $A > 10^{-12}$ cm²,

$$\Delta E_s = 8.8 \times 10^{-6} \sqrt{A} - 5.4 \times 10^{-13}$$

For $10^{-13} < A < 10^{-12}$ the investigator should interpolate between these two formulas. ΔE_s as a function of A is plotted in Figure 2 (curves a and b).

Calculations of ΔE_s have also been carried out for highly dilute films (141) for which $A_0/A \ll 1$. Here the density of polar groups of amphiphilic molecules is too small to bind to themselves all the available surface molecules of water, and we are led to consider some of the water as securely bound to the polar groups while the rest is free to organize itself into kinetic units of flow characteristic of the water itself. The calculations are lengthy, but they nevertheless result in an expression for ΔE_s as a function of A_0 and A, where it will be recalled that A is the area in the surface available to a film-forming molecule while A_0 is its cross-sectional area.

Finally, for $A = A_i$ and i arbitrary,

$$\Delta E_i = \Delta E_{c,i} + \Delta E_s(A_i)$$

When A differs from A_i (for example, $A_{i-1} < A < A_i$) the formulas are slightly more complicated. It has been admitted (143) that in this case the film at rest comprises a mixture of molecules in the states i and $i - 1$. Hence

$$A = (1 - \alpha)A_i + \alpha A_{i-1}$$

in which α is the mole fraction of film molecules in the state $i - 1$. For a condensed state, however, it is generally true that

$$\frac{A_i - A_{i-1}}{A_i} \ll 1$$

so that $\Delta E_s(A)$ changes very little in the interval $A_{i-1} - A_i$. On the other hand, experimental values of ΔE calculated from η are sensitive functions of A, being sections of straight-line plots whose points of discontinuous slope occur at the points $A = A_i$. It is consequently amply justified to write

$$\Delta E_c = (1 - \alpha)\,\Delta E_{c,i} + \alpha\Delta E_{c,i-1}$$

so that

$$\Delta E(A) = (1 - \alpha)\,\Delta E_{c,i} + \alpha\,\Delta E_{c,i-1} + \Delta E_s(A)$$

which is to say

$$\Delta E(A) \simeq 7[(1 - \alpha)W_i(r_i) + \alpha W_{i-1}(r_{i-1})]$$
$$- 5.8[(1 - \alpha)W_{i-l}(r_i) + \alpha W_{i-1-m}(r_{i-1})] + \Delta E_s(A)$$

c. Non-Newtonian Surface Viscosity

We have already obtained Eyring's general equation

$$\sinh\left(\frac{\eta\dot\gamma A}{2kT}\right) = \left(\frac{\dot\gamma h}{2kT}\right)\exp\left(\frac{\Delta E}{kT}\right)$$

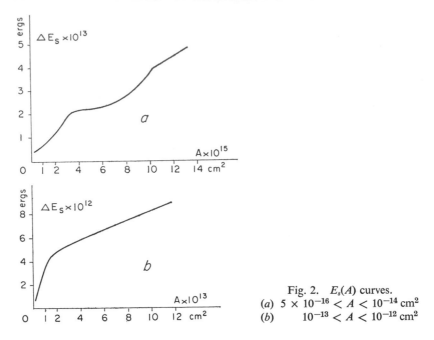

Fig. 2. $E_s(A)$ curves.
(a) $5 \times 10^{-16} < A < 10^{-14}$ cm^2
(b) $10^{-13} < A < 10^{-12}$ cm^2

But for $x < 0.25$, $\sinh x = x$ to an accuracy of 1%, so that at ordinary temperatures the surface viscosity can be written

$$\eta = \frac{h}{A}\, e^{\Delta E/kT}$$

so long as $\eta \dot{\gamma} A < 2 \times 10^{-14}$ erg. Under such conditions, the surface viscosity must necessarily be Newtonian. Experimentally, however, the surface viscosity frequently does not become Newtonian even though $\eta \dot{\gamma} A$ is marked by less than 2×10^{-14} erg, and this suggests that ΔE ceases to be independent of the shear stress. For simplicity the discussion will be limited to the special case $A = A_i$.

We have remarked that the translation of a molecule from its initial position in the film to a neighboring, empty site in a row of molecules parallel to the flow direction produces a deformation of the quasilattice, and hence a temporary displacement of some of the neighboring molecules. If a second translation takes place in this row before the molecules displaced from the neighboring rows have regained their initial positions, the activation energy required for the second motion is not ΔE_i but the smaller quantity $\Delta E_i'$. This difference is principally due to the fact that the second translation requires neither a new local deformation of the lattice nor a change in the state of stability of the displaced molecules.   In first approximation,

$$\Delta E_i - \Delta E_i' \simeq 4[W_i(r_i) - 1.1 W_{i-l}(r_i)]$$

If p_i is the probability that a molecule i which has been displaced from its initial lattice position has not regained it before it has been overtaken by a second molecule from a neighboring row undergoing flow, the activation energy for flow may be written

$$\Delta E(\dot\gamma) = \Delta E_i - p_i(\Delta E_i - \Delta E_i')$$

whence

$$\eta(\dot\gamma) \simeq \frac{h}{A} \exp\left[\frac{\Delta E_i - p_i(\Delta E_i - \Delta E_i')}{kT}\right] = \eta_i \exp\left[\frac{p_i(\Delta E_i' - \Delta E_i)}{kT}\right]$$

It is furthermore legitimate to put $p_i = \exp(-1/\dot\gamma\tau_i)$ where τ_i is analogous to a relaxation time.   From the fact that molecules initially in the state i pass into the state $i - l$ during deformation of the network, τ_i may be regarded as a measure of the mean lifetime of the local aggregate formed by molecules in the state $i - l$ but with a lattice parameter $0.94r_i$ rather than r_{i-l}.   By an extension of Frenkel's theory (144), τ_i to first approximation is

$$\tau_i \simeq 0.94 r_i \sqrt{\frac{2\pi m}{kT}} \exp\left[\frac{W_{i-l}(0.94r_i)}{kT}\right]$$

in which m is the mass of a kinetic unit.

The decrease in surface viscosity with increasing shear rate at constant surface pressure is accompanied by an apparent increase in the area per molecule (38, 145):

$$A(\dot\gamma) = (1 + 0.07 p_i)A_i$$

We have just seen that the removal of a molecule i induces in the neighboring molecules a temporary transition from the state i into the state $i - l$ but with the provision that the lattice parameter shall be $0.94r_i$ rather than r_{i-l}.   As a result of thermal fluctuations it may happen that these molecules do not relax into the state i with lattice parameter r_i but condense with their neighbors into the state $i - l$ with lattice parameter r_{i-l}.

The probability of such an event is

$$\pi_i = \exp\left[\frac{W_{i-l}(0.94r_i) - W_{i-l}(r_{i-l})}{W_{i-l}(0.94r_i) - W_i(r_i)}\right]$$

Moreover, the probability that one of these molecules is still in the state $i - l$ after a time lapse $\dot\gamma^{-1}$ from its condensation is

$$\varphi_i = e^{-1/\dot\gamma\theta_i}$$

in which θ_i is the mean lifetime of a kinetic unit in the aggregate.   To a first approximation

$$\theta_i \simeq r_{i-l} \sqrt{\frac{2\pi m}{kT}} \, e^{W_{i-l}(r_{i-l})/kT}$$

It follows that if in the initial state of rest all the molecules are in state i, then after a flow duration t at shear rate $\dot{\gamma}$, the fraction of molecules converted into the state $i - l$ is

$$z(t) = \pi_i \varphi_i \frac{[\varphi_i(1 - \pi_i)]^{\dot{\gamma}t} - 1}{\ln \varphi_i(1 - \pi_i)}$$

From this formula we may anticipate an increase in the surface viscosity because the activation energy for flow is calculated from

$$\Delta E(t) = \Delta E_i - p_i(\Delta E_i - \Delta E_i') + z(t)[\Delta E_{i-l} - \Delta E_i + p_i(\Delta E_i - \Delta E_i')]$$

The effect is one of progressive thickening under flow, experimental examples of which have been given in Sections I.A.4.c and I.A.4.d.   The explanation is here in terms of a phase change at the molecular level, exhibiting itself by a decrease in the apparent molecular area as flow proceeds.

$$A(t) = (1 + 0.07p_i)A_i + z(t)[A_{i-l} - (1 + 0.07p_i)A_i]$$

In the general case where $A = (1 - \alpha)A_1 + \alpha A_{i-1}$ at rest, all the preceding phenomena repeat themselves, but the final formulas for $\Delta E(\dot{\gamma})$, $A(\dot{\gamma})$, $\Delta E(t)$, and $A(t)$ are more complicated (38, 145).

We have seen that this extension of Eyring's theory has provided explanations of the principal features of surface viscosity.   The most difficult aspect of this theory is an understanding of the mechanism by which a shear force can create an asymmetric potential barrier between two equilibrium positions in a row of molecules parallel to the direction of flow.   Macroscopically the distribution of shear forces at steady flow leads to a zero resultant force on a molecule in this row.   One suggestion to overcome this difficulty has been to introduce an elastic relaxation effect (146).   In the last analysis, however, it is only the perfection of the theory of real liquids which will solve this problem, particularly those aspects of it which relate to the transmission of forces through liquids.

III. THE EFFECT OF THE RHEOLOGICAL PROPERTIES OF MONOLAYERS ON THE MECHANICAL BEHAVIOR OF INTERFACES

The discussion of Section I showed that the rheological parameters characteristic of surface and interfacial films are large enough to make a significant contribution to the overall surface motion. This fact permits them to be measured with a satisfactory precision, and in the following we shall give a number of examples of how a surface film of amphiphilic molecules can modify the macroscopic motion of the fluid interface.

A. Wave Damping

It has long been known that a monomolecular film at a water surface has the ability to change both the wave length and the damping rate of transverse waves generated by an external source of oscillation. The study of this phenomenon has recently been resumed under well-defined experimental conditions (147–149), and the results obtained have been used to examine transitions in surface films (148, 150) and the formation of complexes between the molecules in the film and those in the substrate (142).

The influence of surface tension upon the propagation of waves generated at a surface was studied theoretically in the last century. The principal result is Kelvin's formula (151) which relates the wave length λ of a capillary ripple to its frequency ν and to the surface tension γ:

$$\nu^2 = \frac{g}{2\pi\lambda} + \frac{\gamma}{\rho}\frac{2\pi}{\lambda^3}$$

Here g is the acceleration of gravity and ρ the density of the liquid.

From this formula it can be shown that the pattern of ripples formed in the wake of a moving object (Poncelet's ripples) do not constitute a stable system on a film-covered water surface because of the nonconstancy of the surface tension (152). It appears that changes in γ prohibit the ripple velocity from attaining everywhere the same velocity as that of the moving object.

In the early work no account was taken of the rheological properties of the surface film in attempts to account for the mechanical properties of the interface. In subsequent work it was at first rigid films that were studied (153). Only recently has a Newtonian surface viscosity been introduced into the theory of capillary wave damping (154). It has furthermore been necessary to introduce several rheological parameters in order to account for the departure of the observed damping coefficients from those predicted from simplified theories (155, 156).

The presence of a monomolecular film at the surface of a liquid modifies the motion of that surface to the extent that it influences the components of the stress tensor at different points of the surface.

Let the surface at rest be denoted by the xz plane and consider a plane wave propagated in the x direction. The coordinates of a point in the surface are x, y_s and those of a point in the interior of the liquid are x, y. If v_x and

v_y are the velocity components of a kinetic unit in the surface, then the equation of motion of that kinetic unit is (157)

$$\frac{\partial y_s}{\partial t} = v_y - v_x \frac{\partial y_s}{\partial x} \tag{1}$$

If the liquid is incompressible, its motion is determined by the Navier-Stokes equations plus the equation of continuity.   Let n and r be unit normal and tangent vectors to the surface at the point x, y_s in the plane $z = 0$.   Then the components of the stress tensor are

$$p_{nn} = \left[\left(\frac{\partial y_s}{\partial x}\right)^2 p_{xx} - 2 \frac{\partial y_s}{\partial x} p_{xy} + p_{yy} \right] \left[1 + \left(\frac{\partial y_s}{\partial x}\right)^2 \right]^{-1}$$

$$p_{nr} = \frac{\partial y_s}{\partial x} (-p_{xx} + p_{yy}) \left[1 + \left(\frac{\partial y_s}{\partial x}\right)^2 \right]^{-1} + p_{xy} \tag{2}$$

In the interior of the liquid at a point x, y having velocity components u_x, u_y the components of the stress tensor are

$$p_{xx} = -p + 2\eta_s \frac{\partial u_x}{\partial x}$$

$$p_{yy} = -p + 2\eta_s \frac{\partial u_y}{\partial y} \tag{3}$$

$$p_{xy} = p_{yx} = \eta_s \left(\frac{\partial u_x}{\partial y} + \frac{\partial u_y}{\partial x}\right)$$

in which η_s is the internal or bulk viscosity of the liquid.   At the surface the normal component of the stress tensor p_{nn} is the sum of the static pressure p_0 in the gas phase plus the Laplacian or surface tension contribution due to the curvature of the surface wave.

$$p_{nn} = \gamma \frac{\partial^2 y_s}{\partial x^2} \left[1 + \left(\frac{\partial y_s}{\partial x}\right)^2 \right]^{-3/2} - p_0 \tag{4}$$

Equations 2–4 lead to a boundary condition

$$2\eta_s \left(\frac{\partial u_y}{\partial y}\right)_s - 2\eta_s \frac{\partial y_s}{\partial x} \left(\frac{\partial u_x}{\partial y} + \frac{\partial u_y}{\partial x}\right)_s + 2\eta_s \left(\frac{\partial y_s}{\partial x}\right)^2 \left(\frac{\partial u_x}{\partial x}\right)_s$$

$$= \gamma \frac{\partial^2 y_s}{\partial x^2} + (p - p_0) \left[1 + \left(\frac{\partial y_s}{\partial x}\right)^2 \right] \tag{5}$$

Identifying p_{nr} as the gradient of the surface tension

$$p_{nr} = \frac{\partial \gamma}{\partial r} \tag{6}$$

we have from equations 2, 3 and 6

$$2\eta_s \frac{\partial y_s}{\partial x}\left(\frac{\partial u_y}{\partial y} - \frac{\partial u_x}{\partial x}\right)_s + \eta_s\left[1 - \left(\frac{\partial y_s}{\partial x}\right)^2\right]\left(\frac{\partial u_x}{\partial y} + \frac{\partial u_y}{\partial x}\right)_s$$

$$= \left[1 + \left(\frac{\partial y_s}{\partial x}\right)^2\right]^{1/2}\left(\frac{\partial \gamma}{\partial x} + \frac{\partial y_s}{\partial x}\frac{\partial \gamma}{\partial y}\right) \quad (7)$$

The effect of the wave is to cause a periodic variation in the surface area S, hence also in Γ and consequently in γ. As a result the wave profile is not precisely sinusoidal.

All the quantities entering into the preceding equations can be developed into Fourier series

$$X = X_1 \exp(i\omega t) + X_2 \exp(2i\omega t) + \cdots \quad (8)$$

where $\omega = 2\pi\nu$ and ν is the frequency of the ripple generator. Each X_i is a function of x and y.

In order that equations 5, 7, and 8 be compatible, a relation of the type

$$F_1 \exp(i\omega t) + F_2 \exp(2i\omega t) + \cdots = 0 \quad (9)$$

must be satisfied for arbitrary t, whence it follows that

$$F_1 = F_2 = \cdots = 0 \quad (10)$$

To the first order of approximation ($F_1 = 0$) and defining the wave number by $k = 2\pi/\lambda$ and introducing a parameter $m^2 = k^2 + i\rho\omega/\eta_s$, the analysis (157) leads to

$$u_x = -ikA \exp(ky) + mB \exp(my)] \exp(ikx) \exp(i\omega t) \quad (11)$$

$$u_y = -[kA \exp(ky) - ikB \exp(my)] \exp(ikx) \exp(i\omega t) \quad (12)$$

$$p = p_0 - \rho g y + i\rho\omega A \exp(ky) \exp(ikx) \exp(i\omega t) \quad (13)$$

$$y_s = (i\omega)^{-1}k(-A + iB) \exp[i(\omega t + kx)] \quad (14)$$

in which the unknowns A, B, and k are related by equations 5 and 7 after substitution. To the first order of terms the boundary conditions require

$$A\left(\frac{ik\rho g}{\omega} - i\rho\omega - 2\eta_s k^2 + \frac{ik^3\gamma_0}{\omega}\right) + B\left(\frac{k\rho g}{\omega} + 2ikm\eta_s + \frac{k^3\gamma_0}{\omega}\right) = 0 \quad (15)$$

$$\eta_s[2ik^2A + B(m^2 + k^2)] = \frac{\partial \gamma_1}{\partial x}\exp(-ikx) \quad (16)$$

For an inviscid liquid, equations 15 and 16 reduce to Kelvin's equation

$$\omega^2 = gk + \frac{\gamma k^3}{\rho} \quad (17)$$

At the filmfree interface $(\partial\gamma/\partial x = 0)$ of a liquid of internal viscosity η_s, equations 15 and 16 are linear and homogeneous in A and B, so that k must be chosen to make the determinant of coefficients vanish.

The damping coefficient, defined by $\alpha = d \ln \mathscr{A}/dx$ in which $\mathscr{A}$ is the wave amplitude, takes in this case the simple form

$$\alpha = \frac{2\eta_s k^3}{3\pi\rho\nu} \tag{18}$$

provided that the wave length is not too short, which is to say that

$$\lambda^2 \gg \frac{2\pi\eta_s}{\rho\nu} \tag{19}$$

If a film is present at the interface, the wave generates a variation in the surface concentration Γ, whence for adsorbed, soluble films, fluctuations in the concentration c near the boundary may be expected. The diffusion equation is

$$\frac{\partial c}{\partial t} + u_x \frac{\partial c}{\partial x} + u_y \frac{\partial c}{\partial y} - D\left(\frac{\partial^2 c}{\partial x^2} + \frac{\partial^2 c}{\partial y^2}\right) = 0 \tag{20}$$

in which D is the translational diffusion coefficient, and the equation of continuity at the surface is

$$\frac{d}{dt} \Gamma S = -DS\left(\frac{\partial c}{\partial n}\right)_s \tag{21}$$

in which S is the area of a surface element.

As before, we expand in Fourier series

$$
\begin{aligned}
c &= c_0 + c_1 \exp(i\omega t) + c_2 \exp(2i\omega t) + \cdots \\
\Gamma &= \Gamma_0 + \Gamma_1 \exp(i\omega t) + \Gamma_2 \exp(2i\omega t) + \cdots
\end{aligned} \tag{22}
$$

and reject all but the first-order terms. Then equation 20 leads to

$$c_1 = E \exp(ny)\exp(ilx) \tag{23}$$

with

$$n^2 = l^2 + \frac{i\omega}{D} \tag{24}$$

while from equations 11, 21, and 23 we get

$$i\omega\Gamma_1 = -\Gamma_0(kA - imB)k \exp(ikx) - DEn \exp(ilx) \tag{25}$$

If it is assumed that instantaneous equilibrium is established between the film and the subsolution, then

$$\Gamma_0(kA - imB)k \exp(ikx) + DEn \exp(ilx) = -i\omega E\left(\frac{d\Gamma}{dc_s}\right)_0 \exp(ilx) \tag{26}$$

which implies that $l = k$, that

$$E = - \frac{k\Gamma_0(kA - imB)}{nD + i\omega\left(\frac{d\Gamma}{dc_s}\right)_0} \tag{27}$$

and that

$$\gamma_1 = \left(\frac{d\gamma}{dc_s}\right)_0 E \exp(ikx) \tag{28}$$

Finally from equations 16, 27, and 28,

$$A\left[ik^3\Gamma_0\left(\frac{d\gamma}{dc_s}\right)_0 - 2in\eta_s k^2 D + 2\omega\eta_s k^2\left(\frac{d\Gamma}{dc_s}\right)_0\right.$$
$$\left. + B\left\{k^2 m\Gamma_0\left(\frac{d\gamma}{dc_s}\right)_0 - \eta_s(m^2 + k^2)\left[nD + i\omega\left(\frac{d\Gamma}{dc_s}\right)_0\right]\right\}\right] = 0 \quad (29)$$

For dilute solutions which satisfy Szyszkowski's equation

$$\pi = RT\Gamma_\infty \ln\left(\frac{c}{a} + 1\right) \tag{30}$$

equation 29 may be written

$$A\{2i\eta_s k^3[Dn(c_0 + a)^2 + ia\omega\Gamma_\infty] + ik^3 c_0 RT\Gamma_\infty{}^2\}$$
$$+ B\{\eta_s(m^2 + k^2)[Dn(c_0 + a)^2 + ia\omega\Gamma_\infty] + k^2 m c_0 RT\Gamma_\infty{}^2\} = 0 \quad (31)$$

Equations 15, 29, and 31 are linear and homogeneous in A and B, so that the vanishing of their determinant is sufficient to determine k, but the algebraic result is complicated.

For insoluble films,

$$\eta_s[2ik^2 A + B(m^2 + k^2)] = \Gamma_0\left(\frac{d\gamma}{d\Gamma_0}\right)\frac{k^2}{\omega}(kA - imB) = \frac{\varkappa}{\omega}k^2(kA - imB) \quad (32)$$

in which $\varkappa$ is the compression modulus of the film. If equation 19 is satisfied, then the damping coefficient becomes

$$\alpha = \frac{2\eta_s}{3\lambda^2}\left(\frac{\pi\eta_s}{\rho_2}\right)^{1/2} \tag{33}$$

The agreement of equation 33 with experiment is satisfactory.

To improve the theory, it is necessary to take account of the more complicated rheological properties of the surface film. Thus for the tangential stress we might write (158)

$$p_{nr} = - \frac{\varkappa}{\Gamma_0}\frac{\partial\Gamma}{\partial n} - \frac{\zeta}{\Gamma_0}\frac{\partial^2\Gamma}{\partial x \partial t} \tag{34}$$

in which $\varkappa$ is the compression modulus and ζ is the dilational surface viscosity.

Taking account of the gravitational force (159), the normal stress is

$$p_{nn} = \gamma \frac{\partial^2 y_s}{\partial x^2} \left[1 + \left(\frac{\partial y_s}{\partial x} \right)^2 \right]^{-\frac{3}{2}} - p_0 - \rho g y_s \tag{35}$$

Defining

$$K = k + i\alpha$$

$$m'^2 = K^2 - \frac{i\rho}{\eta_s}\omega$$

$$n'^2 = K^2 - \frac{i\omega}{D}$$

$$y_1 = \frac{\rho\omega^2}{\gamma k^3}\left(1 + \frac{\rho g}{\gamma k^2} \right)$$

$$y_2 = \frac{\alpha}{k}$$

$$n_1 = \frac{\eta_s \omega^2}{\gamma k}\left(1 + \frac{\rho g}{\gamma k^2} \right)^{-1}$$

$$\frac{m'}{k} = u_3 e^{i\theta_3}$$

$$\frac{\varkappa - i\omega\zeta}{1 + in' \dfrac{D}{\omega}(dc/d\Gamma)_{c_0}} = u_2 e^{i\theta_2}$$

$$\varphi = \tan^{-1} y_2$$

$$v = (1 + y_2{}^2)^{\frac{1}{2}}$$

the vanishing of the determinant as above leads to a compatibility equation

$$i\left[\frac{y_1}{v^3} e^{-3i\varphi} - 1 \right]\left[\frac{u_1}{v} e^{-i\varphi} + \frac{u_1 u_3{}^2}{v^3} e^{i(2\theta_3 - 3\varphi)} \right] - 2 \frac{u_1{}^2}{v^2} e^{-2i\varphi}$$

$$- 2 \frac{u_1{}^2 u_3{}^2}{v^4} e^{2i(\theta_3 - 2\varphi)} + 2i \frac{u_1}{v} e^{-i\varphi} + 4 \frac{u_1{}^2 u_3}{v^3} e^{i(\theta_3 - 3\varphi)}$$

$$= u_2 e^{i\theta_2}\left[1 + \frac{y_1 u_3}{v^4} e^{i(\theta_3 - 4\varphi)} - \frac{u_3}{v} e^{i(\theta_3 - \varphi)} \right] \tag{36}$$

If the film is only weakly viscoelastic ($u_2 < 0.01$) the corresponding simplification leads to

$$y_1 = 1 - 2\sqrt{2}u_1^{3/2} + u_2 \cos\theta_2 + 4u_2 u_1^{1/2} \sin\left(\theta_2 - \frac{\pi}{4}\right) \qquad (37)$$

$$y_2 = \tfrac{4}{3}u_1 - \frac{2\sqrt{2}}{3} u_1^{3/2} - \tfrac{1}{3}u_2 \sin\theta_2 + \tfrac{4}{3}u_1^{1/2} u_2 \cos\left(\theta_2 - \frac{\pi}{4}\right) \qquad (38)$$

For strongly viscoelastic films ($u_2 > 1$) the simplification gives

$$y_1 = 1 - \frac{\sqrt{2}}{2} u_1^{1/2} + \frac{u_1}{4} - \frac{u_1}{u_2} \sin\theta_2 + 4\frac{u_1^{3/2}}{u_2} \sin\left(\theta_2 + \frac{\pi}{4}\right) \qquad (39)$$

$$y_2 = \frac{\sqrt{2}}{6} u_1^{1/2} + \frac{11}{36} u_1 + \frac{1}{3}\frac{u_1}{u_2} \cos\theta_2 - \frac{4u_1^{3/2}}{3u_2} \cos\left(\theta_2 - \frac{\pi}{4}\right) \qquad (40)$$

For films of intermediate viscoelasticity the formulas are very complicated

$$y_1 - 1 = \frac{2\sqrt{2}u_1^{3/2} - u_2(1 + 4u_1)\cos\theta_2 - 4u_2 u_1^{1/2} \sin\left(\theta_2 - \frac{\pi}{4}\right) + \frac{\sqrt{2}}{2} u_2^2 u_1^{-1/2}}{1 - 2u_2 u_1^{-1/4} \cos\left(\theta_2 - \frac{\pi}{4}\right) + u_2^2 u_1^{-1}}$$

$$(41)$$

$$y_2 = \frac{4u_1 - 2\sqrt{2}u_1^{3/2} - u_2(1 - 4u_1)\sin\theta_2 - 4u_2 u^{1/2} \cos\left(\theta_2 - \frac{\pi}{4}\right) + \frac{\sqrt{2}}{2} u_2^2 u_1^{-1/2}}{3\left[1 - 2u_2 u_1^{-1/4} \cos\left(\theta_2 + \frac{\pi}{4}\right) + u_2^2 u_1^{-1}\right]}$$

$$(42)$$

More tractable expressions for k and α are obtainable for the limiting cases of zero and infinite viscoelasticity ($u_2 = 0$ and $u_2 = \infty$, respectively). For $u_2 = 0$

$$k = \left(\frac{\rho\omega^2}{\gamma}\right)^{1/3}\left(1 + \frac{\rho g}{\gamma k^2}\right)^{-1/3}\left[1 + \frac{2\sqrt{2}}{3\gamma}\left(\frac{\omega\eta_s^3}{\rho}\right)^{1/2}\left(1 + \frac{\rho g}{\gamma k^2}\right)^{-1}\right] \qquad (43)$$

$$\alpha = \frac{4}{3}\frac{\eta_s\omega}{\gamma}\left(1 + \frac{\rho g}{\gamma k^2}\right)^{-1}\left[1 - \frac{\sqrt{2}}{2}\left(\frac{\omega\eta_s^3}{\rho}\right)^{1/6}\gamma^{-1/3}\left(1 + \frac{\rho g}{\gamma k^2}\right)^{-1/3}\right] \qquad (44)$$

and for $u_2 = \infty$,

$$k = \left(\frac{\rho\omega^2}{\gamma}\right)^{1/3}\left(1 + \frac{\rho g}{\gamma k^2}\right)^{-1/3}\left[1 + \frac{\sqrt{2}}{6}\left(\frac{\omega\eta_s^3}{\rho}\right)^{1/6}\gamma^{-1/3}\left(1 + \frac{\rho g}{\gamma k^2}\right)^{-1/3}\right] \qquad (45)$$

$$\alpha = \frac{\sqrt{2}}{6}\left(\frac{\rho\omega^2}{\gamma^2}\right)^{1/3}\left(1 + \frac{\rho g}{\gamma k^2}\right)^{-2/3}\left(\frac{\omega\eta_s^3}{\rho}\right)^{1/6}\left[1 + \sqrt{2}\left(\frac{\omega\eta_s^3}{\rho}\right)^{1/6}\gamma^{-1/3}\left(1 + \frac{\rho g}{\gamma k^2}\right)^{1/3}\right] \qquad (46)$$

Experimental results obtained from a large number of monomolecular films are in good agreement (order of 7%) with these formulas (160).

In the special case where the dilational surface viscosity ζ is negligible, the calculation simplies, and it is found (161) that the damping coefficient passes through a maximum at moderate values of $\varkappa$.

Indeed, by writing

$$k' = k \sqrt{\frac{\eta_s}{\omega\rho}}$$

$$\alpha' = \alpha \sqrt{\frac{\eta_s}{\omega\rho}}$$

$$\gamma' = \gamma \sqrt{\frac{\rho}{\omega\eta_s^{3}}}$$

$$\varkappa' = \varkappa \sqrt{\frac{\rho}{\omega\eta_s^{3}}}$$

$$g' = g \sqrt{\frac{\rho}{\omega^3\eta_s}}$$

it may be verified that the equations are of the sixth degree in k' and α' and of the second degree in γ' and $\varkappa'$. If mass transport between the film and substrate is negligible, the calculations reduce to

$$\alpha' \simeq \tfrac{4}{3}k'^3 \frac{(\sqrt{2}/8)k'^3\varkappa'^2 + (\sqrt{2}/2)k'^2\varkappa' + 1 - (\sqrt{2}/2)k'}{(k'^4 - (2\sqrt{2}/3)k'^5 - (2/3)g'k'^5)\varkappa'^2 + (\sqrt{2}\,k'^2 - 2k'^3 - (2\sqrt{2}/3)g'k'^3)\varkappa' + 1 - (2/3)g'k'} \tag{47}$$

At the maximum in α' we have effectively

$$\alpha'_{max} \simeq \frac{\sqrt{2}}{3} k'^2_{max} \simeq \frac{\sqrt{3}}{2} \gamma'^{-\frac{3}{2}}$$

while

$$\varkappa'_{max} \simeq -\sqrt{2}\,\gamma'^{\frac{2}{3}}$$

If $\varkappa' \to \infty$, then

$$\alpha' \to \frac{\sqrt{2}}{6} k'^2 \simeq \frac{\sqrt{2}}{6} \gamma'^{-\frac{2}{3}}$$

The experimental agreement is satisfactory for a wide variety of adsorption films (161).

If there is mass transport between the surface film and the solution, the equation of continuity (21) introduces a modification (162) into the expression for α'. In terms of a transfer coefficient

$$\theta = \frac{dc}{d\Gamma} \sqrt{\frac{D}{2\omega}}$$

there results

$$\alpha' = \tfrac{4}{3} k'^3 \frac{(\sqrt{2}/8)k'^3 \varkappa'^2 + k'[(\sqrt{2}/2)k' - (\theta/4)]\varkappa' + 1 - (\sqrt{2}/2)/k' + 2\theta + 2\theta^2}{k'^4[1 - (2\sqrt{2}/3)k']\varkappa'^2 + k'^2(\sqrt{2} - 2k' - 2\theta k')\varkappa' + 1 + 2\theta + 2\theta^2}$$

$$(48)$$

For constant $\varkappa'$, an increase in the dilational viscosity ζ is accompanied by a decrease in α'. If $\theta \ll 1$, then at the maximum

$$\alpha'_{max} \simeq \frac{\sqrt{2}}{2} k'^2 \left(1 - \frac{\theta}{2}\right)$$

$$\varkappa'_{max} \simeq -\sqrt{2}\, k'^{-2}(1 + \theta)$$

but if $\varkappa' \to \infty$, then

$$\alpha' \to \frac{\sqrt{2}}{6} k'^2$$

If the Szyszkowski-Langmuir equation 30 is valid, θ is proportional to $(1 + c/a)^2$ and $\varkappa'$ is proportional to c/a. At high concentrations the limiting value of α' is $\tfrac{4}{3}k'^3$. If θ is large, the surface behaves like that of a pure liquid.

Ordinarily two maxima may be observed for α' with the ratio of the corresponding concentrations dependent on a. When a is small, the second maximum is in general not observed, for it lies at a concentration higher than the critical micelle concentration. When a is large, the two maxima are practically indistinguishable. They may consequently be observed only for intermediate values of a (order of 10^{-7} mole/cm³). The overall agreement with experiment is satisfactory.

B. The Stability of Emulsions, Bubbles, and Foams

It has long been known that the coalescence of two drops of a liquid immersed in a second, immiscible liquid is influenced by the presence of compounds dissolved in one or the other of the liquid phases. In particular, the presence in one of the liquids of a substance capable of diffusing into the other favors the coalescence of the drops (163). A particularly important factor is the adsorption at the liquid/liquid interface of a monomolecular film. The presence of such a film generally exerts a stabilizing influence in which the mechanical properties of the film play a role. The Marangoni effect, for example, and through it the apparent interfacial dilational viscosity tend to stabilize the drops (164). High rigidity or high surface shear viscosity are also stabilizing influences, without at the same time excluding other contributing factors, for in some cases stabilization is known to take place even when the surface viscosity is low.   It is nevertheless true that a good correlation exists between the lifetime of the drops and the interfacial rheological parameters η and G for such additives as the saponins, gelatin, polymethacrylic acid, and carboxymethylcellulose (30).   In a similar way when mercury drops are dispersed in xylene, it is found that aliphatic compounds such as hexadecylamine, palmitic alcohol, stearic acid, or oleic acid extend the lifetime of the drops in the same sense as the magnitude of the interfacial viscosity (122).

A more general question is that of the relation between the stability of emulsions and the rheological behavior of interfacial films (165, 166).   It was suggested long ago that emulsion stability is improved by the presence of highly condensed, interfacial films (167–169), and particular attention has been paid to the correlation between stabilizing power and the viscosity or rigidity of the films (170–173).   For this reason films which are capable of forming strong intermolecular linkages between the film molecules are frequently good stabilizers (174).   Thus mixtures of fatty acids and amines bound together by ionic bonds between the NH_3^+ and COO^- groups exhibit strong cohesion.   Similar behavior is observed with the condensation products of fatty amines or amides with ethylene oxide.   These materials form intermolecular hydrogen bonds, the amines requiring the intervention of water molecules to form structures such as

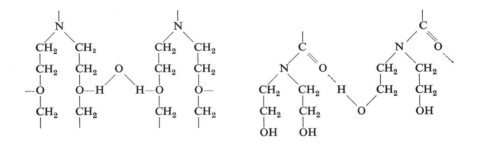

The effect is further enhanced by addition of fatty acids.

The correlation has also been established for protein films (73, 175, 176) or for soaps such as aluminum stearate (177).   It cannot be accepted unequivocally, however, for it is frequently observed that good stabilizing power is obtained with films of low interfacial viscosity (30, 178, 179).

It may also be remarked that interfacial films play a role not only on the stability of emulsions but also upon their macroscopic rheological behavior. It has been shown, for example, that if the film is purely viscous, its presence does not change the viscoelastic character of the emulsion, but the macroscopic viscosity and the relaxation and retardation times are changed (180). If the film is purely elastic, then in steady flow at low shear rates the emulsion behaves like a suspension of solid particles whose viscoelastic behavior can be completely described by two relaxation and two retardation times.

It was suggested long ago that the mechanical properties of adsorbed films ought to play a role in the stability of soap bubbles and of foams (181, 182). The importance of the Marangoni effect and of the phenomena of surface transport have been convincingly demonstrated to be among the factors which determine the lifetime of such liquid lamellae (183, 184).

It is generally recognized that a good foamer is a material that produces at the air/water interface a film which is relatively condensed but which is at the same time fluid and capable of rapid changes in π as the surface area varies (185). These features account for the fact that often the stability of a foam passes through a maximum with the concentration of the foaming agent. Usually the more coherent the adsorbed film, the greater the stability of the foam; and the general trend of the surface viscosity and of the foam lifetime is to increase or decrease together (125). The fine details of this correspondence, however, are not perfect, being good for protein films (186) and rather poor for quaternary ammonium compounds (124). It is also to be remarked that the most stable foams are often obtained with mixtures of foamers, one member of the blend being relatively soluble with a low surface viscosity and constituting a reservoir of surface active substance for the foam, the other member less soluble but with a high surface viscosity, thus assuring the cohesiveness of the mixed film (124).

A somewhat different case is that of solid adsorbed films such as those furnished by the saponins. Their stability is due in great measure to the resistance of the films to bubble deformation, thus preventing collapse as the foam drains (183). On the other hand, if the solid films are fragile, the bubbles break under their own weight, and no stable foam is observed (187). It would seem that a high molecular mobility within the adsorbed film is a prime factor in foam stability (188).

Inasmuch as a foam is stabilized by surface films of certain specified properties, a foam depressant must be able to replace such films by others not having the required characteristics (185). This could be achieved by materials forming solid films (189) or by those whose films are completely fluid, such as the polydimethylsiloxanes (102). Equally effective would be highly insoluble films of low surface activity such as those formed at high temperatures at the air/water interface by the diacylpiperazines or the diethylenetriamines (190).

In a foam, the liquid lamellae are essentially layers of variable thickness of a solution of an amphiphilic substance whose two faces are covered with a monomolecular film whose presence assures the stability of the individual bubbles.   From the start we must recognize the importance of the rate of drainage of excess liquid from the foam (186, 191, 192), which is to say the velocity of fluid flow from the interior of the walls of the bubbles.   For this reason, fluid flow in liquid films has been the subject of a considerable amount of investigation.

Early work ignored the special rheology of monomolecular films.   Drainage rates were assumed to be determined by stationary states in which the bounding surfaces were assumed rigid.   This model leads to a relatively simple result, Frankel's law relating the thickness δ of the lamella to the rate v at which it is drawn from the mother solution:

$$\delta = 1.88 \frac{v^{2/3}\eta_s^{2/3}}{\gamma^{1/6}\rho^{1/2}g^{1/2}}$$

in which η_s is the viscosity of the bulk liquid, γ the surface tension, ρ the fluid density, and g the gravity constant.   This formula has been verified experimentally in a reasonably satisfactory way, as much for solid adsorbed surface films as for fluid ones, except for very small values of v (193, 194). The data indicate that η_s is absolutely constant beyond distances of 100 Å from the surface and is not appreciably anomalous even 10 Å from the bounding surface film (195, 196).   At equilibrium the thickness of the surface film is determined by hydrostatic forces, electrostatic repulsions between the ionic groups, and London attractions between the two opposing monolayers on each side of the lamella (196).

More elaborate calculations have been published in the hope of taking into account the influence of the surface viscosity of the adsorbed films (197).   The flow was assumed to be one dimensional and quasistationary with the surface assigned the properties of a two-dimensional, Newtonian liquid.

For a plane, vertical film of an incompressible, isothermal, Newtonian liquid, let x be the direction of the gravitational field and y be normal to the plane of the film.   Then if u and v are the corresponding components of the velocity vector, the equations of two-dimensional flow under the influence of gravity are

$$\frac{\partial u}{\partial t} + u\frac{\partial u}{\partial x} + v\frac{\partial u}{\partial y} = -\frac{1}{\rho}\left(\frac{\partial p}{\partial x}\right) + g + \nu\left(\frac{\partial^2 u}{\partial x^2} + \frac{\partial^2 u}{\partial y^2}\right)$$

$$\frac{\partial v}{\partial t} + u\frac{\partial v}{\partial x} + v\frac{\partial v}{\partial y} = -\frac{1}{\rho}\left(\frac{\partial p}{\partial y}\right) + \nu\left(\frac{\partial^2 v}{\partial x^2} + \frac{\partial^2 v}{\partial y^2}\right)$$

Here p is the hydrostatic pressure and ρ the density of the liquid with ν its kinematic viscosity.   The equation of continuity is

$$\frac{\partial u}{\partial x} + \frac{\partial v}{\partial y} = 0$$

The inertial terms may be neglected when the Reynolds number Re $\ll$ 1, and if the thickness of the film is negligible with respect to its length, $v \ll u$. Furthermore $\partial p/\partial x \ll \rho g$ so that the equation of motion reduces to

$$\frac{\partial u}{\partial t} = g + \nu\left(\frac{\partial^2 u}{\partial x^2} + \frac{\partial^2 u}{\partial y^2}\right)$$

which may be further simplified by empirically setting $\partial u/\partial t = 0$, whence

$$\nu\left(\frac{\partial^2 u}{\partial x^2} + \frac{\partial^2 u}{\partial y^2}\right) + g = 0$$

We may furthermore reasonably suppose that the surface velocity u_s is much smaller than the value of u at the center of the film where $y = 0$, or in other words that

$$\frac{\partial^2 u}{\partial x^2} \ll \frac{\partial^2 u}{\partial y^2}$$

We thus have for the equation of motion of the film the simple result

$$\nu\frac{\partial^2 u}{\partial y^2} + g = 0$$

If 2δ is the thickness of the film, then the boundary conditions are

$$u = u_s \text{ at } y = \delta \quad \text{and} \quad \frac{\partial u}{\partial y} = 0 \text{ at } y = 0$$

Upon integration, the velocity field is

$$u(x, y, t) = \frac{g}{2\nu}(\delta^2 - y^2) + u_s \tag{49}$$

in which u_s and δ will be functions of the time.   In order to calculate u_s and δ, the mechanical properties of Newtonian adsorption films must be evoked.   Letting m be the density of surface mass and τ_{yx} the shear stress component in the film, the surface motion is governed by the equation

$$m\left(\frac{\partial u_s}{\partial t} + u_s\frac{\partial u_s}{\partial x}\right) = -\tau_{yx} + mg + \frac{\partial \gamma}{\partial x} + (\zeta + \eta)\frac{\partial^2 u_s}{\partial x^2}$$

Assuming m to be sufficiently small that the inertial terms are negligible and that equilibrium is so rapidly established that m is effectively constant, we have

$$\frac{\partial^2 u_s}{\partial x^2} = -\frac{\rho g \, \delta}{\zeta + \eta}$$

whence upon integration and the use of equation 49 together with the boundary conditions

$$u_s = 0 \qquad \text{at} \qquad x = 0$$
$$\tau_{yx} = 0 \qquad \text{for} \qquad x = L$$

L being the total height of the film,

$$u_0 = \frac{\rho g}{\zeta + \eta}\left[x\int_0^L \delta \, dx - \int_0^x ds \int_0^s \delta \, dx \right] \qquad (50)$$

At the surface the equation of continuity is

$$\int_0^\delta \frac{\partial u}{\partial x} \, dy = -\int_0^\delta \frac{\partial v}{\partial y} \, dy = -(v)_{y=\delta} = \frac{d\delta}{dt} + u_s\frac{\partial\delta}{\partial x}$$

so that

$$\frac{\partial\delta}{\partial t} = -u_s\frac{\partial\delta}{\partial x} - \int_0^\delta \frac{\partial u}{\partial x} \, dy = -\frac{\partial}{\partial x}\int_0^\delta u \, dy$$

and from equations 49 and 50

$$\frac{\partial\delta}{\partial t} = -\frac{g}{\nu}\frac{\partial}{\partial x}\int_0^\delta \left\{ \tfrac{1}{2}(\delta^2 - y^2) + \frac{\eta_s}{\zeta + \eta}\left[x\int_0^L \delta \, dx - \int_0^x ds \int_0^s \delta \, dx \right]\right\} dy \qquad (51)$$

Defining

$$D = \frac{\delta}{\delta_L}$$

$$X = \frac{x}{L}$$

$$\alpha = \frac{\delta_L{}^2}{L^2}$$

$$\beta = \frac{\eta_s\delta_L}{\zeta + \eta}$$

$$\theta = \frac{gLt}{\nu}$$

$$U = \frac{u\nu}{gL^2}$$

$$U_s = \frac{u_s\nu}{gL^2}$$

it may be shown from equation 51 that

$$\frac{\partial D}{\partial \theta} = -\alpha \left[D^2 \frac{\partial D}{\partial X} \right]$$

$$- \beta \left[\left(D + X \frac{\partial D}{\partial X} \right) \int_0^1 D \, dX - D \int_0^X D \, dX - \frac{\partial D}{\partial X} \int_0^X dS \int_0^S D \, dX \right]$$

$$U_s = \beta \left[X \int_0^1 D \, dX - \int_0^X dS \int_0^S D \, dX \right]$$

and that

$$U_{y=0} = U_s + \frac{\alpha D^2}{2}$$

If

$$\Delta = \frac{\text{volume of liquid drained at any value of } \theta}{\text{volume of liquid at } \theta = 0}$$

then Δ and D may be calculated as a function of

$$\phi = \theta \beta = \frac{\rho g \, \delta_L L t}{\zeta + \eta}$$

This theory predicts and experiment confirms that the rate of thinning of lamellae depends very little upon the initial conditions. The half-drained lamella ($\Delta = \frac{1}{2}$) is achieved at $\varphi = 1.36$. The drainage half-time is thus

$$t_{1/2} = \frac{1.36(\zeta + \eta)}{\rho g L \delta_L}$$

whence it appears that the dilational viscosity is the dominant factor in determining drainage rates.

Experimental values of $t_{1/2}$ are of the order of 1 min, in reasonable agreement with expectations based upon the known range of dilational viscosities (119).

In a foam, the junction of any three lamellae forms a sort of capillary full of liquid whose normal cross section is a curvilinear, concave triangle. Flow within these capillaries plays an important role in foam drainage (198).

Let e be the thickness of a bubble wall and r_0 the radius of curvature of the wall surrounding one of these capillaries. Then in cylinder coordinates with z the long axis of the capillary the equations of motion simplify to

$$\frac{1}{r} \frac{\partial}{\partial r} \left(r \frac{\partial v_z}{\partial r} \right) + \frac{1}{r^2} \frac{\partial v_z}{\partial \theta^2} = -h_e$$

where

$$h_e = \frac{\rho g_e}{\eta_s} \quad \text{and} \quad g_e = g_z - \frac{1}{\rho}\frac{\partial p_i}{\partial z}$$

with g_z the z component of the acceleration of gravity and the pressure p_i inside the capillary related to the pressure p_0 inside the bubbles by the Laplace and Young equation,

$$p_0 - p_i = \frac{\gamma}{r_0}$$

When the boundary conditions are introduced, we have

$$\frac{\partial^2 v_z}{\partial \theta^2} = -\frac{\eta_s r_0{}^2}{\eta}\frac{\partial v_z}{\partial r}$$

in which η is the surface shear viscosity of the adsorbed monolayer. From these beginnings a complete theory of foam drainage rates can be developed. It is found that the efflux from a foam depends critically upon the dimensionless ratio $\eta_s r_0/\eta$, whence it is apparent that the surface viscosity of the adsorbed film plays a major role in foam stability.

C. Mass Transport at Interfaces

In the absence of an interfacial film, mass transport across the boundary between two immiscible, confluent fluid phases is a diffusion-controlled process depending essentially upon the molecular dimensions of dissolved substances, solvent viscosity, and the importance of convection currents.

A film adsorbed at an interface modifies the rate of mass transport either directly because of its degree of permeability or indirectly because of its effect upon the convection currents. The rheological properties of films thus play a role in mass transport at interfaces.

One of the most thoroughly investigated problems is that of the evaporation of water through a monomolecular layer spread at the air/water interface (199, 200). Experiments indicate that the presence of condensed films slows the evaporation rate very considerably. A specific evaporation resistance coefficient r has been defined by

$$r = \frac{1}{\alpha}\sqrt{\frac{2\pi m}{kT}}$$

in which m is the mass of a water molecule and α is the accommodation coefficient. This latter is the fraction of water molecules in the vapor phase which penetrate the film upon collision.   If E is the activation energy needed for a molecule of water to penetrate the film, either during the evaporation or the condensation step, and energies of the different degrees of freedom of the vapor molecules are described by a Maxwell distribution, it may be shown that

$$r = \pi\left(\frac{m}{2E}\right)^{1/2} \exp\left(\frac{E}{kT}\right)\left[1 + \frac{kT}{2E} - \left(\frac{kT}{2E}\right)^2 + \cdots\right]^{-1}$$

The results of experiments show that for mesomorphic films, r is almost independent of the surface pressure while for solid films, $\log r$ is a linear function of the surface pressure.   For long-chain aliphatic compounds, $\log r$ increases linearly with the number of carbon atoms and is also linear in $1/T$.

A similar study has been carried out for the rate of evaporation of water droplets upon which a cetyl alcohol film has been adsorbed from the vapor phase.   When the surface concentration is near saturation, the rate of evaporation is seriously reduced (201).

It would be incorrect to say that the effectiveness of a film as a retarder of evaporation is a result of its surface viscosity.   It is rather that the close correlation between r and η comes from the fact that both depend upon the cohesiveness of the film.   Thus for a molecule of water to pass through a film of aliphatic molecules, a hole approximately the size of the half-cross section of one of the film molecules must be created.   It would thus appear that E is rather close to W, the energy of interaction of a film molecule with its neighbors.   In Section II we noted that W is part of the activation energy for flow.   It follows that the permeability of a monomolecular film is a function of its viscosity in the sense that in first approximation the permeability will be low to the extent that the viscosity is high.

This correlation is also noted in the effect of surface waves upon a film. The oscillatory disturbance increases the surface area (Section III.A) and permits a greater fluidity in the film (202), together with a significant increase in its permeability (203).

Because the molecules in the film are firmly bound to molecules in the substrate (Part I, Section II.B), the mobility of substrate molecules close to the surface is less, the higher the rigidity of the monomolecular film.   The film thus acts to damp convection currents near interfaces, and the effect upon the concentration of dissolved substances (204) and upon temperature gradients (205) near interfaces can be significant.

Material transport from one liquid phase to another can be profoundly influenced by these concentration gradients and by these modifications of the physical condition of liquids in the boundary region.

IV. APPLICATIONS OF SURFACE RHEOLOGY

In Sections I and II we described a wide spectrum of rheological behavior in monomolecular films, and noted for surface viscosity, at least, that the molecular theory has been developed to a reasonable state of precision. Computations have shown that measured values of the surface viscosity are simply related to an activation energy for flow, and that the latter is completely determined by intermolecular interaction in the film, meaning its molecular structure and a sensitivity to variations in the mean intermolecular distance.   From the fact that rather small changes in the activation energy for flow produce large changes in the surface viscosity, it follows that surface viscosity is a sensitive function of molecular structure and interaction. We conclude that surface viscometry is a useful experimental tool in the study of surface films, and we shall review rapidly its principal applications here.

It has been shown that the molecular weights of flexible-chain high polymers cannot be determined from their compression isotherms in the limit of low surface pressure (50, 206, 207), because Guastalla's method is only applicable to rather rigid macromolecules (208).   Such molecular weights can, however, be determined from surface viscometry (98), which is to say that η is a function of the degree of polymerization.   For example, films of polyvinyl acetate display a relation of the form

$$\log \eta = A\sqrt{M} + B$$

in which A is a constant ($A = 1.755 + 10^{-3}$) and B is a function of the surface pressure ($B = 0.1634\pi - 6.255$).   Use of this method permits a determination of the molecular weight of polyvinyl acetate to $\pm 3\%$.

In a different method (100) the intrinsic surface viscosity $[\eta]$ was introduced (see Section II.C.4 in Part I and Section I.B.4 in Part II) with the analog of the Staudinger law

$$[\eta] = KM^{\alpha}$$

Some results are given in Table XXXV.

TABLE XXXV
Staudinger's Constants for Intrinsic Surface Viscosity

Polymer	K	α
Cellulose acetate	1.26×10^{-7}	0.97
Polyvinyl acetate	3×10^{-5}	0.63
Polyacrylic acid	10^{-7}	1.2

A. The Determination of Energies of Activation and of Interaction

The discussion of Section II.B.2.a established a relationship between surface viscosity and the activation energy for flow ΔE in a monomolecular film, each kinetic unit being understood to be a film molecule together with its bound water. The necessary computations have been completed for a fair number of substances, but principally for aliphatic compounds (37, 38, 40, 108, 141). If we refer to Section II.B.2.b, the contribution ΔE_s to the activation energy for flow of the water molecules in the substrate can be calculated directly from the molecular area of the film. It is therefore easy to derive the contribution ΔE_c to the activation energy due exclusively to the film molecules. Representative results are listed in Table XXXVI for films exhibiting Newtonian surface viscosity.

From the formulas of Section II.B.2.c, by extrapolation of the curves $\eta(\dot{\gamma})$ for non-Newtonian films it is possible to determine the limiting value ΔE for the activation energy for flow at zero shear rate and the limiting value $\Delta E'$ at infinite shear rate. Some results of this sort are given in Table XXXVII. The reader should note that those amphiphilic substances which form fluid but non-Newtonian films possess structures susceptible to the formation of intermolecular hydrogen bonds (37, 38, 40, 209).

In Section II.B we showed that to a reasonable approximation it is possible to predict experimental values of the surface viscosity as well as activation energies for flow from the interaction energy of a film molecule with its neighbors (37, 38, 209). Some typical results are collected in Tables XXXVIII and XXXIX.

B. The Determination of Molecular Conformation

If hydrogen bonds are not formed between the amphiphilic molecules in the film, the molecular interactions are essentially electrostatic between charged groups, of the Debye or Keesom type between polar groups, and of the London type between all groups, polar or nonpolar. These forces are uniquely determined by the molecular conformation and the distances between functional groups. If we imagine a fixed molecular conformation with free rotation about an axis perpendicular to the interface and centered in the region of bonding of the molecule to the interface, it becomes possible to calculate the interaction energy W for an assigned molecular area (108, 141). Conversely by the examination of successive molecular models, it is possible to investigate those mean molecular conformations compatible with the experimentally determined values of W determined from the surface viscosity. Such information, however crude, gives an approximate idea of the various molecular shapes assumed when molecules are spread at an interface and the mean molecular area is changed. Fifty such conformations

TABLE XXXVI
Activation Energy for Flow of Newtonian Films of Aliphatic Compounds

Film and substrate	T (°C)	A (Å^2)	$\Delta E \times 10^{13}$ (erg)	$\Delta E_c \times 10^{13}$ (erg)
Myristic acid on 0.01 M HCl	17	22.7	7.23	5.75
		26	7.06	5.36
		31.2	7.07	5.02
		39	7.35	5.13
	22	32.5	7.06	4.96
		39	7.33	5.11
Pentadecylic acid 0.01 M HCl	25	21	8.31	6.96
		21.5	7.93	6.53
Palmitic acid on 0.01 M HCl	17	22	7.35	5.92
		24.5	7.13	5.63
		25.5	7.25	5.58
	25.3	22	7.5	6.07
		24.5	7.38	5.78
		27.3	7.25	5.48
		29	7.7	5.77
Stearic acid on 0.01 M HCl	20	20.1	7.7	6.42
		20.5	7.61	6.29
		21	7.55	6.2
		22	7.37	5.94
Stearic acid on 0.001 M HCl	18	20.1	7.89	6.61
		20.5	7.90	6.58
		21	7.72	6.37
		22	7.47	6.04
		22.5	7.42	5.97
		23.5	7.31	5.79
Oleic acid on 0.01 M HCl	17	34.9	6.73	4.58
		36	6.87	4.7
		39	7.2	4.98
Ethyl 11-oxystearate on water	20	109	7.13	2.91
Eicosanoic acid on 0.01 M HCl	20.5	80.5	7.32	4.44
Tricaproin on water	20	83	6.86	3.88
		89.5	6.97	3.7
Tricaprylin on water	20	83	7.31	4.33
		89.5	7.39	4.12
Tricaprin on water	19.5	83	7.42	4.44
		89.5	7.44	4.17
Trilaurin on water	16.25	83	7.58	4.6
		89.5	7.62	4.35
	22	89.5	7.48	4.21
Triolein on water	20	103.5	7.28	3.3
Triricinolein on water	20	103.5	6.54	2.56

TABLE XXXVII

Activation Energy for Flow of Non-Newtonian Films of Aliphatic Compounds

Film and substrate	T (°C)	A (Å²)	$E \times 10^{13}$ (erg)	$E' \times 10^{13}$ (erg)
Lauryl alcohol on water	20	37	8.44	7.79
Myristyl alcohol on water	20	20	8.62	7.375
		20.5	8.17	7.175
		22	8.15	7.125
		23.5	8.18	7.42
Cetyl alcohol on water	24.8	19.25	10.37	9.67
	20	19.5	9.06	7.65
		20	8.85	7.08
		20.5	8.73	7.07
		21.5	8.45	7.405
Stearyl alcohol on water	20	19.5	9.16	7.71
		20	8.955	7.655
		20.5	8.8	7.12
	25	19.75	9.895	8.685
Eicosyl alcohol on water	25.1	19.45	9.255	8.305
Stearylamide on water	20	21.5	10.03	8.025
		23.5	9.5	7.555
		24.5	9.33	7.475
Alkoxyethanol $C_{14}OC_2H_4OH$ on water	25	18.35	10.445	9.64
Alkoxyethanol $C_{16}OC_2H_4OH$ on water	25.1	19.9	10.32	9.53
Alkoxyethanol $C_{18}OC_2H_4OH$ on water	24.9	19.65	9.615	8.665
Alkoxyethanol $C_{20}OC_2H_4OH$ on water	25.1	18.65	10.27	9.115

for aliphatic compounds (108, 141, 210) have been determined by this technique of successive approximations. These structures correspond to discrete states of molecular stability postulated to explain the general properties of monomolecular films, the course of their compression isotherms, and the nature of the different order transitions (142, 143, 211). The results may be summarized by stating that the conformations are such that for each molecular area examined, the number of contacts between methylene groups along the chains is maximized.

C. Transitions in Monomolecular Films

The existence in monomolecular films of numerous transitions of first or higher order is well known, such transitions being a function of the surface pressure and of the temperature (6, 27, 142, 143). These transitions are the

TABLE XXXVIII
Molecular Interaction Energy of Aliphatic Compounds Whose Surface Viscosity
is Newtonian

Film and substrate	T (°C)	A (Å²)	$W \times 10^{13}$ (erg)
Myristic acid on 0.01 M HCl	17	22.7	5
		26	4.67
		31.2	4.36
		39	4.46
	23	32.5	4.32
		39	4.45
Pentadecylic acid on 0.01 M HCl	25	21	6.06
		21.5	5.68
Palmitic acid on 0.01 M HCl	17	22	5.15
		24.5	4.9
		25.5	4.85
	25.3	22	5.27
		24.5	5.03
		27.3	4.76
		29	5.02
Stearic acid on 0.01 M HCl	20	20.1	5.58
		20.5	5.47
		21	5.39
		22	5.17
Stearic acid on 0.001 M HCl	18	20.1	5.75
		20.5	5.72
		21	5.54
		22	5.25
		22.5	5.19
Oleic acid on 0.01 M HCl	17	34.9	3.98
		36	4.09
		39	4.33
Tricaproin on water	20	83	3.38
		89.5	3.22
Tricaprylin on water	20	83	3.77
		89.5	3.58
Tricaprin on water	19.5	83	3.86
		89.5	3.62
Trilaurin on water	16.25	83	4
		89.5	3.78
	22	89.5	3.66
Triolein on water	20	103.5	2.87
Triricinolein on water	20	103.5	2.23

TABLE XXXIX

Molecular Interaction Energy of Aliphatic Compounds Whose Surface
Viscosity is Non-Newtonian

Film and substrate	T (°C)	A (Å^2)	$W \times 10^{13}$ (erg)
Lauryl alcohol on water	17	30	9.78
Myristyl alcohol on water	20	19	9.95
		19.5	9.75
		20.5	9.81
Cetyl alcohol on water	20	18.2	13.11
		18.5	10.03
		19.5	9.88
Stearyl alcohol on water	20	18.5	13.17
		19.5	10.32
		20	10.23
		20.5	10.16
Stearylamide on water	19	18.5	13.62
		20.5	10.44
		21.5	10.3

result of changes in molecular conformation (143). Because the surface viscosity changes practically exponentially with the intermolecular interaction energy, and, as has been discussed above, these interactions depend uniquely upon the molecular structure and intermolecular distance, we may anticipate that transitions in monomolecular films are accompanied by large changes in the surface viscosity.

This expectation is realized in practice. We conclude that measurements of the surface viscosity furnish a sensitive method of detecting transitions in monolayers (6, 32, 108), even if such transitions have only a weak influence upon the compression isotherm $\pi = f(A)$. The method has been much used in the study of higher-order transitions in numerous aliphatic compounds (32, 108). Specifically it has been used with good precision to determine the transition temperature from the plastic to the nonplastic state of the adsorption films of the long-chain sodium soaps (C_{12}–C_{18}) as a function of pH (212). Even-numbered aliphatic alcohols (C_{16}–C_{22}) have been studied at temperatures between 15 and 30°C and at shear rates between 0.12 and 1.8 sec^{-1}; and surface viscometry shows an exact agreement for the transition surface pressures revealed by the isotherms $\pi = f(A)$ (213).

It has been observed that foam bubbles may be classified into two types according to whether their drainage rate is fast or slow (214). For a given foaming solution at constant composition, one type may be converted into the other simply by changing the temperature (215). It is furthermore recognized that slow drainage is associated with adsorption films of high viscosity, and that the transition temperature at which a slow drainer is converted into a fast drainer coincides with a dramatic fall in the surface viscosity (124, 216).   It follows that the study of η as a function of T permits the determination of transition temperatures in drainage rates.   The method has been applied to the study of the influence of lauric and cetyl alcohols on the drainage transition temperatures of foamed solutions of polyoxy-ethylenelauryl alcohols containing from 12 to 23 ethylene oxide residues (217).

A special type of transition detected with ease by surface viscometry is a transition induced by the flow itself (145, 218).   This occurs in films of cetyl alcohol and stearyl amide in which the intermolecular interaction energy is high.

Finally, as has been mentioned in Section I.B.4.c, the α–β transition can be observed in monomolecular films of polypeptides.   Thus with films of poly-γ-methyl-L-glutamate, this transition in the presence of 0.02 M formic acid causes a pronounced fall in the surface viscosity at constant molecular area (71).

D. The Study of Molecular Interaction

Because the surface viscosity is directly related to the energy of interaction between the molecules in a film, every alteration of this energy by the intrusion of foreign molecules into the film is bound to have an effect upon the surface viscosity.   We conclude that surface rheology is a sensitive technique for the study of intermolecular interaction.

As an example, the study of wave damping by surface films together with measurements of the Gibbs elasticity have been applied to a study of the departure of adsorption films from ideality (219).   Any departure from ideality has an influence upon gradients in γ created by the wave motion, and hence also upon E_G.   At a given bulk concentration c, departures from ideality are revealed by values of π and of Γ in excess of those predicted for ideal solutions.   It follows that $\varkappa$, which is proportional to the gradient of γ, is larger and less sensitive to diffusive exchanges of matter between the film and the substrate.   For nonideal solutions we therefore anticipate that a plot of the damping coefficient against c will show a sharp maximum, that damping by highly soluble films is more efficient than for insoluble ones (see Section III.A), and that E_G will be higher in the nonideal than in the ideal case (see Section II.A.1).   For these reasons, the relative position and breadth of the maximum in a plot of the damping coefficient α against c is a more sensitive index of molecular interaction in surfaces than is the measurement of γ.

1. Interaction between Film and Substrate

Two types of film–substrate interaction have been investigated: interactions between film molecules and substrate ions, and between film molecules and uncharged species in the substrate. The interest in the latter case arises because of its application to tanning operations.

Many experiments have been performed testing the effect of ions upon the surface viscosity of monomolecular and adsorption films. Thus solutions of sodium laurate at high pH show no appreciable increase in surface viscosity upon addition of sodium salts to the substrate, even at salt concentrations as high as 0.05 M (220). A contrasting behavior is that of films of octadecyltrimethylammonium bromide (44), as shown in Table XL.

The interaction between Ca^{2+} ions and fatty acid films has been much investigated. Consider a film of stearic acid at $A = 30$ Å^2 and temperatures from 5 to 30°C spread upon a substrate of pH 5.2. If a concentration 5 × 10^{-4} M of calcium ions is injected into the substrate, the surface viscosity grows until the free energy of activation for flow in the film is close to 11 kcal/mole. The apparent kinetic order of the adsorption reaction is $\frac{2}{3}$ at 21°C, and this order depends upon the molecular area. If $A = 30$ Å^2, the order stays at 0.66, but reduction of the area to $A = 28$ Å^2 increases the order to a maximum of 0.8, after which it falls again almost to zero as A approaches 24 Å^2. When the pH is less than 5, stearic acid molecules are no longer ionized, and there is no interaction with calcium ions (221).

The effect of calcium ions on α-substituted fatty acids has also been studied (222). An ethyl group in the α position of lauric, myristic, and palmitic acids hinders the solidification of the film by calcium ions in a substrate of pH 7.5. Even a methyl group offers sufficient steric hindrance to interfere with the solidification, but with carbon chains longer than C_{16}, normal solidification takes place.

When straight-chain acids solidify, the mechanism does not appear to be the formation of a di-soap but rather the creation of a polymeric network, for double-chain molecules such as the phospholipids yield only fluid films

TABLE XL
Effect of Salts on Surface Viscosity of Octadecyltrimethylammonium bromide

A (Å^2)	Salt	Salt concentration (mole/l)	η
85	NaCl	0.1–2	increases
85	NaI	>3 × 10^{-2}	increases
85	NaF	>0.5	increases
170	NaCl	>10^{-2}	decreases

(35).   The same phenomenon is observed with oleic and elaidic acids, whose molecular areas are too large to permit the formation of a polymeric network in the presence of calcium ions.

Most studies of soap formation in the presence of salts have been performed with stearic acid.   The increasing viscosity of the film can be used to follow the course of soap formation (223).   With some cations, soap formation is accompanied by the appearance of elasticity in the film.   These mechanical properties are evidently a function of the cation used, but they also depend upon the temperature and upon the pH of the solution (224).   Some representative results are given in Table XLI.

The high rigidity induced by Co^{2+} ions in alkaline solution is attributed to the interaction of the stearate ions in the film with complex cobalt ions in the solution (225), said interaction leading to the formation of a two-dimensional network.   According to the rheological properties of the films formed, metallic ions have been classified into three groups (226): Li^+, Ca^{2+}, Sr^{2+}, and Ba^{2+} convert stearic acid films into Voigt bodies; Th^{2+}, Fe^{3+}, Al^{3+}, Co^{2+}, and Zn^{2+} convert them into Maxwell bodies; but Na^+, K^+, Rb^+, and NH_4^+ do not form solid films with fatty acids.

Surface viscometry has also been applied to the study of polypeptides. Poly-1-benzyl-L-histidine spread on water, for example, shows an expansion of the film accompanied by an increase in the surface viscosity when the substrate is made 0.01 M in potassium sulfate.   The same effect is noted with potassium chloride and sodium acetate at pH 5.6.   If cupric sulfate is introduced into the substrate to the extent 0.01 M at 16°C, a further expansion of the film occurs, together with a considerable increase in the surface viscosity (227).   This effect is attributed to the formation of complexes between the hystidyl residues and the cupric ions, leading to the formation of an interlocked network.   If the percentage of histidyl residues is low as in the copolymer 2:2:2:1 (glycine, O-benzyl-DL-serine, β-benzyl-L-aspartate, 1-benzyl-L-histidine), the effect is absent.

The interaction of polybenzylhistidine with Cu^{2+} occurs over a rather wide pH range (4.8–6.7) with the maximum effect between pH 5.1 and 6.2.

TABLE XLI
Effect of Salts on Stearic Acid Films

Salt	pH at which solidification is complete
$CuCl_2$	5.5
$FeCl_3$	2.7
$AlCl_3$	3.4–4.2
$Al_2(SO_4)_3$	3.4–4.2

Calcium ions, however, have very little effect upon this polypeptide (228). In order of decreasing activity the ions fall into the sequence Cu^{2+}, Zn^{2+}, Co^{2+}, and Ca^{2+}. The network formed by cobalt ion is less viscous than that formed by zinc ions, whose interaction is maximal between pH 5.1 and 6.2. For Co^{2+} this maximum is in the pH range 5.6–6.2. The weak action of Ca^{2+} appears between pH 5.6 and 6.7.

Surface rheology may also be usefully employed in the study of the interaction of films with substances other than metallic ions. Thus the transition from neutral to acid soap brought about by CO_2 may be detected by the appearance of plasticity in the surface films (212).

The presence of saccharose in substrates supporting films of proteins and polypeptides has an effect upon their rheological properties (94). Sucrose in the substrate causes an expansion of the film together with an increase in its surface viscosity for pepsin, insulin, trypsin, lysozyme, serum albumin, and polyalanine, all spread on water at pH 6.0. Sucrose, however, is without effect upon films of polyvinyl acetate or stearate. It has been suggested that the mechanism of the sucrose action is to modify the hydrogen bonds between the ceto-imide groups of neighboring chains. Apparently the sucrose molecules are solvated by so many water molecules that not enough of the latter are available to form hydrogen bonds between the CO and NH groups, thus liberating them to hydrogen bond with each other.

Surface rheology offers particular advantages for the study of tanning. It appears that tanning is accompanied by the formation of an extremely viscous film, as may be confirmed by the injection of tannic acid into the substrate beneath a fluid protein film (229). The large increase in surface viscosity apparently corresponds to the formation of linkages between the protein chains (230). Depending upon the tanning agent used, the mechanism of this network formation varies (231). Thus catechol causes the film to condense, suggesting multiple points of association between the tannin and the protein chains and leading to a compact structure. By contrast, chromium sulfate induces a slight expansion in the film caused by electrovalent links formed between the chromium cations and the negative carboxylate groups, leading to a rather open network. This hypothesis is supported by the fact that chrome alum causes an expansion and solidification of a film of myristic acid in the same way that it induces tanning in a film of collagen, while at the same time not tanning a film of gliadin containing few carboxylate groups (232).

The viscosity of collagen films is increased more than a thousandfold by the addition of mimosa tannin to a substrate of pH 3, but it increases only fourfold when the pH exceeds 6. Methoxymethyl nylon shows the same behavior as collagen when spread on tannic acid solution at pH 6, but its interaction with mimosa tannin at this pH is weaker (233). This same effect upon substituted nylon shows that ionic groups are not necessary for reaction with vegetable tannins.   On the other hand, collagen with about three times the number of ceto-imide groups per unit length of chain as are possessed by methoxymethyl nylon reacts about three times as fast in the isoelectric region.   Similar results are obtained when a resorcinol–formaldehyde mixture is used as the tanning agent, thus confirming the nonionic character of the tanning mechanism.   Films of collagen may also be tanned by phenolic compounds not usually considered to be tanning agents, provided that hydrogen peroxide is present and traces of peroxidases (234).

With gelatin, rheological measurements have been carried out under conditions where the gelatin film is without viscoelasticity ($\pi = 5$ dyne/cm, $T = 18°C$) in the absence of a tanning agent.   Very low concentrations of vegetable tannin suffice to produce a significant viscoelasticity (96).   On the other hand, neither chrome nor potassium alums nor copper sulfate solutions will produce any marked viscoelasticity until after rather large additions of the tanning agent.   Spread on chromium hydroxysulfate solutions, the films are highly elastic.   These films can be described by a rheological model containing four parameters.   Their elasticity appears between pH 3.5 and pH 6, rising to a sharp maximum at pH 5.5.   Analogous results are obtained with methylated gelatin.   Although the elasticity is not as large, the maximum occurs at pH 5.3.

Silicic acid is another tanning agent which has been studied through surface viscometry.   It reacts with insulin, albumin, and nylon over a wide pH range, but the films are tanned only in the neighborhood of pH 6.   Other than the formation of ionic bonds and hydrogen bonds with the molecules in the film, it appears that tanning also involves the formation of polymeric silicic acids (235).   Between pH 5.4 and 6.1 insulin at low surface pressures spread on 0.005 M silicic acid solution is indifferent to the presence of the acid, but as soon as π achieves 6 dyne/cm, the film becomes rigid.   Near the isoelectric points of insulin and albumin, histidine and lysine are capable of forming salt bridges with silicic acid.   Nylon-4 and nylon-1.5 do not interact with silicic acid, for too few functional sites are available; but nylon-6.6/6.10/6 interacts between pH 2 and 9 and is tanned between pH 4.5 and 6 owing to the formation of hydrogen bonds.   It follows that in the tanning of films of insulin and of albumin, hydrogen bonds are formed between the ceto-imine groups on the proteins and the hydroxyl groups of the silicic acid.   For collagen and gelatin, tanning by silicic acid occurs between pH 3 and 8, probably by the formation of networks between the protein chains rather than by the polymerization of the silicic acid as happens with the globular proteins (236).   Silicic acid reacts with films of pepsin between pH 3.5 and 7, but tanning does not occur.   It will, however, tan laminarin at pH 5.8.   Laminarin is a linear polysaccharide containing 20

β-D-glucopyranose groups; and the tanned film, even at low surface pressures, is solid and unyielding.   No tanning occurs with films of cellulose acetate (237).   We conclude, therefore, that there are two types of tanning with silicic acid: network formation between the protein or glucosidic chains or the polymerization of the silicic acid itself.   Only certain conformations of the film molecules make the first type possible (238).

2. Mixed Films and Penetrated Films

Another phenomenon that may be studied through surface rheology is the influence of impurities upon the films, particularly the effect of more or less complete elimination of the spreading solvent.   Such impurities can have a profound effect upon the rheological properties of the films, particularly protein films (95).   Ovalbumin, for example, spread at pH 4.5 yields the same compression isotherm whatever the spreading solvent, but the rheological behavior is very different depending upon the use as a spreading solvent of n-propyl, isopropyl, n-amyl, isoamyl, alcohols, acetone, or pyridine. Furthermore, if spread without the use of a spreading solvent, ovalbumin films display an instantaneous elasticity, while with the use of a spreading solvent the elasticity is delayed.   It also appears that the critical molecular area for the appearance of the delayed elasticity decreases with rising concentration of spreading solvent.   We therefore conclude that surface rheology is a highly sensitive method for the study of the action of plasticizers and other impurities in monomolecular films.

Another area of great usefulness for surface rheology lies in the study of mixed films, those composed of a mixture of constituents at least one of which is amphiphilic, whether soluble or insoluble.

A well-known example is solutions of sodium lauryl sulfate mixed with lauryl alcohol (124, 239).   At a fixed concentration of sodium lauryl sulfate, the surface viscosity increases with the concentration of lauryl alcohol.   At a fixed concentration of lauryl alcohol, the surface viscosity drops abruptly when the critical micelle concentration of the sulfate has been exceeded, for above this concentration the lauryl alcohol solubilizes in the lauryl sulfate micelles (216).   Analogous results are observed in mixtures of sodium stearyl sulfate with lauryl alcohol.   For mixtures of all three constitutents: sodium lauryl sulfate plus sodium stearyl sulfate plus lauryl alcohol, the adsorption film displays a high mechanical resistance.   Identical behavior is observed when lauryl alcohol is added to sodium laurate at high pH, for there is a pronounced increase in the surface viscosity (220).

Insoluble mixed films possess surface viscosities which are far more sensitive to interaction between the film constituents than are either the molecular area or the surface potential.   Binary mixtures of stearic acid with octadecanol or with arachidic acid show log η plots which are linear in π, as is also the case for the pure constituents alone (33).   The surface viscosity of the mixture lies between the surface viscosities of the constituents, increasing with the mole fraction of the more viscous component.   Mixtures of stearic acid with stearyl alcohol are Newtonian only over a region of surface pressure which narrows as the proportion of alcohol increases.

The free energy of activation for flow in a binary mixture may be written

$$\Delta F = x \, \Delta F_1' + (1 - x) \, \Delta F_2'$$

in which x and $1 - x$ are the mole fractions and $\Delta F_1'$, $\Delta F_2'$ the partial molar free energies of activation for flow of the pure constituents.   If the mixture is ideal, meaning without interaction, and if the molecular areas of the components are close ($A_1 \simeq A_2$), Eyring's formula (Section II.B.2.a) for the surface viscosity leads to

$$\log \eta = x \log \eta_1 + (1 - x) \log \eta_2$$

where η_1 and η_2 are the surface viscosities of the components.   In the non-ideal case where there is interaction but where $A_1 \simeq A_2$, the variation in the surface viscosity as a function of composition may be represented empirically by

$$\log \eta = x \log \eta_1 + (1 - x) \log \eta_2 + x(1 - x)\mathscr{T}(x)$$

Experimental values of $\mathscr{T}(x)$ are a measure of the importance of interaction between the film components.

In mixtures of stearic with arachidic acid the departure from linearity appears only above $\pi = 5$ dyne/cm.   In mixtures of stearic acid with stearyl alcohol, the surface viscosity decreases slightly from that for stearic acid alone when the mole fraction of alcohol is less than 0.2; but with further additions, the viscosity increases rapidly (33).

Mixtures of fatty acids with triglycerides have been studied by surface viscometry (240).   When myristic acid is mixed with trimyristin in a film spread on 0.01 M HCl at 21°C, the rheological behavior is completely different depending upon whether or not there is more or less than one molecule of trimyristin for every ten of mytistic acid.   From a consideration of their molecular areas, this ratio corresponds to that required to surround each trimyristin molecule completely by myristic acid molecules, so that the flow at mole fractions of trimyristin less than 0.1 takes place in an environment of practically pure myristic acid, indistinguishable from that of the pure material.   This example demonstrates that changes in rheological properties in mixed films are not necessarily due to the formation of complexes but simply to the relative change in their spacial distributions.

Mixed films of lecithin with cholesterol (241) show continuous changes in physical properties except at two compositions: three molecules of lecithin to one of cholesterol or the reverse molecular ratio. Despite this fact, the surface viscosity does not change much from those of the pure constituents, which are in any case very close. We therefore conclude that there is no strong interaction between these two molecules. The observed discontinuity in the physical properties is due simply to a rearrangement in their relative geometric configurations.

The type of equation displayed above to express the surface viscosity of a mixed, insoluble film can be extended to mixed adsorbed films by interpreting x in terms of the thermodynamic parameters of each constituent and from their adsorption isotherms (241). The final equations are not simple, but they can be used numerically in an attempt to estimate the importance of the intermolecular interactions. Studies of this sort have shown that there is no particular interaction between the molecules of the two saponins, senegin and digitonin.

Surface viscometry can also be applied to the study of penetrated films, meaning mixed films in which one component is insoluble and the other soluble in the substrate into which it is ordinarily injected. Despite this fact, rather little research has been published upon this subject; but some complexes obtained by the penetration method (243, 244) have been studied in this way (108). Sample results are shown in Table XLII, all obtained by the oscillation method under a constant pressure of 14 dyne/cm at 20°C.

The data suggest that the surface viscosities of the 1:1 complexes are higher than those of the 1:2 and the 1:3, but there is not enough evidence to generalize safely.

For mixtures of cholesterol with digitonin, experiments have been carried out via the rotation method (242). Some results are given in Table XLIII.

TABLE XLII

Surface Viscosity of Complexes Obtained by the Penetration
Method ($\pi = 14$ dyne/cm; $T = 20°C$)

Film	$\eta \times 10^3$ (g/sec)
Cholesterol	1.1
1 cholesterol + 1 colchicine	2.2
1 cholesterol + 2 colchicine	1.6
1 cholesterol + 1 sodium cetyl sulfate	2.5
1 cholesterol + 3 sodium cetyl sulfate	1.5
1 cholesterol + 1 digitonin	1.2
1 cholesterol + 3 digitonin	7
Lecithin	1.4
1 lecithin + 1 sodium taurocholate	1.9
1 lecithin + 1 sodium glycocholate	1

TABLE XLIII

Surface Viscosity for Mixtures of Cholesterol With Digitonin

Surface concentration of cholesterol $\times 10^{11}$ (mole/cm^2)	Volume concentration of digitonin $\times 10^7$ (g/cm^3)	$\eta \times 10^3$ (g/sec)
8.3–33	0	2.4
0	1–40	3.3
8.3–33	1–40	3.5–300

These results indicate a strong interaction between molecules of cholesterol and digitonin (a very pure sample of molecular weight 1,230).

E. The Study of the Deformability and of the Internal Cohesion of Macromolecules

In Section II.B.2.b it was shown how the contribution of the liquid sub-phase to the activation energy for flow of a surface phase could be calculated directly from the area of the kinetic units, and how as a result experimental values of the surface viscosity could be used to calculate activation energies ΔE_c for flow characteristic of the amphiphilic film molecules themselves. The formulas for ΔE_s show that this term increases rather rapidly with molecular area A for films composed of rigid molecules in condensed films. Most macromolecules in condensed states have molecular areas which are proportional to the degree of polymerization, and it follows that extremely high values of the surface viscosity are to be expected.   This expectation is, however, frequently not fulfilled, even for molecules of very high molecular weight.   It is found, furthermore, for almost all monomolecular films of high polymers whose surface viscosities have been published that values of ΔE computed under the supposition that each molecule is a single kinetic unit are smaller the ΔE_s values for the same molecular areas.

It is thus certain that the totality of water molecules firmly bound to an arbitrary film molecule do not move as a unit, and hence that macromolecules deform during flow.   Because by definition a kinetic unit is undeformable, we must conclude that a single macromolecule with its associated bound water cannot comprise only one kinetic unit.

Certain evidence that shear forces responsible for flow also deform a macro-molecule in a film lies thus in a calculated value of ΔE from measured values of the surface viscosity.   If ΔE is less than ΔE_s predicted for a kinetic unit consisting of a rigid macromolecule together with its bound water having the same composition and degree of molecular entanglement as the film molecule,

TABLE XLIV

Deformability of Several High Polymers Spread as Monomolecular Films

Film and substrate	T (°C)	A (Å²)	A_r (Å²)	η (g/sec)	$\Delta E_D \times 10^{13}$ (erg)	η_i (g/sec)	$W_D \times 10^{13}$ (erg)
Nylon-6 on water	20	1,050	7	7×10^5	15.13	1.8×10^5	13.15
		1,800	12	1.3×10^4	13.46	1745	11.65
		3,750	25	7.8×10^3	12.75	132	11.11
Polyvinyl stearate on 0.01 M HCl	25	6,620	27.5	2.75×10^{-2}	7.73	3.5×10^{-4}	6.73
		11,300	50	1.25×10^{-3}	6.21	5×10^{-6}	5.4
Polyvinyl acetate on 0.01 M HCl	25	5,610	12	1.85×10^{-3}	7.28	2.7×10^{-4}	6.33
		6,550	14	5.32×10^{-4}	6.71	5.96×10^{-5}	5.84
		7,480	16	1.62×10^{-4}	6.13	1.25×10^{-5}	5.33
		30,500	12	5.2×10^{-3}	7.71	7.45×10^{-4}	6.71
		35,500	14	1.49×10^{-3}	7.12	1.6×10^{-4}	6.19
		40,600	16	3.4×10^{-4}	6.43	2.6×10^{-5}	5.58
Polyvinyl alcohol on water	25	15,600	10	5.5×10^{-3}	7.72	9.36×10^{-4}	6.7
		21,900	14	8×10^{-3}	6.88	9×10^{-5}	5.98
		25,100	10	1.22×10^{-2}	8.07	2.25×10^{-3}	7.02
		35,100	14	1.25×10^{-3}	7.04	1.245×10^{-4}	6.12
Polymethyl acrylate on water	35	17,000	17	6.5×10^{-3}	7.9	4.7×10^{-4}	6.85
		23,000	23	4.3×10^{-3}	7.44	1.2×10^{-4}	6.47
Polymethyl methacrylate on water	24	20,300	20.3	10	10.46	0.41	9.11
	35	17,000	17	200	12.33	15.5	10.75
		23,000	23	2.2	10.13	6.9×10^{-2}	8.82

TABLE XLV

Deformability of Several Polypeptides Spread as Monomolecular Films

Film and substrate	T (°C)	A (Å²)	A_r (Å²)	η (g/sec)	$\Delta E_D \times 10^{13}$ (erg)	η_i (g/sec)	$W_D \times 10^{13}$ (erg)
Poly-DL-alanine on water	9	6,600	22	0.17	8.2	4.25×10^{-3}	7.13
		7,800	26	4.46×10^{-2}	7.49	5.85×10^{-4}	6.5
		9,000	30	1.48×10^{-2}	6.81	8.8×10^{-5}	5.93
		10,200	34	5.56×10^{-3}	6.32	2.2×10^{-5}	5.49
	24	10,400	14.3	4×10^{3}	13.47	9.23	11.7
Poly-γ-glutamic acid							
on water at pH 1.6	22		26	7.23×10^{-2}	8.08	1.115×10^{-3}	7.03
on water at pH 4.4				5.45×10^{-2}	7.98	8.45×10^{-4}	6.95
on water at pH 4.8				1.89×10^{-2}	7.53	2.86×10^{-4}	6.56
Poly-γ-methyl-L-glutamate							
on water	10		11	0.065	8.24	8.89×10^{-3}	7.17
			15	0.042	7.94	3.13×10^{-3}	6.9
on 0.02 M formic acid			11	0.225	8.78	3.62×10^{-2}	7.62
			15	2.5×10^{-3}	6.86	1.97×10^{-4}	5.96

Substance	Temp	Mol. wt.					
Poly-γ-benzyl-L-glutamate on water	10		23	0.266	8.36	5.74×10^{-3}	7.7
			28	0.021	7.01	1.49×10^{-4}	6.1
Poly-γ-benzyl-DL-glutamate on water	10		23	0.125	8.08	2.81×10^{-3}	7.02
			28	0.021	7.01	1.49×10^{-4}	6.1
Poly-DL-α-amino caproic acid on water	25	10,000	14	0.15	9.02	0.016	7.84
Poly-DL-α-amino-caprylic acid on water	25	9,000	18	0.18	8.94	1.04×10^{-2}	7.78
		10,000	20	7.75×10^{-2}	8.53	3.3×10^{-3}	7.43
Poly-DL-α-amino capric acid on water	25	15,500	22	0.33	9.02	1.02×10^{-2}	7.85
		17,000	24	0.105	8.4	2.1×10^{-3}	7.31
Poly-DL-α-amino lauric acid on water	25	16,800	28	0.245	8.6	2.9×10^{-3}	7.48
		18,000	30	0.09	8.05	7×10^{-4}	7

TABLE XLVI

Deformability of Several Copolypeptides Spread as Monomolecular Films

Film and substrate	T (°C)	A_r (Å^2)	η (g/sec)	$\Delta E_D \times 10^{13}$ (erg)	η_i (g/sec)	$W_D \times 10^{13}$ (erg)
Copoly-glycine-alanine on water	22	10	0.18	9.09	2.64×10^{-2}	7.84
		14	0.065	8.58	6.55×10^{-3}	7.47
Poly-L-propyl-L-leucylglycine on water	6.9	7	0.1345	8.47	2.99×10^{-2}	7.35
		7.65	0.0406	8.02	9.06×10^{-3}	6.96
		8.35	0.0132	7.56	2.48×10^{-3}	6.57
	16.7	6.67	0.142	8.79	3.44×10^{-2}	7.64
		7.55	2.79×10^{-2}	8.14	6.38×10^{-3}	7.08
		8.35	3.03×10^{-3}	7.26	6.3×10^{-4}	6.32
	21.5	6.35	0.1325	8.9	3.38×10^{-2}	7.74
		7	8.79×10^{-2}	8.27	6.7×10^{-3}	7.2
		7.65	6.98×10^{-3}	7.74	1.65×10^{-3}	6.73
	30.4	5.67	0.169	9.26	4.86×10^{-2}	8.05
		6.35	0.028	8.54	7.57×10^{-2}	7.42
		7.35	6.98×10^{-3}	8.01	3.34×10^{-3}	6.97
Copoly 1:1:1 (L-proline, L-leucine, DL-alanine) on water	4.7	7	0.138	8.4	3.14×10^{-2}	7.31

		8	2.68×10^{-2}	7.77	5.22×10^{-3}	6.75
		9	8.15×10^{-3}	7.2	1.09×10^{-3}	6.25
	16.7	7	6.75×10^{-2}	8.51	1.61×10^{-2}	7.4
		8	1.045×10^{-2}	7.78	2.5×10^{-3}	6.77
	20.5	6	0.156	8.94	4.6×10^{-2}	7.78
		7	3.49×10^{-2}	8.35	8.83×10^{-3}	7.26
		8	7.45×10^{-3}	7.74	1.73×10^{-3}	6.73
	29.9	6	9.4×10^{-2}	9.03	2.53×10^{-2}	7.85
		7	1.58×10^{-2}	8.41	5.19×10^{-3}	7.32
		8	1.85×10^{-3}	7.42	4.35×10^{-4}	6.45
Copoly 1:2:1 (L-lysine, L-leucine,	7	14	6.9×10^{-2}	8.12	6.38×10^{-3}	7.07
L-glutamic acid) on water at pH 1.6		15	2.67×10^{-2}	7.7	1.97×10^{-3}	6.7
at pH 5.8		14	4.45×10^{-2}	8.85	4.32×10^{-2}	7.7
		15	4.45×10^{-3}	7.02	3.43×10^{-4}	6.1
at pH 7		21	0.20	8.25	6×10^{-3}	7.17
		26	7.77×10^{-3}	6.72	9×10^{-5}	5.84
	14	21	0.12	8.21	3.3×10^{-3}	7.14
			3.67×10^{-2}	7.55	5.86×10^{-4}	6.56
at pH 8.3	7	19	0.142	8.21	5.78×10^{-3}	7.15
		21	0.01	7.1	3.08×10^{-4}	6.18
at pH 9.2		15	0.312	8.64	2.43×10^{-2}	7.52
		16	7.55×10^{-2}	8.07	4.98×10^{-3}	7.02

TABLE XLVII
Deformability of Several Proteins Spread as Monomolecular Films

Film and substrate	T (°C)	A (Å^2)	A_r (Å^2)	η (g/sec)	$\Delta E_D \times 10^{13}$ (erg)	η_i (g/sec)	$W_D \times 10^{13}$ (erg)
Bovine serum albumin on water at pH 2.2	24	7500	12.7	0.36	9.39	0.104	8.17
		9400	16	8.45×10^{-4}	6.77	6.3×10^{-5}	5.88
at pH 5.7		9400	16	0.36	9.25	2.67×10^{-2}	8.05
		14100	24	2.44×10^{-3}	6.89	5.5×10^{-5}	5.99
at pH 6	25	6100	10.37	37	11.3	1.1	9.82
		10200	17.37	4	10.24	0.258	8.92
		11260	19.15	1	9.62	0.05	8.35
at pH 11.9	24	7500	12.7	0.165	9.07	2.08×10^{-2}	7.89
		9400	16	5.43×10^{-2}	8.48	4.14×10^{-3}	7.38
		14100	24	2.41×10^{-3}	6.88	5.5×10^{-5}	5.98
Horse serum albumin on water at pH 2	7	10000	17	9.7×10^{-3}	7.53	5.9×10^{-4}	6.54
		13200	22.4	1.3×10^{-3}	6.5	3.4×10^{-5}	5.65
Human serum albumin on water at pH 6	25	11200	19.1	4	10.24	0.204	8.87
		12850	21.9	1	9.48	3.03×10^{-2}	8.15
Bovine γ-globulin on water at pH 2.3–11.9	24	17000	12.7	0.275	9.28	0.036	8.08
		21500	16	2.69×10^{-2}	8.15	1.85×10^{-3}	7.1
		32200	24	1.25×10^{-4}	5.7	3×10^{-6}	4.95
Pepsin on water at pH 6	25	5950	18.45	4	10.14	0.18	8.83
		8250	25.6	1	9.27	1.65×10^{-2}	8.05
Insulin on water at pH 6	25	1770	11	3	10.36	0.239	9.03
		2040	12.1	1	9.83	0.134	8.55
Lysozyme on water at pH 10.5	14	2190	17	1.5×10^{-2}	7.63	9.1×10^{-4}	6.63
		2320	18	2.7×10^{-3}	6.88	1.37×10^{-4}	5.98
		2580	20	4×10^{-4}	6.07	1.58×10^{-5}	5.27

then deformation occurs. Surface viscometry thus enables the investigator to characterize the deformability of a macromolecule under the influence of shear stresses (209, 245, 246).

It is interesting to establish a scale of deformability by means of surface viscometry. To achieve this, let us arbitrarily take each monomer or group of monomers (as for copolymers) of the macromolecule occupying an area A_r to be an independent kinetic unit. We define by ΔE_D an apparent energy of activation for deformation. This energy is equal, by definition, to the activation energy for flow (exclusive of the part due to the bound water) in a model system of independent kinetic units of area A_r, and where the model system has the same surface viscosity as that measured for the experimental film. For the same model system we define the apparently internal cohesion energy W_D as that energy of interaction which must exist between the kinetic units of area A_r to make the surface viscosity of the model equal to that observed in the macromolecular film under investigation.

It is then possible to write $\Delta E_D = \Delta E_r - \Delta E_{rs}$ in which ΔE_r is defined by

$$\eta = \frac{h}{A_r} \exp\left(\frac{\Delta E_r}{kT}\right)$$

with η the experimental value of the surface viscosity. $\Delta E_{rs} = \Delta E_s(A_r)$ is the contribution to the activation energy for flow of the water bound to a kinetic unit of area A_r (see Section II.B.2.b). The relation between W_D and ΔE_D is evidently the same as between W and ΔE_c defined for undeformable molecules; that is, $W_D \simeq 0.87\Delta E_D$. It is also noteworthy that an apparent internal viscosity for macromolecules spread in monolayers may be defined by

$$\eta_i = \frac{h}{A_r} \exp\left(\frac{\Delta E_D}{kT}\right)$$

It is important to recognize the arbitrary character of the parameters ΔE_D, W_D, and η_i. Although they allow the classification of macromolecules, they are still "apparent" or "equivalent" quantities, for they are defined in relation to model systems, simpler than those studied experimentally, but possessing the same surface density, the same chemical composition, and the same surface viscosity. Their use is justified only to the extent that it is legitimate in first approximation to compare the deformation of a macromolecule to the flow of a model liquid whose kinetic units are the monomer segments of the macromolecule. The determination of these parameters from experimental values of the surface viscosity has been carried out for several high polymers, notably for synthetic polypeptides and for proteins. Examples are given in Tables XLIV to XLVII.

Acknowledgment

I am greatly indebted to Professor F. C. Goodrich for the careful translation of the entire French manuscript.

Symbols

A	molecular area
A_r	surface area per residue
E_G	Gibbs elasticity
G	surface elastic or shear modulus
S	surface area
U	surface energy per unit area
W	interaction energy
W_D	apparent internal cohesive energy
h	Planck's constant
k	wave number
r	specific evaporation resistance coefficient
v	compression rate
ΔE	energy of activation for flow
ΔE_D	apparent energy of activation for deformation
ΔE_s	part of the activation energy for flow due to bound water molecules
ΔF	free energy of activation for flow
$\Delta S_+^{\ddagger}$	entropy of activation
Γ	surface concentration
α	damping coefficient of surface waves
δ	mean amplitude of random translation
γ	surface or interfacial tension
$\dot{\gamma}$	rate of shear
ζ	surface dilational viscosity
η	surface shear viscosity
$[\eta]$	intrinsic surface viscosity
η_i	apparent internal viscosity
η_0	bulk viscosity of subphase
ν	frequency
ρ	density
θ	relaxation time
$\varkappa$	surface compression modulus
ξ	surface flexibility
π	surface pressure
τ	retardation time
τ_0	period of oscillation

References

1. L. Fourt and W. D. Harkins, *J. Phys. Chem.*, **42,** 897 (1938).
2. G. C. Nutting and W. D. Harkins, *J. Am. Chem. Soc.*, **62,** 3155 (1940).
3. M. Joly, *J. Chim. Phys.*, **44,** 206 (1947).
4. Z. Knor, M. Kalousek, and V. Bohačkova, *Collection Czech. Chem. Commun.*, **24,** 1373 (1959).
5. M. Joly, in *Recent Progress in Surface Science*, Vol. 1, J. F. Danielli, K. G. A. Pankhurst, and A. C. Riddiford, Eds., Academic Press, New York, 1964, p. 1.
6. D. G. Dervichian and M. Joly, *J. Phys. Radium*, **10,** 375 (1939).
7. E. D. Goddard, S. R. Smith, and O. Kao, *J. Colloid Interface Sci.*, **21,** 320 (1966).

8. A. V. Deo, S. B. Kulkarni, M. K. Charpurey, and A. B. Biswas, *Nature*, **191**, 378 (1961).
9. R. N. Shukla, M. K. Charpurey, and A. B. Biswas, *J. Colloid Interface Sci.*, **23**, 1 (1967).
10. G. E. Hibberd and A. E. Alexander, *J. Phys. Chem.*, **66**, 1854 (1962).
11. J. H. Brooks and B. A. Pethica, *Trans. Faraday Soc.*, **61**, 571 (1965).
12. H. E. Ries, N. Beredjick, and J. Gabor, *Nature*, **186**, 883 (1960).
13. J. G. Hawke and A. E. Alexander, *J. Colloid. Sci.*, **11**, 419 (1956).
14. P. M. Jeffers and J. Dean, *J. Phys. Chem.*, **69**, 2368 (1965).
15. H. C. Parreira, *J. Colloid Sci.*, **20**, 742 (1965).
16. J. A. Spink, *J. Colloid Sci.*, **18**, 512 (1963).
17. M. Rosoff and C. Aron, *J. Phys. Chem.*, **69**, 21 (1965).
18. V. L. Schneider, R. T. Holman, and G. O. Burr, *J. Phys. Colloid Chem.*, **53**, 1016 (1949).
19. D. Chapman, N. F. Owens, and D. A. Walker, *Biochim. Biophys. Acta*, **120**, 148 (1966).
20. M. K. Bernett, N. L. Jarvis, and W. A. Zisman, *J. Phys. Chem.*, **68**, 3520 (1964).
21. G. Weitzel, A. M. Fretzdorff, and S. Heller, *Z. Physiol. Chem.*, **290**, 32 (1952).
22. G. Weitzel, A. M. Fretzdorff, and S. Heller, *Z. Physiol. Chem.*, **288**, 189 (1951).
23. G. Weitzel, A. M. Fretzdorff, and S. Heller, *Z. Physiol. Chem.*, **288**, 200 (1951).
24. D. G. Dervichian, *J. Phys. Radium*, **6**, 221 (1935).
25. S. Heller, *Kolloid-Z.*, **136**, 120 (1954).
26. W. Rabinovitch, R. F. Robertson, and S. G. Mason, *Can. J. Chem.*, **38**, 1881 (1960).
27. D. G. Dervichian, *J. Chem. Phys.*, **7**, 931 (1939).
28. E. Stenhagen and S. Stallberg-Stenhagen, *Nature*, **159**, 814 (1947).
29. R. Matuura, *Mem. Fac. Sci. Kyushu Univ. Ser. C*, **1**, 47 (1948–1949).
30. L. E. Nielsen, R. Wall, and G. J. Adams, *J. Colloid Sci.*, **13**, 441 (1958).
31. K. Motomura and R. Matuura, *Bull. Chem. Soc. Japan*, **35**, 289 (1962).
32. G. E. Boyd and W. D. Harkins, *J. Am. Chem. Soc.*, **61**, 1188 (1939).
33. G. E. Boyd and F. Vaslow, *J. Colloid Sci.*, **13**, 275 (1958).
34. N. L. Jarvis, *J. Phys. Chem.*, **69**, 1789 (1965).
35. D. W. Deamer and D. G. Cornwell, *Biochim. Biophys Acta*, **116**, 555 (1966).
36. K. D. Dreher and D. F. Sears, *Trans. Faraday Soc.*, **62**, 741 (1966).
37. M. Joly, *Kolloid-Z.*, **126**, 35 (1952).
38. M. Joly, *J. Colloid Sci.*, **11**, 519 (1956).
39. R. Chaminade, D. G. Dervichian, and M. Joly, *J. Chim. Phys.*, **47**, 883 (1950).
40. S. S. Katti, S. B. Kulkarni, M. K. Charpurey, and A. B. Biswas, *J. Colloid Interface Sci.*, **22**, 207 (1966).
41. A. A. Trapeznikov, *Acta Physicochim. USSR*, **10**, 65 (1939).
42. A. A. Trapeznikov, *Acta Physicochim. USSR*, **19**, 553 (1944).
43. A. A. Trapeznikov, *Acta Physicochim. USSR*, **20**, 589 (1945).
44. J. T. Davies and E K. Rideal, *J. Colloid Sci. Suppl.*, **1**, 1 (1954).
45. N. L. Gershfeld and C. Y. C. Pak, *J. Colloid Interface Sci.*, **23**, 215 (1967).
46. S. Ikeda and T. Isemura, *Bull. Chem. Soc. Japan*, **33**, 753 (1960).
47. R. G. Paguette, E. C. Lingafelter, and H. V. Tartar, *J. Am. Chem. Soc.*, **65**, 686 (1943).
48. J. T. Davies, *Biochim. Biophys. Acta*, **11**, 165 (1953).
49. J. T. Davies, *J. Colloid Sci. Suppl.*, **1**, 9 (1954).
50. H. Hotta, *J. Colloid Sci.*, **9**, 504 (1954).
51. M. Muramatsu and H. Sobotka, *J. Phys. Chem.*, **66**, 1918 (1962).
52. M. Muramatsu and H. Sobotka, *J. Colloid Sci.*, **18**, 625, 636 (1963).
53. K. Motomura and R. Matuura, *J. Colloid Sci.*, **18**, 52 (1963).
54. J. M. Hammond, M. H. Williams, and W. G. P. Robertson, *Nature*, **189**, 549 (1961).

190   RHEOLOGY OF MONOMOLECULAR FILMS. II

55. M. J. Schick, *J. Colloid Sci.*, **17**, 801 (1962).
56. J. Llopis and J. A. Subirana, *J. Colloid Sci.*, **16**, 618 (1961).
57. J. Jaffé, C. Berliner, and M. Lambert, *J. Chim. Phys.*, **64**, 499 (1967).
58. H. Hotta, *Bull. Chem. Soc. Japan*, **28**, 64 (1955).
59. J. Jaffé and C. Berliner, *J. Chim. Phys.*, **63**, 389 (1966).
60. H. Hotta and T. Isemura, *Bull. Chem. Soc. Japan*, **30**, 464 (1957).
61. T. Isemura, H. Hotta, and S. Otsuka, *Bull. Chem. Soc. Japan*, **27**, 93 (1954).
62. H. Hotta, *Bull. Chem. Soc. Japan*, **27**, 412 (1954).
63. J. Jaffé and J. M. Ruysschaert, *J. Polymer Sci.*, [A] **3**, 4047 (1965).
64. S. Ikeda, *Ann. Rept. Sci. Works Fac. Sci. Osaka Univ.*, **10**, 13, 23 (1962).
65. S. Ikeda and T. Isemura, *Bull. Chem. Soc. Japan*, **34**, 416 (1961).
66. T. Isemura and K. Hamaguchi, *Bull. Chem. Soc. Japan*, **26**, 425 (1953).
67. T. Isemura and K. Hamaguchi, *Bull. Chem. Soc. Japan*, **27**, 339 (1954).
68. E. Mishuck and F. R. Eirich, *J. Polymer Sci.*, **16**, 397 (1955).
69. T. Isemura, K. Hamaguchi, and H. Kawasato, *Bull. Chem. Soc. Japan*, **28**, 185 (1955).
70. K. Hamaguchi, *J. Biochem. Japan*, **43**, 83 (1956).
71. T. Isemura and K. Hamaguchi, *Mem. Inst. Sci. Ind. Res. Osaka Univ.*, **9**, 134 (1952).
72. T. Isemura and K. Hamaguchi, *Bull. Chem. Soc. Japan*, **25**, 40 (1952).
73. C. W. N. Cumper and A. E. Alexander, *Trans. Faraday Soc.*, **46**, 235 (1950).
74. K. Imahori, *Bull. Chem. Soc. Japan*, **27**, 146 (1954).
75. M. Kashiwagi, *Bull. Chem. Soc. Japan*, **31**, 176 (1958).
76. N. W. Tschoegl and A. E. Alexander, *J. Colloid Sci.*, **15**, 155 (1960).
77. K. Hamaguchi, *J. Biochem. (Tokyo)*, **42**, 705 (1955).
78. S. Ikeda, *Ann. Rept. Sci. Works Fac. Sci. Osaka Univ.*, **10**, 35 (1962).
79. B. S. Harrap, *J. Colloid Sci.*, **9**, 522 (1954).
80. J. D. Arnold and C. Y. C. Pak, *J. Colloid Sci.*, **17**, 348 (1962).
81. J. Llopis and A. Albert, *Arch. Biochem. Biophys.*, **81**, 146 (1959).
82. J. Llopis and A. Albert, *Arch. Biochem. Biophys.*, **81**, 159 (1959).
83. M. Demeny, S. Kochwas, and H. Sobotka, *J. Colloid Interface Sci.*, **22**, 144 (1966).
84. K. Hamaguchi, *J. Biochem. (Tokyo)*, **43**, 355 (1956).
85. F. Krum, *Kolloid-Z.*, **153**, 47 (1957).
86. K. Wulf and K. Edelmann, *Kolloid-Z.*, **182**, 86 (1962).
87. H. E. Ries, R. A. Ahlbeck, and J. Gabor, *J. Colloid Sci.* **14**, 354 (1959).
88. D. G. Dervichian, *Kolloid-Z.*, **126**, 15 (1952).
89. F. Mac Ritchie, *J. Colloid Sci.*, **18**, 555 (1963).
90. K. Motomura, *J. Phys. Chem.*, **68**, 2826 (1964).
91. K. Motomura and R. Matuura, *J. Colloid Sci.*, **18**, 295 (1963).
92. T. Tachibana and K. Inokuchi, *J. Colloid Sci.*, **8**, 341 (1953).
93. K. Inokuchi, *Bull. Chem. Soc. Japan*, **28**, 453 (1955).
94. F. Mac Ritchie and A. E. Alexander, *J. Colloid Sci.*, **16**, 57 (1961).
95. T. Tachibana, K. Inokuchi, and T. Inokuchi, *Biochim. Biophys. Acta*, **24**, 174 (1957).
96. T. Tachibana, K. Inokuchi, and H. Kakiyama, in *Recent Advances in Gelatin and Glue Research*, G. Stainby, Ed., Pergamon Press, London, 1958, p. 243.
97. N. W. Tschoegl and A. E. Alexander, *J. Colloid Sci.*, **15**, 168 (1960).
98. T. Isemura and K. Fukuzuka, *Mem. Inst. Sci. Ind. Res. Osaka Univ.*, **13**, 137 (1956).
99. T. Yamashita, *Bull. Chem. Soc. Japan*, **38**, 430 (1965).
100. J. Jaffé and J. M. Loutz, *J. Polymer Sci.*, **29**, 381 (1958).
101. T. Isemura and K. Fukuzuka, *Mem. Inst. Sci. Ind. Res. Osaka Univ.*, **14**, 169 (1957).
102. N. L. Jarvis, *J. Phys. Chem.*, **70**, 3027 (1966).
103. T. Yamashita and T. Isemura, *Bull. Chem. Soc. Japan*, **38**, 426 (1965).
104. S. Ikeda and T. Isemura, *Bull. Chem. Soc. Japan*, **32**, 659 (1959).
105. T. Yamashita and T. Isemura, *Bull. Chem. Soc. Japan*, **38**, 420 (1965).
106. T. Isemura and K. Hamaguchi, *Bull. Chem. Soc. Japan*, **27**, 125 (1954).

107. K. Hamaguchi and T. Isemura, *Bull. Chem. Soc. Japan*, **28**, 9 (1955).
108. M. Joly, *J. Chim. Phys.*, **44**, 213 (1947).
109. M. Joly, *Biochim. Biophys. Acta*, **2**, 624 (1948).
110. J. Pouradier, *J. Chim. Phys.*, **46**, 627 (1949).
111. J. Llopis and A. Albert, *Ann. R. Soc. Esp. Fis. Quim.*, **55B**, 109 (1959).
112. S. Ikeda and T. Isemura, *Bull. Chem. Soc. Japan*, **33**, 137 (1960).
113. J. T. Davies and C. R. A. Mayers, *Trans. Faraday Soc.*, **56**, 691 (1960).
114. S. C. Ellis, A. F. Lanham, and K. G. A. Pankhurst, *J. Sci. Instr.*, **32**, 70 (1955).
115. D. Platikanov, I. Panajotov, and A. Scheludko, *Proceedings of the Third International Symposium on Surface Active Substances*, vol. 2, Akademie Verlag, Berlin, 1967, p. 773.
116. J. R. Van Wazer, *J. Colloid Sci.*, **2**, 223 (1947).
117. K. J. Mysels, M. C. Cox, and J. D. Skewis, *J. Phys. Chem.*, **65**, 1107 (1961).
118. J. A. Kitchener, *Nature*, **195**, 1094 (1962).
119. F. Van Voorst Vader, Th. F. Erkens, and M. Van Den Tempel, *Trans. Faraday Soc.*, **60**, 1170 (1964).
120. L. K. James and J. N. Labows, *J. Phys. Chem.*, **68**, 1122 (1964).
121. L. Gargallo and F. Mac Ritchie, *Kolloid-Z.*, **212**, 169 (1966).
122. H. Sonntag, *Z. Physik. Chem. Leipzig*, **225**, 284 (1964).
123. W. E. Ewers and R. A. Sack, *Australian J. Chem.*, **7**, 40 (1954).
124. A. G. Brown, W. C. Thuman, and J. W. Mac Bain, *J. Colloid Sci.*, **8**, 491 (1953).
125. J. T. Davies, *Proc. Intern. Congr. Surface Activity, 2nd, London, 1957*, Vol. 1, p. 220.
126. D. W. Criddle and A. L. Meader, *J. Appl. Phys.*, **26**, 838 (1955).
127. K. V. Zotova and A. A. Trapeznikov, *Kolloidn. Zh.*, **26**, 190 (1964).
128. A. A. Trapeznikov and K. V. Zotona, *Kolloidn. Zh.*, **27**, 614 (1965).
129. L. Erdélyi, M. Gara, and A. Lörinc, *Proceedings of the Third International Symposium on Surface Active Substances*, Vol. 2, Akademie Verlag, Berlin, 1967, p. 829.
130. B. Biswas and D. A. Haydon, *Proc. Roy. Soc. (London) Ser. A*, **271**, 296 (1963).
131. B. Biswas and D. A. Haydon, *Proc. Roy. Soc. (London) Ser. A*, **271**, 317 (1963).
132. B. Biswas and D. A. Haydon, *Kolloid-Z.*, **186**, 57 (1962).
133. H. Devaux, *Compt. Rend. Soc. Biol.*, **119**, 1124 (1935).
134. D. Van Den Tempel, J. Lucassen, and E. H. Lucassen-Reynders, *J. Phys. Chem.*, **69**, 1798 (1965).
135. B. A. Pethica, *Trans. Faraday Soc.*, **50**, 413 (1958).
136. M. Blanck and J. S. Britten, *J. Colloid. Sci.*, **20**, 789 (1965).
137. J. Frenkel, *Trans. Faraday Soc.*, **33**, 58 (1937).
138. R. H. Ewell and H. Eyring, *J. Chem. Phys.*, **5**, 726 (1937).
139. W. J. Moore and H. Eyring, *J. Chem. Phys.*, **6**, 391 (1938).
140. S. Glasstone, K. J. Laidler, and H. Eyring, *The Theory of Rate Process*, McGraw-Hill, New York, 1941.
141. M. Joly, *J. Phys. Radium*, **7**, 83, 112 (1946).
142. M. Joly, in *Surface Chemistry*, Butterworths, London, 1949, p. 37.
143. M. Joly, *J. Colloid Sci.*, **5**, 49 (1950).
144. J. Frenkel, *Kinetic Theory of Liquids*, Oxford Press, 1946, p. 6.
145. M. Joly, in *Surface Phenomena in Chemistry and Biology*, J. F. Danielli, K. G. A. Pankhurst, and A. C. Riddiford, Eds., Pergamon Press, London, 1958, p. 88.
146. M. Mooney, *Trans. Soc. Rheol.*, **1**, 63 (1957).
147. E. Ferroni and A. Ficaldi, *Atti. Accad. Nazl. Lincei, Rend. Classe Sci. Fis. Mat. Nat.*, **28**, 207 (1960).
148. W. D. Garrett and J. D. Bultman, *J. Colloid Sci.*, **18**, 798 (1963).
149. D. Tissen and A. Sheludko, *Dokl. Akad. Nauk SSSR*, **163**, 939 (1965).
150. W. D. Garrett and W. A. Zisman, *Am. Chem. Soc. Abstr. Papers*, **150**, 23, I (1965).
151. W. Thomson, (Lord Kelvin), *Phil. Mag.*, **42**, 368 (1871).
152. R. Merigoux, *Compt. Rend.*, **205**, 105 (1937).

153. V. Levich, *Acta Physicochim. USSR*, **14**, 307, 321 (1941).
154. F. C. Goodrich, *Proc. Roy. Soc. (London) Ser. A*, **360**, 481, 490, 503 (1961).
155. R. G. Vines, *Australian J. Phys.*, **13**, 43 (1960).
156. F. C. Goodrich, *J. Phys. Chem.*, **66**, 1858 (1962).
157. M. Van Den Tempel and R. P. Van de Riet, *J. Chem. Phys.* **42**, 2769 (1965).
158. R. S. Hansen and J. A. Mann, *J. Appl. Physics*, **35**, 152 (1964).
159. R. S. Hansen, *J. Appl. Physics*, **35**, 1983 (1964).
160. J. A. Mann and R. S. Hansen, *J. Colloid Sci.*, **18**, 805 (1963).
161. J. Lucassen and R. S. Hansen, *J. Colloid. Interface Sci.*, **22**, 32 (1966).
162. J. Lucassen and R. S. Hansen, *J. Colloid. Interface Sci.* **23**, 319 (1967).
163. G. E. Charles and S. G. Mason, *J. Colloid Sci.* **15**, 236 (1960).
164. P. A. Rehbinder and A. B. Taubmann, *Proc. Intern. Congr. Detergency, 3rd, Cologne, 1960*, p. 209.
165. J. E. Carless and G. Hallworth, *Chem. Ind.*, 30 (1966).
166. J. E. Carless and G. Hallworth, *J. Colloid Interface Sci.*, **26**, 75 (1968).
167. C. Robinson, *Trans. Faraday Soc.*, **32**, 1424 (1936).
168. J. H. Schulman and E. G. Cockbain, *Trans. Faraday Soc.*, **36**, 651 (1940).
169. A. E. Alexander, *J. Roy. Inst. Chem.*, **4**, 221 (1948).
170. A. S. C. Lawrence, *Nature*, **170**, 232 (1952).
171. C. G. Sumner, *Chem. Ind. (London)*, 1066 (1960).
172. P. Becher, *Am. Perfumer*, **77**, 21 (1962).
173. P. A. Rehbinder and A. B. Taubmann, *Z. Physik. Chem.*, **228**, 184 (1965).
174. R. E. Ford and C. G. L. Furmidge, *J. Colloid Interface Sci.*, **22**, 331 (1966).
175. P. A. Rehbinder and A. A. Trapeznikov, *Acta Phys. Chim. USSR*, **62**, 257 (1938).
176. S. N. Srivastana, *J. Indian Chem. Soc.*, **41**, 279 (1964).
177. A. B. Taubmann and A. F. Koretzky, *Kolloidn. Zh.*, **20**, 676 (1958).
178. E. G. Cockbain and T. S. McRoberts, *J. Colloid Sci.*, **8**, 440 (1953).
179. B. Biswas and D. A. Haydon, *Kolloid-Z.*, **185**, 31 (1962).
180. J. G. Oldroyd, *Proc. Roy. Soc. (London) Ser. A*, **232**, 567 (1955).
181. R. E. Wilson and E. D. Ries, *Colloid Symp. Monogr.*, **1**, 145 (1923).
182. D. Talmud and S. Suchowoloskaja, *Z. Phys. Chem., A*, **154**, 277 (1931).
183. W. E. Ewers and K. L. Sutherland, *Australian J. Sci. Res. A*, **5**, 697 (1952).
184. A. Scheludko, *Kolloid-Z.*, **155**, 39 (1957).
185. D. G. Dervichian, *Bull. Soc. Chim. France*, 15 (1956).
186. F. Mac Ritchie and A. E. Alexander, *J. Colloid Sci.*, **16**, 61 (1961).
187. A. A. Trapeznikov and P. A. Rehbinder, *Compt. Rend. Acad. Sci. USSR*, **18**, 427 (1938).
188. A. L. Jocoby, *J. Phys. Colloid. Chem.*, **52**, 689 (1948).
189. A. E. Alexander, *Proc. Roy. Soc. (London) Ser. A*, *179*, 486 (1942).
190. J. G. Hawke and A. E. Alexander, *J. Colloid Sci.*, **11**, 419 (1956).
191. R. Matalon, in *Surface Chemistry*, Butterworths, London, 1949, p. 195.
192. S. Okazaki, *Bull. Chem. Soc. Japan*, **37**, 144 (1964).
193. J. Lyklema, *Rec. Trav. Chim.*, **81**, 890 (1962).
194. J. Lyklema, P. C. Scholten, and K. J. Mysels, *J. Phys. Chem.*, **69**, 116 (1965).
195. K. J. Mysels and M. C. Cox, *J. Colloid. Sci.*, **17**, 136 (1962).
196. K. J. Mysels, *J. Phys. Chem.*, **68**, 3441 (1964).
197. W. Johannes and S. Whitaker, *J. Phys. Chem.*, **69**, 1471 (1965).
198. R. A. Leonard and R. Lemlich, *A.I.Ch.E. J.*, **11**, 18 (1965).
199. R. J. Archer and V. K. La Mer, *Ann. N.Y. Acad. Sci.*, **58**, 807 (1954).
200. R. J. Archer and V. K. La Mer, *J. Phys. Chem.*, **59**, 200 (1955).
201. B. V. Derjaguin, V. A. Fedoseyev, and L. A. Rosenzweig, *J. Colloid Interface Sci.*, **22**, 45 (1966).

202. T. Tachibana and M. Okuda, *Kolloid-Z.*, **171**, 15 (1960).
203. T. W. Healy and V. K. La Mer, *J. Phys. Chem.*, **68**, 3535 (1964).
204. T. Seimiya and T. Sasaki, *J. Colloid Interface Sci.*, **21**, 229 (1966).
205. N. L. Jarvis, *J. Colloid Sci.*, **17**, 512 (1962).
206. J. C. Benson and R. L. Mac Intosh, *J. Colloid Sci.*, **3**, 323 (1948).
207. T. Isemura, H. Hotta, and T. Miwa, *Bull. Chem. Soc. Japan*, **26**, 380 (1953).
208. J. Jaffe, *J. Chim. Phys.*, **51**, 243 (1954).
209. M. Joly, in *Dritte Intern. Vortragstagung Grenzflächenaktive Stoffe*, Akademie-Verlag, Berlin, 1967, p. 683.
210. M. Joly, in *Proc. Intern. Congr. Rheol., 1st, Amsterdam, 1949*, **2**, 35.
211. D. G. Dervichian, in *Surface Chemistry*, Butterworths, London, 1949, p. 47.
212. E. J. Burcik and R. C. Newman, *J. Colloid Sci.*, **12**, 10 (1957).
213. G. S. Patil, S. S. Katti, and A. B. Biswas, *J. Colloid Interface Sci.*, **25**, 462 (1967).
214. G. D. Miles, J. Ross, and L. Shedlovsky, *J. Am. Oil. Chemists' Soc.*, **27**, 168 (1950).
215. M. B. Epstein, J. Ross, and C. W. Jakob, *J. Colloid Sci.*, **9**, 50 (1954).
216. J. Ross, *J. Phys. Chem.*, **62**, 531 (1958).
217. P. Becher and A. J. Del Vecchia, *J. Phys. Chem.*, **68**, 3511 (1964).
218. M. Joly, in *Compt. Rend. 2ième Reun. Chim. Phys., Paris, 1952*, p. 477.
219. J. Lucassen and E. H. Lucassen-Reynders, *J. Colloid Interface Sci.*, **25**, 496 (1967.)
220. M. Camp and K. Durham, *J. Phys. Chem.*, **59**, 993 (1955).
221. R. P. Enever and N. Pilpel, *Trans. Faraday Soc.*, **63**, 781 (1967).
222. K. Durham, *J. Appl. Chem.*, **5**, 686 (1955).
223. A. A. Trapeznikov, *Mon. Inst. Phys. Chem.* (ed. by Acad. Sci. USSR, Moscow, 1957), p. 3.
224. J. A. Spink and J. V. Sanders, *Trans. Faraday Soc.*, **51**, 1154 (1955).
225. R. Matsuura and H. Kimizuka, *Bull. Chem. Soc. Japan*, **28**, 668 (1955).
226. H. Kimizuka, *Bull. Chem. Soc. Japan*, **29**, 123 (1956).
227. T. Yamashita and T. Isemura, *Bull. Chem. Soc. Japan*, **37**, 742 (1964).
228. T. Yamashita and T. Isemura, *Bull. Chem. Soc. Japan*, **38**, 699 (1965).
229. J. H. Schulman and E. K. Rideal, *Proc. Roy. Soc. (London) Ser. B*, **122**, 46 (1937).
230. K. G. A. Pankhurst, in *Surface Phenomena in Chemistry and Biology*, J. F. Danielli, K. G. A. Pankhurst, and A. C. Riddiford, Eds., Pergamon Press, London, 1958, p. 100.
231. S. C. Ellis and K. G. A. Pankhurst, *Discussions Faraday Soc.*, **16**, 170 (1954).
232. J. H. Schulman and M. Z. Dogan, *Discussions Faraday Soc.*, **16**, 158 (1954).
233. A. F. Lanham and K. G. A. Pankhurst, *Trans. Faraday Soc.*, **52**, 521 (1956).
234. W. E. Elstow, D. E. Hathway, and K. G. A. Pankhurst, *Res. Correspondence*, **8**, 64 (1955).
235. S. G. Clark, P. F. Holt, and C. W. Went, *Trans. Faraday Soc.*, **53** (1), 1500 (1957).
236 S. G. Clark and P. F. Holt, *Trans. Faraday Soc.*, **53**, 1509 (1957).
237. P. F. Holt and C. W. Went, *Trans. Faraday Soc.*, **55**, 1435 (1959).
238. P. F. Holt and C. W. Went, *Proc. Intern. Congr. Surface Activity, 3rd, 1960*, **2**, 49.
239. L. Osipaw, F. D. Snell, and J. Hickson, *Proc. Intern. Congr. Surface Activity, 2nd, London, 1957*, **1**, 273.
240. L. De Bernard and D. G. Dervichian, *Bull. Soc. Chim. Biol.*, **37**, 943 (1955).
241. L. De Bernard, *Bull. Soc. Chim. Biol.*, **40**, 161 (1958).
242. P. Joos, R. Vochten, and R. Ruyssen, *Bull. Soc. Chim. Belges*, **76**, 601 (1967).
243. D. G. Dervichian and M. Joly, *Bull. Soc. Chim. Biol.*, **28**, 426 (1946).
244. M. Joly, *Nature*, **158**, 26 (1946).
245. M. Joly, *Biorheol.*, **4**, 11 (1966).
246. M. Joly, *Cah. Groupe Fr. Rheol.*, **1**, 217 (1967).

The Physical Chemistry of Detergency

ANTHONY M. SCHWARTZ

The Gillette Company Research Institute, Rockville, Maryland 20850

I. INTRODUCTION

Detergency as it is generally defined is without doubt a colloidal phenomenon, an effect that depends on the physicochemical behavior of matter at phase interfaces.   Since cleaning is a practical art, however, most of the very extensive literature on detergency has been concerned specifically with soil removal (or the appearance of soil removal) in practical or simulated practical systems.   Such systems are far too complex to be directly amenable to treatment by the established theories of colloid science, and therefore prior efforts to construct a comprehensive theory of detergency have generally fallen short of the mark.   Consider, for example, a soiled work shirt being put into a washing machine.   The shirt is typically constructed of a fiber blend, cotton and polyester.   It bears a soil consisting typically of human sebum (itself a complex mixture of water-insoluble organic compounds) skin detritus, and several other solid and oily species depending on where and how long it has been worn.   The wash liquor contains the hardness ingredients of the tap water and a detergent that consists of a dozen or more organic and inorganic ingredients.   The vigor with which the shirt is agitated in the machine and the duration of the treatment are more or less arbitrary.   Since the parameters of this system are so numerous and so poorly defined, it is essentially impossible to use them in developing meaningful generalizations.   This system, however, like most detersive systems, can be resolved without undue difficulty into a number of simpler systems, each composed of three distinct characterizable phases and the three corresponding interfacial boundaries.   The behavior of these simple component systems (or their idealized models) can usually be described and explained satisfactorily in terms of generally accepted theory.   By suitable combination, therefore, it should be possible to construct a valid theoretical description of the detersive process, although such a description will necessarily comprise several more or less independent parts.   In the present discussion we shall attempt an analysis of detergency along these lines.

The first section includes a general description of practical detersive systems and of the individual model systems into which they can be resolved. The next three sections describe the mechanisms involved in the removal and redeposition of liquid, solid, and mixed soils.   The mechanisms described are macroscopic rather than molecular, and the treatment is for the most part qualitative.   Rigorous treatments of the various molecular mechanisms would be far too lengthy for our present scope, and many of the more important ones are discussed in other chapters of this treatise.   A discussion of the kinetic aspects of detergency concludes the analysis.   In the last part of the chapter the application of this analytical approach is illustrated, using as examples some of the more pertinent studies in both the recent and older literature.

In practical systems detergent performance is judged according to practical criteria, which are not always wholly related to actual soil removal. In laundering, for example, it is the visual appearance of the fabric that forms the basis of judgment, not the total absence of foreign matter on it. In the present discussion, however, we limit our concern to the separation of soil from substrate and the necessary accompanying effects.

II. PRACTICAL AND MODEL DETERSIVE SYSTEMS

A. Practical Systems

1. General Considerations

Cleaning of a solid object (referred to as the substrate) consists in removing unwanted foreign matter (soil) from its surface. The more restricted term "detergency" will refer in this discussion to the cleaning effect obtained in systems having the following characteristics. (1) The cleaning is accomplished by a liquid medium, the bath. (2) The cleaning action of the bath is not due primarily to a dissolving action on the soil, although such dissolving action may take place on certain of the soil constituents. Nor is the cleaning action effected simply by hydraulic shearing of the bath against the soiled substrate. (3) The cleaning effect is caused primarily by interfacial forces acting among substrate, soil, and bath. These forces operate to loosen the soil–substrate bond and thereby facilitate soil removal. Although pure water is a surprisingly effective bath for separating some soil–substrate combinations, the bath in most practical detersive systems contains a special solute (or mixture of solutes), the detergent, that enhances the cleaning effect. In most detersive systems the bath is aqueous. There are some industrially important nonaqueous cleaning systems fulfilling the above requirements for a true detersive system, but unless otherwise specified the following discussion refers only to aqueous systems.

The cleaning procedure typically includes the following stages or operations. (1) The bath is applied in liberal quantity to the soiled substrate, usually by immersion, sometimes by sponging, spraying, or streaming it on. (2) The bath is worked over the surface of the soiled substrate; that is, mechanical and/or hydraulic action is applied in an appropriate manner. It is in this washing stage that the soil becomes separated from the substrate and isolated from it by the bath. The soil may or may not form a stable dispersion in the bath. Isolation of the soil by the bath is necessary; dispersion of the soil is not. (3) The substrate is removed from the fouled bath (or vice versa) and is rinsed, sometimes with fresh unfouled bath, usually with pure detergent-free solvent. It is, of course, important that the soil remain isolated from the substrate during rinsing. In systems where the detergent-laden bath is a much more effective cleaner than the detergent-free solvent, there is usually a tendency for soil to redeposit on the substrate during rinsing. Some redeposition of separated soil may also take place during the washing stage. (4) After rinsing, the cleaned substrate is usually dried in some appropriate manner, but this is not properly a part of the detersive process and will not be considered in the present discussion.

The meaning of "clean" and the specification of cleanness require clear definition. Conceptually a clean surface (solid–gas or solid–liquid interface) is one that contains no molecular species other than those in the interior of the two phases. Such a state is seldom reached, even under laboratory conditions, and is of theoretical rather than utilitarian interest. For practical purposes the type and quantity of foreign material that will be considered tolerable must be prespecified, and when these prespecifications are met the surface is considered clean. White wearing apparel, for example, is considered clean when it is free of visible soil even though it may carry a relatively heavy load of starch or softening finish. This same material would be rejected as dirty if it were going to be dyed, since a starch coating seriously interferes with dyeing. A piece of polished brass, eminently clean from the decorative point of view, may be far too dirty to be suitable for electroplating or painting. Cleanness is often judged visually or optically, as in the case of household linen. Many other criteria are used, however. The cleanness of some substrates, such as dishes and glassware, may be judged by water wettability or other criteria as well as by appearance. For substrates that carry a relatively heavy burden of oily soil, such as raw wool, the weight of soil per unit weight of substrate is frequently used as a measure of cleanness (or dirtiness). It is evident that detergency must be regarded not as a removal of all foreign matter from the substrate, but as a maximum displacement of undesirable foreign matter. Unobjectionable foreign matter present with the soil is often allowed to remain on the substrate, and new unobjectionable foreign matter is invariably added in the form of adsorbates from the bath.

2. Substrates

Although objects to be cleaned vary endlessly in size, shape, and chemical composition, they are usually divided into two groups: textiles or fabrics (including paper and similar fibrous materials), and "hard surfaces." The difference lies much more in their shape and the way they must be handled than in their chemical or physical properties. Fabric surfaces have a highly complicated configuration and a very high ratio of surface to mass. They can hold soil mechanically as well as by the physicochemical forces. They are, however, highly flexible; and it is therefore easy to subject them to effective mechanical action. Objects other than fabrics, that is, the hard surface substrates, have a low ratio of surface to mass and are substantially inflexible. Some sort of external device is needed to work the bath over their surfaces during the cleaning operation. The great importance of this difference in geometry can be illustrated by many materials. Nylon fabric, for example, is cleaned by the same general laundering procedures used for wool or cotton. Nylon plastic panels are cleaned by the procedures used for metal or ceramic panels. Similar considerations apply to glass, polyester, and acrylic resins, etc. Both fibrous and nonfibrous substrates vary in absolute hardness, that is, in the ease with which they are indented. Soft, easily indented substrates are more readily soiled by solid particulate soil, and retain it more tenaciously under washing conditions (1).

Substrates should not, of course, be subjected to baths that attack them irreversibly, but a reversible effect is often desirable. Many fibrous substrates, particularly the naturally occurring fibers, are swollen by water; most of the commonly encountered hard-surface substrates are not. Swelling greatly changes the surface properties of the substrate and usually makes cleaning easier. On drying and deswelling the clean substrate is recovered unchanged.

3. Soils

The soils encountered in practical detersive systems are even more numerous than the substrates, but from the technical point of view they can be classed simply as liquid, solid, or mixed. A liquid soil may be arbitrarily defined as one sufficiently fluid to move at a significant rate under the influence of its own surface forces at the prevailing temperatures of the system. Gummy or plastic soils having a high yield value are a special case. With respect to the mechanism by which they are removed from the substrate during washing, they must be regarded as solids. They may, however, have been in a fluid state when they originally became attached to the substrate, and therefore, with regard to mode of attachment, may resemble liquid soils.

Solid soils are characterized by being particulate, and particle size is one of the most important factors governing their ease of removal. If we assume a roughly equidimensional particle shape, and a surface energy in the median range, particles having a diameter greater than about 5 μ are generally quite easy to remove from the substrate. Particles less than about 10 mμ (10^{-6} cm) are often essentially unremovable from ordinary textile fiber surfaces by normal detersive processes. Particles in this size range are responsible for the gradual irreversible graying of white goods on repeated soiling and laundering. Fortunately, they also have a strong tendency to clump or cluster, and the clusters often show the general behavior of large individual particles. Particles in the size range 0.1–1.0 μ are frequently unremovable by water alone but removable by detergent solutions. This, therefore, is the size range of greatest interest in detergent science. Particle shape also has a considerable effect on ease of removal. Lamellae tend to cling more tenaciously to a substrate because of their larger area of attachment. They also provide less area for traction by dislodging mechanical forces.

A solid soil–substrate system can be regarded from two broad points of view. In the first place it is an *adhesive system*. The phase interfaces of interest are solid–solid interfaces. The two solids bordering any interface can be regarded as typical adherends, and it is the molecular forces acting across the interface to hold the solids together that must be overcome in the detersive process. Secondly, when immersed in the bath the solid soil–substrate system becomes a typical *lyophobic colloidal system*. Complete soil removal consists in dispersing the agglomerated mixed colloid consisting of the substrate surface and those particles which are directly adherent to it. The applicable theory in this case describes the attachment–separation mechanism of a small, essentially equidimensional particle to a semi-infinite planar wall (sometimes referred to in current literature as a "half space"). The particle and the wall are composed of different materials. Incomplete soil removal can occur when the soil consists of agglomerates, if the bath is capable of dispersing the agglomerate but incapable of breaking the soil–substrate bond.

The chemical and physicochemical properties of soils, both liquid and solid, can of course vary widely. In some practical detersive systems, for example, the scouring of goods being processed in a textile mill, or machined metal parts being cleaned for plating, the composition of the soil is well known. In other systems, for example, household laundering, the soil composition is variable and poorly defined. In most systems the soil is a mixture of liquid and solid, usually a single liquid phase (or a mixture that can become a single liquid phase at washing temperatures) and a multiplicity of solid phases, each in particulate form. The possible disposition of liquid and soil on the substrate surface is shown in Figure 1. In these mixed soil systems (Figure 1, x, y, and z) there are three possible modes of attachment; solid only, liquid only, or solid and liquid contacting the substrate. It is evident that we have three separation processes to consider, two soil–substrate separations and the liquid soil–solid soil separation.

4. Baths

The bath, particularly the solute which is responsible for the cleaning effect, is the key component of a detersive system. The solute, usually a

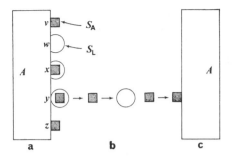

Fig. 1.   Model for solid, liquid, and mixed soil detergency, and solid soil redeposition. S_A is solid soil particle, S_L liquid soil droplet.

mixture of several compounds, is called the detergent.   "Detergent" is also the term applied in a more restricted sense to an organic surfactant of high detersive power.   Many metallic and ceramic substrates, however, can be well cleaned by baths containing inorganic alkalis or other nonsurfactant materials in the complete absence of surfactants.   Surfactants are usually the most important detersive ingredients in baths designed for washing fabrics and organic polymeric materials.   Such baths almost always contain certain specific inorganic salts or alkalis, referred to as builders, which augment the cleaning action.   Modern laundering formulations, based on a combination of synthetic surfactant and builder, also contain antiredeposition or soil-suspending agents.   These materials, of which sodium carboxymethylcellulose is presently most widely used, prevent solid soil that has already been removed from subsequently going back onto the fabric before the fouled bath can be drained and rinsed away.   Laundering formulations also contain a variety of other special-purpose ingredients such as anticorrosion agents, fluorescent whitening agents, etc., which do not contribute to actual soil removal.

Since the characteristic active bath constituent in most detersive systems is the surfactant it is appropriate to review briefly the properties of surfactants, particularly as they relate to detergency.   A surfactant or surface-active agent may be defined as a solute which, when present in relatively low concentrations, lowers the surface tension of the solvent to an unusual extent. The key to surface activity lies in the highly asymmetric structure of the surfactant molecule.   Molecules of the aqueous surfactants in which we are interested are typically elongated, having one end which is nonpolar and hydrophobic, the other end being polar and hydrophilic.   The term "amphipathic" has been applied to this type of structure.   The balance between the two ends with regard to both mass and polarity is such that the compound is water-soluble, but the solutions have several unusual and characteristic properties.   One of the most notable is that the surfactant has a strong tendency to become adsorbed at most phase boundaries of the solution regardless of the chemical nature of the bordering phase. Adsorption at the air or vapor interface is responsible for the low surface tension. Adsorption from solution is governed by the well-known Gibbs adsorption isotherm, and any solute that lowers the interfacial free energy is accordingly adsorbed positively. The amphipathic character of the surfactant molecules enables them to be adsorbed from aqueous solutions onto a very wide variety of solid and liquid surfaces. The molecules tend to become oriented in the adsorbed layer with the polar end toward the polar phase and the nonpolar end toward the nonpolar phase. There are thus relatively few phase interfaces involving aqueous solutions that will not have their free energy reduced by an adsorbed layer of surfactant.

A second unusual property of surfactants is that their molecules associate into soluble micelles when the solution reaches a certain critical concentration. The association is reversible, and the critical concentration for micelle formation (the cmc) is a characteristic of the surfactant species. For most surfactants that are used in detergent formulations it is in the range 10^{-4}–10^{-2} M. Above this concentration the aqueous surfactant solution is capable of dissolving considerable quantities of various organic materials that are quite insoluble in pure water. This phenomenon, solubilization, plays an important role in the detergency of liquid soil systems. Solubilization is attributed to molecular association of the material being solubilized with the hydrophobic portion of the surfactant. The extent to which solubilization occurs is dependent not only on the chemical constitutions of surfactant and solubilizate respectively, but also on the structure of the micelle, that is, on the number and arrangement of surfactant molecules composing it. In general, micellar structure changes in a discontinuous manner as the concentration is increased above the cmc. The micelles which first form are roughly spherical or equi-dimensional in shape, and may contain from about 50 to 500 molecular units. These are arranged with the hydrophobic "tails" tucked together in the interior of the structure, and the polar "heads" in the exterior adjacent to the aqueous solvent molecules. At concentrations roughly 10–50 times the cmc the micellar structure of many common surfactants change drastically. The molecules assume a long-range order and in some instances appear to form, together with the solvent, a liquid crystal structure. The cmc itself, the "secondary cmc" at which the micellar form changes and the detailed structure of the micelles themselves are affected by temperature, by the presence of salt and other nonsurfactant solutes, and by the presence or absence of solubilizable organic material. Concentrated aqueous solutions of surfactants can interact with polar oils to form ternary liquid phases, the overall macroscopic effect being a "solubilization" of the oil. This can be an important mechanism in removing oily soils from both hard and fibrous substrates. Many technically important products such as emulsion concentrates, disinfectant concentrates, and a variety of so-called soluble oils are also mixtures of this type.

The electrical charge characteristics of surfactants have an important bearing on their detersive properties. This is to be expected since the charge on a surface is a major factor in determining whether it will be repelled or attracted by a neighboring surface. The surface charge frequently results from adsorption of ions from solution, and surfactant ions usually have a strong tendency to become adsorbed. Surfactants are classed as anionic, cationic, ampholytic (or amphoteric), and nonionic, depending on the charge of the ion which contains the hydrophobic group.

Cationics are seldom used as detergents. There are many reasons for this. One is that several of the most common substrates including most textile fibers are negatively charged. They therefore tend to take up excessive quantities of cationic surfactant from solution, and retain it tenaciously. This firmly held surfactant is often undesirable on the substrate. Although many cationics can provide good detergency at impractically high concentrations, at normally low concentrations they tend to deposit the dirt and anchor it to the fabric rather than remove it.

Anionic surfactants behave in just the opposite manner, and include among their members the most widely used detergents as well as the oldest, namely, soap. The soaps are acid insoluble and form highly insoluble salts with the alkaline earth and heavy metal cations. The term "synthetic anionic detergent" commonly refers to the sulfates, sulfonates, and phosphates that are acid soluble and form relatively soluble lime and heavy metal salts. Whereas the cationics sorb onto negatively charged surfaces via coulombic attraction and orient with their hydrophobic tails outward, the anionics sorb onto negatively charged surfaces by van der Waals and/or hydrophobic bonding, orienting with their polar heads outward. They are relatively easy to desorb by rinsing, and when incompletely removed tend to provide a hydrophilic finish on the substrate. Ampholytic surfactants behave like anionics at high pH and like cationics at low pH. The adsorption behavior of all ionogenic surfactants is, of course, strongly influenced by pH. The pH acts in two ways: it affects the degree of dissociation of weakly ionized surfactants, for example, carboxylic acid anionics or nonquaternary nitrogen-base cationics; it also affects the surface charge on the substrate, which comes to an adsorption equilibrium with H^+ and OH^- in the surrounding medium.

Nonionic surfactants are, in general, less firmly sorbed than either of the ionogenic types. Regardless of the surface charge of the substrate they tend to be sorbed via a van der Waals or hydrophobic bonding mechanism and to orient with their hydrophilic groups in the aqueous phase.   Most nonionics owe their solubility to a plurality of ether oxygen and/or hydroxyl groups. Like the synthetic anionics, they remain dissolved in the presence of both acids and salts.

It is again worth emphasizing that surface activity is not always necessary for detergency.   Some detersive mechanisms depend on the low liquid–vapor and liquid–liquid interfacial energies provided by surfactants; others do not. Some hydrophilic polymers and even some sol-forming minerals such as bentonite are outstanding cleaning agents even though they have little effect on the surface tension of their aqueous medium.   The simple alkalis exert a strong cleaning effect on certain substrates because they furnish an excess of hydroxyl ions that charge and hydrate the surface.   Sequestering agents can act as powerful detergents in systems where the soil is bound to the substrate by bridges of heavy metal ions.   An empirical knowledge of which cleaning agents are highly effective in which systems will often indicate which detersive mechanism is operating, and vice versa.

Builders are used in laundering detergents, in which the major soil-removing ingredient is a surfactant.   From a practical point of view the function of the builder is to potentiate the surfactant, so that soil will be effectively removed at lower surfactant concentrations than would be required if the builder were absent.   Builders have therefore been traditionally sought among the less expensive materials, especially the inorganic salts. It has been known for a long time that soap is very effectively built for cotton laundering by the inorganic alkaline silicates, carbonates, and ortho-phosphates.   These materials are used either singly or in combination, and are presumed to exert their effect by any of three different mechanisms. First, since soaps are converted at acidic pH levels to the insoluble ineffective fatty acids, these alkaline builders serve to keep the pH buffered at a high level.   Second, all three of these materials form insoluble calcium salts in the same manner as soap itself does.   They are especially useful, therefore, in softening hard-water baths and allowing the soap to function at low concentrations.   In the absence of these line-precipitating builders the first increments of soap would simply be precipitated by the hardness in the bath water, and additional soap would remain ineffective until all the hardness had been removed.   The third physicochemical effect of these soap builders, a minor effect exerted more strongly by the silicates than by carbonates or orthophosphates, is to keep the solid soil deflocculated and dispersed in the bath.   This deflocculating action helps to remove the main mass of a large soil agglomerate from the substrate leaving only those primary particles that are in actual contact with it.   The degree of deflocculation depends largely on the nature of the soil, being quite pronounced with certain clays.

It was discovered early in the history of synthetic surfactant development that sodium carbonate has essentially no building action on the cotton washing powers of alkylbenzene sulfonates and fatty alkyl sulfates. Orthophosphate is similarly ineffective and silicate has only a slight effect which may be ascribed to its deflocculating power. In one sense this was not unexpected, since the calcium salts and free acids of these surfactants are quite soluble in water. It is a well-established fact of colloid chemistry, however, that calcium ions have a strong tendency to agglomerate negatively charged sols, and should therefore have an antidetersive effect. This is indeed the case. The common sulfonated surfactants do wash soiled cottons far better in soft than in hard water. From this point of view it is surprising that sodium carbonate, which does precipitate calcium ion, does not build these surfactants satisfactorily. Probably because some calcium ion is intimately held by the fibrous substrate and at the soil–substrate interface, only the very powerful calcium sequestering agents are good builders in these commercially important systems. Sodium tripolyphosphate is notably effective and has for many years been the standard builder in household heavy-duty laundering detergents. The recent search for tripolyphosphate replacements, stimulated by the possible unfavorable role of phosphates in eutrophication, has shown that the strong sequestrants such as nitrilotriacetic acid are generally much more effective builders than weaker sequestrants of equal capacity.

Building action is specific with regard to the surfactant and the substrate. The mechanism of the building action also varies with the system. Sodium sulfate, for example, is a good builder for the sulfonated surfactants in washing wool. The effect here is simply one of lowering the critical micelle concentration without adding any strongly flocculating cations. Even when the mechanism is sequestration, the builder–surfactant–substrate interaction is specific. For example, carbonates are reasonably good builders in the washing of cottons with nonionic polyoxyethylene surfactants.

The remarkable effect of carboxymethyl cellulose (abbreviated NaCMC) in reducing redeposition of soil onto fabrics is attributed to its being strongly sorbed onto both the fabric and the soil particles. The rate and extent of sorption is greatly increased by the presence of builder salts (2). Current practice is to include about 0.3–1 % of NaCMC by weight in laundering formulations. Since the formulation is used at a level of 0.1–0.3 % in the bath, the concentration of NaCMC necessary to produce a noticeable practical effect is well under 30 ppm.

In the discussion that follows relatively little attempt will be made to isolate the effects of the various bath ingredients, except where they are reasonably well established as in the illustrations just considered. In most practical systems the interaction effects among the bath components appear to be important, but their form and their effect on performance remain as yet unexplored. In our first-order approach to detergency theory the bath can be regarded simply as a single liquid phase in contact with soil and substrate simultaneously, and acting to weaken the soil–substrate bond. Mechanisms for this effect are intricate even when the bath is a pure liquid. They are less clearly understood when the bath contains one solute component, and still less so in the case of multicomponent baths.

B. Model Liquid Soil System

In a model liquid soil system the soil tyipcally consists of a single-phase "oily" liquid, that is, a liquid having essentially no solubility or at best a limited solubility in water. The soiled substrate may, of course, bear watery or water-miscible liquid soil as a second liquid phase in addition to the oily soil. This water-miscible material, however, will dissolve in the aqueous bath at the start of the washing operation, leaving the oil as the only material to be removed by detersive processes.

The oily soil may consist of one component or, more typically, of several components. Sometimes a multiple-component soil will consist of a mixture that behaves physicochemically like a single component. An example of such a soil is ordinary mineral oil. More often a multiple-component oily soil will comprise compounds of varying behavior, for example, the mineral oils, glyceride oils, and fatty alcohols which are often combined in cosmetic creams. Sebum, one of the commonest oily soils encountered on apparel similarly contains constituents of widely varying polarity. Oily soils, although by definition insoluble in water, may often contain or consist entirely of acidic materials. These can be dissolved if the pH of the bath is raised to a high enough level. The most common representative soils of this type are the fatty acids. They cannot only be removed from the substrate by alkalis, but during the process of being removed they form surface-active soaps which aid in removing the remaining unreacted fatty acid and any other soil that may be present.

The substrate for the model liquid soil system has many forms, as do substrates in practical systems. A major differentiation among the model substrates is between those that are swellable in the aqueous bath, for example, most natural textile fibers, and those that are not, for example, metals and ceramics. A second important differentiation is on the basis of geometrical shape. Substrate surfaces that have reentrant depressions or elevations in the surface, as shown in Figure 2, will behave quite differently from smooth or nonreentrant surfaces, especially in the model roll-back soil removal process to be discussed later. Some important practical substrates, notably the polyester textile fibers, can be appreciably penetrated by certain oily soils. This effect becomes significant at elevated temperatures that are

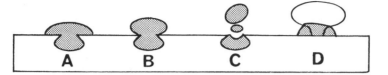

Fig. 2. A–C, oil incompletely removed from reentrant depression, would be completely removed by roll-back from a smooth surface. D, oil trapped by overhanging elevation.

still well within the washing range. The soils can thereby move into the interior of the substrate, beyond the range of the bath's action (3).

The bath in the model liquid soil system will be considered to consist of a single aqueous phase. In the general case it will contain at least one and usually more than one dissolved component. Some baths that are used in practice contain other phases, for example, water-immiscible solvents which may or may not be emulsified in the main aqueous phase. Other baths may contain particulate solids such as bentonite or abrasives which may or may not be colloidally dispersed. For obvious reasons these need not be considered in the model.

The soil–substrate attachment in the model liquid soil system, as in most practical systems, extends over the whole apparent area of contact. This is one of the major differences between liquid and solid soils. The most usual type of intermolecular force that binds the soil to the substrate in practical systems, particularly when the soil is nonpolar, is the London-van der Waals dispersion force. In the model system as well as in many practical systems, however, other forces are involved. The proportion of the total attachment force due to the dispersion forces can be determined, at least for one component liquids, by suitable comparisons of data on contact angles, heats of wetting and heats of adsorption (4). The magnitude of the liquid soil–substrate binding force is measured by the free energy of the interface, γ_{SL}. This quantity is related to the contact angle in air by the familiar Young's equation

$$\gamma_{SV} = \gamma_{SL} + \gamma_{LV} \cos \theta$$

where the gammas are interfacial free energies, the subscripts S, V, and L signify the solid, vapor (air), and liquid phases, and θ is the contact angle. Of two liquids having the same surface tension, the one having the smaller contact angle against a given solid substrate forms the interface of lower free energy against that substrate; that is, it is the more strongly attached. The absolute value of γ_{SL} is a thermodynamic quantity characteristic of the chemical composition of the substrate–soil pair. It is not changed by changes in the other two interfaces of the system.   If, however, it is relatively high the substrate–soil bond will be relatively easy to break; that is, the cleaning will be accomplished more easily.

C. Model Solid Soil System

Solid soil systems are much more complicated, both in theory and practice, than liquid soil systems.   In the first place solid soils consist in most instances of fine particles.   Both particle size and particle shape are major parameters governing the ease of soil removal.   Even if the soil on a given substrate consists of a single pure crystalline chemical species (e.g., graphite or Fe_3O_4) the ease of removal in a given bath will vary enormously with variations in the magnitude of these parameters.   Secondly, most solid soils encountered in practice contain many different species of particle.   Common dirt found on floors or in carpets, for example, normally contains siliceous and argillaceous particles, soot (carbon in various states of surface oxidation), iron oxides, fiber lint, and other materials.   It is to be expected that these will vary in the ease with which they can be removed from the substrate. The third complicating factor is that many solid soil "particles" are in fact agglomerates of smaller particles.   The majority of these smaller particles are not in contact with the substrate at all.   The agglomerate is held to the substrate only by the few constituent smaller particles that contact the substrate.   Two distinct actions may accordingly take place during cleaning. (1) The bond between the substrate and its adjacent contacting soil particle may be broken, releasing the whole agglomerate.   (2) The agglomerate may be dispersed, releasing most of the soil but leaving some of the constituent particles adhering to the substrate.   This effect is illustrated in Figure 3. As a final and not at all unusual complication the soil agglomerates may in themselves be heterogeneous with regard to particle size and particle species. Under a fixed set of conditions (temperature, bath composition, etc.) a single agglomerate may therefore become *partially* deflocculated rather than deflocculating completely or remaining unaffected.

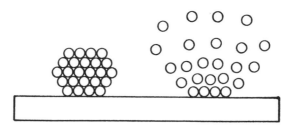

Fig. 3.   Partial removal of soil by dispersion of adhering agglomerate.

Some solid soils are not finely particulate but may be present as relatively brittle continuous sheaths surrounding the substrate. Dried paints and sizings on fabrics are in this category. In this type of system the soil–substrate interfacial energy (i.e., the specific adhesion) must be greatly modified by the bath if soil removal is to be accomplished.

The substrates and baths of the model solid soil system are similar to those described for the model liquid soil system.

The attachment of a solid soil particle to a solid substrate, in the absence of any oily soil, can advantageously be regarded as an example of adhesion and can be analyzed broadly from that point of view. Regardless of the molecular nature of the adhesion forces, one of the parameters determining the force required to separate the adherends is dependent on the area of true contact. "True contact" is not easy to define. Solids are for the most part rigid and, even if they are not ideally elastic, possess a yield point. They also have rough surfaces. The dimensions of the rugosities are usually very much larger than the separation of typical molecules in a crystal lattice, but any rugosities comparable in dimension to a soil particle can afford a great increase in the area of true contact. If (for the time being) we define true contact as the situation in which the separation of unlike molecules across the interface is little if any greater than the separation of like molecules within the bulk, it seems probable that the area of true contact will be quite small compared with the area of macroscopically apparent contact, even when both surfaces are quite smooth by ordinary standards. Possibly a more realistic definition of the area of true contact is the area over which the separation of the adherends is sufficiently small for significant forces of attraction to be mutually exerted by the adherends. In any event, the area of true contact multiplied by the average normal force of attraction per unit area gives the total force holding the adherends (soil particle and substrate in this case) together.

The absolute area of true contact, however, is less important in particle attachment and the ease of particle removal from a massive substrate than two other quantities: the ratios $A_c/A - A_c$ and A_c/m where A_c is the area of true contact, A is the total surface area of the particle, and m is the mass of the particle. The force holding the particle to the substrate is proportional to A_c. Any noninertial force tending to remove the particle must exert its traction over the area $A - A_c$. If the ratio $A_c/A - A_c$ is large the traction tending to separate the particle must be correspondingly large. Similarly the magnitude of inertial or gravitational forces tending to remove the particle is proportional to m. The smaller the mass of the particle (shape and density remaining constant), the greater, in general, are both ratios, $A_c/A - A_c$ and A_c/m. This is the very simple theoretical basis for the experimental fact that solid soils become much more difficult to remove from any substrate as their particle size decreases.   This effect, which has been demonstrated many times (5), has been attributed in the case of cotton and other fiber substrates to mechanical entrapment of the soil particles in the crevices on the fiber surface (6).   Since the particles and the crevices are both in the size range $<1\,\mu$ it is very difficult to distinguish mechanical entrapment from adhesion.   There is good evidence, however, that adhesion rather than entrapment is the mode of attachment, at least in the case of carbon particles on a cotton fiber (7).   Mechanical entrapment of the particles among the fibers of a fibrous substrate such as felt or paper is of course a common mode of soil attachment, but trivial in the present discussion.   A simple opening of the trap in such a case enables the particle to separate from the substrate.

Particle adhesion like liquid soil adhesion is generally considered to result from the same types of intermolecular forces that cause cohesion of the condensed phases of matter.   Those most commonly encountered in soil–substrate systems are the van der Waals forces and the coulombic, ionic, or electrostatic forces.   These are the so-called long-range forces which can act to establish an area of contact between particle and substrate as well as to maintain it (8).   Under certain soiling conditions hydrogen bonds or even stronger short-range bonds may become established between soil and substrate.   This is an unusual condition, however, with solid soils. It is not uncommon in the case of stains and similar quasidyeing effects which are not removable by strictly detersive operations.

A detailed discussion of the origin and physical nature of the two major types of adhesive bonding force, van der Waals and coulombic, is beyond the scope of our present discussion but is available from several good sources (9–12).

D. Model Mixed Soil System

The model mixed soil system can be regarded as a linear combination of the liquid and solid soil systems so far as attachment of soil to substrate is concerned.   It differs from either of these systems, however, in that the liquid and the solid soil particles are attached to each other.   It is therefore possible, in both theory and practice, to separate either liquid or solid from the total soil–substrate complex without bringing about complete cleaning. If both solid and liquid soils are attached to the substrate as well as to each other, three attachments must be broken to remove all soil from the substrate. These are solid soil–substrate, liquid soil–substrate, and liquid soil–solid soil.   The considerations which apply to separating liquid from solid soil particles are identical to those which apply to separating liquid soil from substrate.

III. MECHANISMS OF SOIL REMOVAL

A. Soil Removal in Model Liquid Systems

1. Roll-Back Mechanism

Consider a smooth solid surface of a material that is not swollen or otherwise attacked by the liquids in the system, and a water-insoluble oil deposited on this surface.   Let the equilibrium contact angle at the air–oil–solid boundary line be zero, as it is in a very wide variety of practical systems. If the ratio of the volume of oil to the area of oil–solid interface is small, the oil will have the form of thin adherent film covering the solid surface.   Let this oiled solid now be immersed in an aqueous bath.   Wherever the water has a chance to contact the underlying solid as well as the oil, there will be a tendency for the oil–water interface and the solid surface to assume the contact angle characteristic of the system.   For convenience we can measure the contact angle of the oil–water–solid system in the oil and refer to the angle as θ_{SOW} (supplemental to θ_{SWO}, the angle measured in the water). If θ_{SOW} is positive the thin film of oil will tend to form isolated islands on the solid surface as shown in Figure 4.   If θ_{SOW} is 180° the water will spontaneously displace the oil from the solid surface leaving it clean (of oil).   At values of θ_{SOW} less than 180° but greater than 90° the oil will not be displaced spontaneously but larger proportions of it can be removed by hydraulic currents.   As shown in Figures 4 and 5 the 90° contact angle is critical for easy oil removal.   This is especially true in capillary systems composed of packed cylindrical rods, such as ordinary textile yarns and fabrics.   It is easy to demonstrate (13) that in such a system, if $\theta_{SOW} > 90°$, the oil will spontaneously move from the interior spaces of the yarn to the surface fibers, from which it is removable in the same manner as from a flat plate.

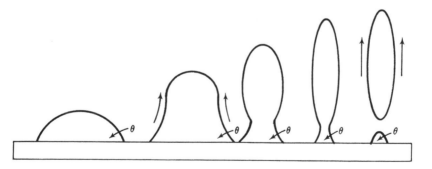

Fig. 4.   Rupture and incomplete removal of large oil droplet by hydraulic currents (arrows) when θ remains constant at <90°.   A small droplet remains attached to the substrate.

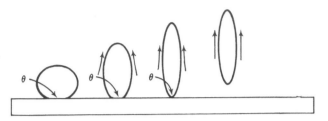

Fig. 5. Complete removal of oil droplet from substrate by hydraulic currents (arrows)
when θ remains constant at $>90°$.

If the contact angle is less than 90° at least part of the oil will tend to remain in the spaces between the fibers.

This spontaneous balling up of oily soil in an aqeuous detergent bath is generally referred to as the "roll-back" mechanism of detergency, and was first clearly described for oiled textile fibers by Adam (14) and by Kling and co-workers (15). These investigators and many others since then also showed that solutions of the usual water-soluble surfactants give much greater values of θ_{SOW} than plain water. In many instances the addition of surfactant to the water raised θ_{SOW} from a value near zero to a value of 180°. It is important to note that the *water-advancing angle* is the controlling parameter in this oil removal process. Many oil–water–solid systems show considerable contact angle hysteresis. If a drop of oil is placed against the surface of a solid submerged in water, the oil–solid interface will expand until θ_{SOW} has come to its oil-advancing value. This may be considerably greater than the final value assumed by θ_{SOW} when a water drop is placed against a solid submerged in oil (the water-advancing angle). The fact that it may be impossible to get a drop of oil to stick to a solid surface submerged in water does not guarantee that submersion in water will remove oil from the pre-oiled solid.

In the roll-back mechanism the function of the detergent is to reduce γ_{SW} while leaving γ_{SO} substantially unaffected. In this way θ_{SOW}, the primary governing parameter, is increased. This effect is concomitant with adsorption of the detergent at the SW interface. If the detergent is a typical surfactant the molecules may become sorbed in an oriented mode, with the hydrophobic nonpolar portions laying down on the solid surface and the hydrophilic polar portions extending outward into the water. For detergents that are not amphipathic the orientation is of little importance. Such substances as hydroxyl ion, for example, are powerful detergents in many systems by virtue of being strongly sorbed at the SW interface and lowering the value of γ_{SW}. Since they have no great effect on the LV

interface (and in fact usually *increase* γ_{LV} to a slight extent) they are not classed as surfactants.

The theory of capillarity and of contact angle phenomena indicates that several factors other than the water-advancing value of θ_{SOW} will influence oily soil removal even when roll-back is the only mechanism operating. One of these is the roughness of the surface. It has been shown above that if θ_{SOW} is 90° or greater, substantially all the oil can be displaced from a plane solid surface by relatively gentle hydraulic currents. Consider, however, a surface pitted with perpendicular cylindrical wells as shown in Figure 2. It is evident that when θ_{SOW} is 90° hydraulic action at the three-phase line boundary will have no tendency to remove oil from the wells. If the wells are reentrant, with openings smaller than the interior, the oil cannot escape without being disrupted even if θ_{SOW} is 180°.

A group of other factors relate to the rate at which θ_{SOW} is approached and the oil displaced. One of these is the value of the oil–water interfacial tension. This tension is the main driving force tending to bring θ_{SOW} to its water-advancing value, that is, to roll back the oil. If this oil–water tension is high the system will approach its equilibrium condition at a correspondingly rapid rate; consequently it is desirable to maintain a high oil–water interfacial tension. This contrasts with the situation in solid–liquid–vapor (*SLV*) systems when it is desired to displace the vapor (usually air) by the liquid, that is, to "wet" the solid. As in *SOW* systems, the driving force in this case is the liquid–vapor interfacial tension γ_{LV}. In *SLV* systems, however, there is a direct relationship between γ_{LV} and θ_{SVL}. According to the quantitative rule discovered by Zisman and co-workers a low value of γ_{LV} corresponds to a high value of θ_{SVL} (or in the more usual notation, a low value of θ_{SLV}), that is, to a displacement of vapor by liquid. Contact angle is a more important factor than interfacial tension in the displacement process, and it is therefore generally favorable in *SLV* systems to keep γ_{LV} as low as possible. In *SOW* systems, however, there is no simple connection between θ_{SOW} and γ_{OW}. Young's equation, and the corresponding diagram of Figure 2, shows that the relative values of γ_{SO} and γ_{SW} govern the displacement. As γ_{OW} diminishes in value it has correspondingly less influence on θ_{SOW}; and as γ_{OW} approaches zero, θ_{SOW} must approach either 0 or 180° or, in the very special case that $\gamma_{SW} = \gamma_{SO}$, 90°. In *SOW* systems, therefore, if γ_{SO} is greater than γ_{SW} by even a small margin, a high value of γ_{OW} favors rapid oil removal. Another reason why a low value of γ_{OW} should not favor good roll-back detergency is connected with the surface roughness effect discussed previously. If part of a mass of oily soil lies in a trough or hole in the solid surface, it may tend to become separated from the projecting portion of oil where the latter is removed. This separation is, in fact, a yielding of the *OW* interface, and it will occur under low external shear stresses if γ_{OW} is correspondingly low.   If, however, γ_{OW} is sufficiently high the shear stresses may be able to remove all the oil from the solid surface as a single coherent mass.

The major force opposing displacement of one liquid phase by the other is viscosity.   It is therefore desirable to keep the viscosity of both phases as low as possible.   This can be done by increasing the temperature.   It can also be done by adding low-viscosity solvents to the system to thin the oily phase, and by avoiding the presence of hydrophilic polymers or other thickeners in the aqueous phase.

The roll-back mechanism of soil removal as described above is most frequently encountered in cleaning heavy loads of oil from metals or similar nonswellable substrates.   When the substrate is swellable by the aqueous bath, as many textile fibers are, the roll-back effect can be materially accelerated.   The value of γ_{SW} is obviously lowered when water permeates the fiber, and the substrate becomes hydrated.   The value of γ_{SO} also changes, approaching the value of γ_{WO}.   If γ_{WO} is higher than γ_{SO} the net effect must be an increase in θ_{SOW}.   A less expected effect occurs in SOW systems when the substrate is water permeable and the aqueous phase contains a solute such as a salt or detergent.   In such systems droplets of water will form and grow at the oil–solid interface and thus tend to push the oil off the surface (16, 17).   This has been shown to be an osmotic effect, the water coming through the substrate.   It can also be observed with impermeable substrates such as glass, if a trace of salt is present on the glass under the oil and the oil itself is reasonably permeable to the water.

2. Emulsification Mechanism

Consider a smooth solid surface, a nylon or glass fiber or a metal coupon, for example, bearing a relatively massive amount of oil.   Let the oil–solid system be of such a nature that when it is placed in contact with an aqueous bath, W, the value which θ_{SOW} finally reaches is very low; that is, the bath has little or no tendency to roll back the oil.   It is still possible in some such situations to remove a large proportion of the oil by emulsifying it into the bath.   It is necessary, of course, that both the oil and the bath have a composition conducive to forming the oil-in-water (OW) emulsion.   Furthermore the emulsion should preferably be relatively stable and must be producible with a minimum of mechanical agitation.   More generally, the emulsion must be producible under the conditions of temperature, time, chemical composition and concentration, and energy input that prevail in the cleaning system.   Fortunately, both the theoretical and empirical knowledge of emulsification are quite extensive.   If the chemical composition of the oily soil is known it is often not difficult to formulate an aqueous bath that will carry the soil into emulsion. The HLB procedure for matching the aqueous surfactant composition and the composition of the oil to form an easily emulsifiable system is convenient to use and effective. It was developed empirically as a guide to the selection of emulsifying agents (18) but it has been shown to rest on sound theoretical grounds (19). There are, of course, many other clues in the theory and technology of emulsions that can be used as guides to more effective aqueous detergent formulations (20).

In some instances the oily soil may be of such a nature that the aqueous bath cannot practically be made to emulsify it. It may still be possible to form an emulsion by deliberately adding an oil-soluble emulsification promoter to the system. This will dissolve in the oily soil and make it susceptible to the emulsifying action of the aqueous bath. In effect, the oily soil is converted to a "soluble oil" type of emulsifiable composition. Fatty acids are the most common materials used for this purpose (21).

Rate effects and the effects of mechanical action are very important in the emulsification process. Emulsification involves the breaking up of a large mass of oil into small droplets. This is a mechanical process which invariably requires an input of mechanical energy, but the amount of agitation required varies greatly from system to system. In some cases fluid flow engendered by concentration gradients, or other chemical potential gradients across the oil–water interface, is sufficient to form the emulsion. Such systems are said to be self-emulsifying, and an aqueous bath that forms a self-emulsifying system with an oily soil will obviously be effective in removing that soil from its substrate. A bath that requires excessive agitation to emulsify a given oily soil will not be of practical value as a detergent for the soil even though the emulsion, once formed, is stable. Stable emulsions almost always have an interfacial film surrounding each droplet and preventing it from coalescing with its neighbors. Regardless of its composition, this film requires a finite time to form and become organized. Agitation that is too severe may accordingly disrupt an emulsion as fast as it is formed. Since emulsions tend to change with time an oil–water system may form an emulsion quickly and easily, and yet this emulsion may become unstable a short while later. These considerations emphasize the importance of well-controlled timing and agitation in removing oily soil by means of an emulsifying bath.

How completely an oiled surface can be cleaned by an emulsifying bath is an important question. At the beginning of this discussion it was noted that emulsification and roll-back are in theory quite independent of each other. Emulsification involves only the liquid–liquid interface; roll-back involves the liquid–liquid–solid boundary line and two liquid–solid interfaces. Consider, however, the case of an already emulsified droplet colliding with the substrate. In this situation the theory of roll-back rather than the theory of emulsification is applicable. The droplet may maintain a 180°

contact angle and bounce off, or it may assume a contact angle between 0 and 180° and remain attached.   The droplet will tend to assume the equilibrium contact angle characteristic of the oil–bath–substrate system (θ_{SOW}). The fact that it is stably emulsified (so that it resists coalescing with other oil droplets when it collides with them) does not necessarily mean that it will resist "coalescing" with the solid, and many otherwise stable emulsions are known to deposit their oil in adherent droplets on the walls of the container or other solid with which they may be in contact.   The eventual thickness which such a "redeposited" oil layer may reach depends on the value of θ_{SOW}, the size and size distribution of the oil droplets, and the rate at which they spread after making contact with the solid surface.   It is evident, however, that as long as oil droplets cannot coalesce with each other the oil layer on the solid surface can never become as thick as the diameter of a single oil droplet.

If, instead of starting with a clean surface and an emulsion, we start with an oiled surface and a clear aqueous solution of a detergent that is capable of emulsifying the oil, the situation described above is reversed.   Emulsification will proceed only until the residual oil layer has become as thin as the diameter of the smallest oil droplet that can be produced by the action of the detergent solution.   Thus an oiled surface cannot be completely de-oiled by emulsification alone.   Unless the contact angle θ_{SOW} at the solid–oil–bath boundary line can be brought to 180°, that is, unless complete roll-back is involved, some oil will remain attached to the substrate.   If the initial oil layer is completely spread over the solid surface, no portion of the solid can be completely freed of oil unless θ_{SOW} is brought to a value greater than zero, that is, unless some roll-back is involved.

3. Solubilization Mechanism

a. Solubilization at Low Surfactant Concentrations

Aqueous solutions of surfactants that are above their critical micelle concentration (cmc) but are still relatively dilute are capable of dissolving appreciable proportions of various water-insoluble oily materials.   If the oily substance happens to constitute a soil on a solid surface this dissolving effect can presumably be an important avenue of soil removal.   The molecular mechanisms of solubilization, and the effects of chemical constitution of the solubilizing surfactant and the solubilized oil, have been the subject of much study (22, 23).

We may loosely regard the micelle as a more or less spherical agglomerate of about 50–400 surfactant units, arranged with their nonpolar tails pointing inward and their polar heads outward toward the aqueous medium.   The solubilizate can become associated with the micelle (and thereby dissolved in the water–surfactant mixture) in any of the following ways.   (1) If the solubilizate is a hydrocarbon, that is, essentially nonpolar, it can become dissolved, in the classical sense, in the nonpolar interior of the micelle. Aliphatic hydrocarbons, mineral oils, and many aromatic and halogenated hydrocarbons dissolve in surfactant solutions according to this mechanism. (2) If the solubilizate molecules have an amphipathic structure but are water insoluble, for example, primary fatty alcohols, amines or carboxylic acids, they can arrange themselves in the micelle parallel to the surfactant molecules, that is, tails in and heads out.   (3) Solubilizate molecules that have two polar ends, for example, esters of dicarboxylic acids, can become associated with the polar outer portions of the micelle.   (4) If the surfactant is of the polyoxyethylene nonionic type it may solubilize certain types of polar molecules by association through the hydrophilic polyoxyethylene moiety.

The introduction of solubilized material into a surfactant solution has an effect on the critical micelle concentration, the micelle size, and other micelle-related properties.   It also affects the solubility of the surfactant in the aqueous medium, or to be more precise, the shape of the composition–temperature phase diagram of the total system, and a great array of secondary utilitarian properties.   Regarding the relationship between solubilization and detersive phenomena, however, the quantities of greatest interest are the amount of oil that can be solubilized and the rate at which it is taken into solution.   The quantity that is solubilized at equilibrium depends primarily on the concentration of surfactant micelles in solution.   It is therefore conveniently expressed as grams of oil solubilized per gram of surfactant in the system, or as a percentage dissolved oil based on the surfactant.   This percentage varies quite widely with the chemical structures of both oil and surfactant, as might be expected.   It also varies to a certain extent with temperature.   If the solubilization exceeds 10% the oil is considered to have a reasonably high solubility in the surfactant, and in the relatively dilute solutions we are discussing the solubilization seldom exceeds 50–60%.   It is evident that the solubilization will increase with increasing surfactant concentration because of the increased proportion of surfactant in micellar form.   Relatively little data is available on the rate at which oils become solubilized.   The rate is presumably diffusion controlled, and depends also on the area of the oil–water interface, that is, on the size of the oil droplets.

An oil-soiled surface can be cleaned via solubilization to about the same extent as by the action of conventional solvents for the oil.   It is probable that surfactant which is strongly sorbed on the solid surface will retain a certain amount of associated oil, but this will be of no practical consequence in most cases.   Solubilization can accordingly be an important mechanism for removing the small amounts of oil that cannot be removed by roll-back or emulsification.

It should be noted that the material solubilized by this mechanism need not be an "oil" in the sense of being a liquid at the temperature of the process. Cetyl alcohol, for example, can be readily solubilized at temperatures well below its melting point by aqueous solutions of fatty alkyl sulfate surfactant.

b. Solubilization at High Surfactant Concentrations (Penetration; Phase Transition)

At high concentrations, in the range of 10–100 times the cmc, aqueous surfactant solutions solubilize organic materials by a somewhat different molecular mechanism. Over a rather wide range of water–surfactant–oil proportions the system consists of a single liquid phase, which is usually liquid crystalline in nature. As at lower surfactant concentrations, the quantity of oil solubilized depends on the molecular structures of surfactant and oil. Polar oils are solubilized to a greater extent than nonpolar oils. The complete phase diagrams for a large number of surfactant–water–oil systems have been published (24, 25). The ratio of oil to surfactant in the homogeneous single-phase region is about the same as it is at low concentrations. In this phase the surfactant apparently does not exist in the form of small spherical micelles. The surfactant molecules are presumed to form extended sheets in which they are oriented perpendicular to the plane of the sheet. The sheets lie parallel to each other with heads facing heads, and tails facing tails. Water is concentrated between the heads. Polar oils are disposed between the tails and partly interspersed in the surfactant sheets. Nonpolar oils are held between the tails. The whole system forms a smectic or a nematic liquid crystal (26).

Concentrated surfactant solutions can dissolve oil from a solid surface to about the same extent as dilute solutions, but the action seems more extensive simply because the higher concentration of surfactant allows a higher absolute quantity of oil to be solubilized. The rate at which oil is solubilized when the proportions of surfactant and water are correct is very rapid, as in most phase changes, being limited only by the rate at which the latent heat can be transferred.

At certain proportions some surfactant–water–oil systems form micro-emulsions (27). These appear to be homogeneous and are difficult to distinguish from the single-phase solubilized systems. For purposes of practical detergency there is probably little difference between the two. The particle size of the oil droplets in microemulsions is so small that the considerations of breaking at the solid surface (discussed above in connection with the emulsification mechanism of cleaning) probably do not apply. In either case the oil appears to be removed from the solid surface as it would be by an organic solvent. During rinsing, furthermore, the surfactant is diluted and microemulsified oil may become truly solubilized via the micellar solubilization mechanism. Concentrated surfactant solutions are notably good cleaning agents, and their effect is in many cases due to their solubilizing action rather than to roll-back or other mechanisms.

4. Oil Removal by Surface Film Formation

Certain water-soluble liquids when placed on a water surface will spread indefinitely, forming at first a duplex film and eventually a monomolecular film. Fatty glycerides and fatty acids, as well as many other amphipathic substances, generally behave in this manner. If a solid substrate, for example a metal strip, is coated with such an oil and is dipped part way into water, the oil will start to spread over the water just as if the substrate were not there. The oil will essentially be transferred from the metal surface to the water surface. The extent of this transfer will depend on the amount of free water surface available for the oil to spread over. By repeatedly dipping the oiled strip into fresh portions of water a very large proportion of the oil can be removed from the metal surface (28, 29). This effect can be an important mechanism of detergency if the soil is of a type that spontaneously spreads on water. It is of interest that the presence of dissolved surfactant in the water inhibits rather than promotes oil removal by this mechanism (30). This is not unexpected, since it is the difference in surface tension between the oil and water which causes the spreading. Surfactants lower the surface tension of the water, thus diminishing the driving force.

One mechanism of oily soil removal that is of great practical importance involves a true chemical reaction and therefore does not strictly conform to our definition of detergency. Many oily soils contain a considerable proportion of fatty acid. If the aqueous bath is sufficiently alkaline it will convert the fatty acid to the corresponding water-soluble surface active soap. Soap generated in situ in this manner has a powerful emulsifying action on the remaining oil. It also promotes solubilization and mesophase formation.

B. Soil Removal in Model Solid Systems

The solid soil–substrate–bath system in its initial state, immediately after the soiled substrate has been immersed in the bath, can advantageously be regarded as a flocculated or agglomerated lyophobic colloidal system. Soil removal is the dispersion or deflocculation of this system. In the general case of a substrate bearing soil particles that are in themselves agglomerates of different species of smaller particles there are really three model systems to consider: (1) the mixed colloid consisting of the semi-infinite planar wall of the substrate and the adherent soil particles, (2) the homocolloid consisting of agglomerated similar soil particles, and (3) the mixed colloid consisting of agglomerated dissimilar soil particles. As pointed out previously, the dispersion or deflocculation of the first system will remove all the soil from the substrate.   If only the second and/or third systems are deflocculated only part of the soil will be removed.   All three model systems, however, can be treated theoretically in the same manner.   Two general theories of the dispersion–agglomeration mechanism are applicable.   They are quite similar except with regard to the nature of the forces that oppose or prevent particle agglomeration.   Coulombic forces are assigned this role in the well-known theory developed independently by Derjaguin and Landau (31) and Verwey and Overbeek (32), referred to for brevity as the DLVO theory. It is particularly applicable in detersive systems where the bath contains no surfactant or a surfactant (ionic or nonionic) at a level well below the critical micelle concentration.   In the alternative theory, which might better be called a hypothesis since it is not on a firm quantitative basis, solution or osmotic forces oppose the union of soil particles to one another or to the substrate.   This theory is more applicable when the bath contains surfactants above their critical micelle concentrations.   The theories are not contradictory, and in any real system both mechanisms can work simultaneously.

The theories can both be developed along the same lines, starting with a lyophobic colloid in the dispersed state.   The particles are in Brownian motion and, according to the classical theory of Smoluchowski their collisions cause their number to diminish at a rate given by the expression

$$-\frac{dn}{dt} = 4\pi D r n^2$$

where n is the total number of particles present at time t; D is the diffusion coefficient of the particles; and r is the collision radius, that is, the distance between particle centers when they unite.   The value of r can conveniently be taken as equal to $2a$ where a is the radius of a single particle.   The value of D is given by the Einstein formula

$$D = \frac{kT}{6\pi\eta a}$$

where k is Boltzmann constant, T is the absolute temperature, η is the viscosity of the medium, and a is the radius of the particle.

By combining the two equations and integrating, we can get an expression for the half life, $t_{1/2}$, of a colloidal dispersion, that is, the time for the number of particles to become halved:

$$t_{1/2} = \frac{3\eta}{4kTn_0}$$

where n_0 is the number of particles present at the start.

For dispersions of moderate concentration, in the range of 10^9 particles/ cm^3, $t_{1/2}$ has a value on the order of a few seconds.

The above derivations assume that there are no barriers to collision and that every collision is effective. Since stable dispersions exist, we can assume an energy barrier, W, which tends to prevent collisions. The equation for coagulation rate can then be written

$$-\frac{dn}{dt} = 4\pi D r n^2 \exp\left(-\frac{W}{kT}\right)$$

and the expression for half life becomes

$$t_{1/2} = \frac{3\eta \exp(W/kT)}{4kTn_0}$$

If W is in the range of 15–$20kT$, the half life is in the range of several days rather than several seconds, and the dispersion can be considered reasonably stable. The problem of colloid stability thus becomes a problem of defining and understanding the behavior of the forces that unite the particles when they collide, and of the energy barrier W that opposes the collision.

The interaction between two small particles suspended in a liquid medium is conveniently represented by a diagram in which the interaction potential is plotted as a function of the distance between the particles. Figure 6 is such a plot. The two particles a and a' are represented in this case as spherical and of identical radius r. The distance of closest approach of their centers, without distorting the particles or otherwise invoking very strong repulsion forces, is $2r$ at which distance the net potential W_{2r} is at a minimum and is one of attraction; that is, the energy that must be put into the system to bring a' from an infinite distance to a distance $2r$ from a is negative. Curve 3, representing the net potential, is formed from the algebraic sum of curves 1 and 2, which represent the attraction potential and the repulsion potential, respectively. It is important to note that the ordinate in Figure 6 represents the *potential energy* of the two-particle system due to the forces of attraction and of repulsion that the particles exert on each other. If we regard the position of particle a as fixed with its center at $X = 0$, and start with particle a' at $X = \infty$ and push it toward a, the ordinate of each point on curve 3 corresponding to an abscissa $X = i$ gives the value E of the integral

$$E = \int_{X=\infty}^{X=i} F\, dx$$

where F represents the force which the two particles exert on each other. The value of F corresponding to any value of X is given by the *slope* of curve 3 at that point. The maximum in curve 3 at X_1 represents a distance

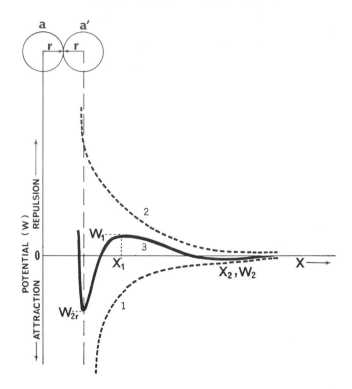

Fig. 6.   Attraction–repulsion potentials (W) between two particles (a, a') as a function of distance (X) between centers.   Curve 1 shows attraction potential; curve 2, repulsion potential; curve 3, resultant net potential.

at which the net force acting between the particles is zero, and the ordinate W_1 represents the energy barrier which must be surmounted to bring the particles close enough so that the net force between them becomes one of attraction.   In many colloidal systems the shape of curves 1 and 2 is such that another point of zero net force, corresponding to a minimum in curve 3, occurs at a considerably greater distance of separation.   This is shown in Figure 6 to occur at separation distance X_2 corresponding to a slight net potential of attraction W_2.   This dip in the curve is referred to as the "secondary minimum," to contrast with the primary minimum at $X = 2r$, and represents a position of stability for the $a - a'$ system, although one from which it is easily displaced.

Curves 1 and 2 are monotonic in opposite directions.   The form of these curves and the physical situation they represent is at the heart of the theory of colloidal stability.   The attraction potential represented by curve 1, as discussed previously, is generally considered to be due primarily to the London dispersion forces or van der Waals forces, although other forces can be involved. The strong repulsion potential represented by the portion of curve 2 left of $X = 2r$ in Figure 6 can be considered the result of Born forces and is of little interest in the present discussion. The form of curve 2 to the right of $X = 2r$ may represent the effect of either coulombic forces or osmotic forces or a combination of the two.

According to the DLVO theory, which is most applicable in systems that contain either no surfactant or an ionogenic surfactant well below the cmc, the repulsion potential is determined by the thickness and charge density of the electrical double layer around the particles which in turn are determined by the nature of the ionic species adsorbed at the interface, the degree of adsorption, and the ionic strength of the medium. The quantitative aspects of DLVO theory, and of double layer theory (i.e., the structure, formation, and interactions of electrical double layers at phase interfaces) are outside the scope of this article, but are available from several excellent sources (32, 33). Qualitatively, high charge density increases the repulsion forces and thus shifts curve 3 upward, increasing the potential W, and decreasing W_{2r}. High ionic strength shrinks the double layer, lowering curve 3, lowering W_1, and tending to increase W_{2r}. In most detersive systems the charges acquired by both substrate and solid soil are negative. The adsorption of detergent anions increases the effective density of negative charge and tends to increase the double layer repulsion potentials. The counterions, in this case metallic cations, exert the controlling effect on ionic strength, with increasing valence greatly magnifying the effect. Thus the calcium ions characteristic of hard water have a much greater effect than sodium ions in shrinking the double layer and promoting agglomeration.

One of the few experimental methods for estimating double layer potentials depends on the electrokinetic effect. If two electrodes are placed in a colloidal suspension, and a voltage is impressed across them, the particles will move toward the electrode of opposite charge. For nonconducting solid spherical particles the equation controlling this motion is

$$u = \frac{RfV\epsilon\zeta}{6\pi\eta}$$

where u = velocity of particles
   V = applied field (V/cm)
   ϵ = dielectric constant of medium
   ζ = zeta potential
   η = viscosity of medium
   R = factor for electrical relaxation
   f = factor for size of spheres

This equation is a reasonable model of electrokinetic behavior, although for theoretical studies there are many corrections that must be considered. Correction must always be made for electrokinetic effects at the wall of the cell, since this wall also carries a double layer. Correction is also required for the solvated ions through the medium, surface and bulk conductivity of the particles, nonspherical shape of the particles, etc. The parameter zeta, determined by measuring the particle velocity and substituting in the above equation, is a measure of the potential at the surface dividing the moving particle and its adherent layer of solution from the stationary bulk of the solution. Since this surface of shear lies at an indeterminate distance from the true particle surface the measured zeta potential usually correlates only semiquantitatively with the net repulsion potential, even when this is predominantly due to double layer forces.

The DLVO theory of double layer repulsion has been most successful in describing the behavior of systems in which the particles are either inherently charged or charged by virtue of having adsorbed small nonamphipathic ions. It cannot explain the fact that nonionic surfactants stabilize lyophobic suspensions and often exert a detersive effect even in solutions of high salt content. Not only nonionic detergents but even anionic surfactants can overcome to a great extent the agglomerating effects of salt. To explain this phenomenon, it is postulated that the surfactant molecules are adsorbed at the solid–solution interface in an oriented manner with the strongly hydrophilic heads in the solution. This is the expected orientation since it has the effect of lowering the surface free energy. The net result is that the original hydrophobic surface becomes essentially coated with a two-layer coating, the outer layer of which consists of groups that would by themselves be water soluble. The whole particle therefore has a tendency to behave after the manner of a soluble molecule vis-à-vis the surrounding aqueous medium. If two such particles approach too closely an osmotic pressure is built up, forcing them apart. Agglomeration can occur only if the particles approach each other with sufficient kinetic energy to break through the hydrophilic (and presumably highly hydrated) barrier over a large area. Conversely, if two particles that are adherent over a small area of contact are immersed in a surfactant solution, oriented adsorption on the non-contacting areas, followed by hydration, can presumably break the adhesive bond and force the particles apart. The energetics of this effect are similar so the energetics of solution or of diffusion (34). Since wetting is associated with low values of the solid–liquid interfacial free energy, this picture would suggest some degree of correlation between the wetting power of a surfactant for a given material and its stabilizing power for soils of the same material. Such a correlation has indeed been found by Lange (35) using paraffin wax with both nonionic and anionic surfactants.

It is probable that the cleaning of metal and ceramic surfaces by surfactant-free alkaline baths also involves a solvation mechanism. In this case, the inorganic oxide layers adsorb the strongly hydrated hydroxyl ions and/or builder anions. The solvation mechanism is in fact applicable to most situations where roll-back of oily soil occurs. The adsorbed species may be totally solvatable, as in the case of hydroxyl ion, or it may be amphipathic and adsorbed with the solvatable portion oriented outward as in the case of conventional amphipathic surfactants.

Regardless of which molecular mechanism governs the form and height of the repulsion potential curve its action in soil removal is exactly the same as in agglomeration. To apply the above arguments and the situation described by Figure 6 to primary soil removal we can regard a as an extended surface of substrate and a' as an initially attached soil particle. When this system is immersed in the bath either one or both surfaces adsorb surfactant and/or build up electrical double layers. This has the effect of pushing curve 2 toward the right, lowering the energy barrier which must be surmounted to separate the two surfaces far enough for the net force between them to become a repulsion rather than an attraction.

The action of certain water-soluble polymeric materials in aiding soil removal and inhibiting soil redeposition is somewhat analogous to that of nonionic surfactants. The polymers are not amphipathic in the ordinary sense. They can be adsorbed, however, to form relatively thick layers or coils with a statistically high proportion of their strongly hydrophilic groups outward (36). This layer forms an energetic and in a certain sense a mechanical barrier against flocculation. The effect of such hydrophilic polymers has long been recognized as "protective colloid action."

Although the coulombic and the osmotic or solvation mechanisms of colloid stabilization can in theory act independently there is little doubt that in most practical situations both are operative, interacting, and influencing each other. This is evidenced, for example, by the disproportionately strong effect of added surfactants on the electrokinetic behavior of lyophobic colloids (37, 38).

C. Redeposition

The term "redeposition of soil" suggests the concept that a bath can act via interfacial forces to separate soil from a substrate, and that sometime later in the same bath the soil will again become attached to that substrate. This can and does happen, and it is easy to understand if rate factors are taken into consideration. Beginning with the immersing of soiled substrate into the bath the chemical compositions and free energies of the various interfaces in the system are continuously changing. The rates of change are generally slow enough so that equilibrium is not reached during the periods of immersion associated with practical cleaning.   If the substrate is swellable and penetrable by the bath ingredients (as, for example, are most natural fibers) the bulk composition of the bath can also change significantly during the washing period.   Accordingly, it is quite possible in theory to have even a single-component soil removed early in the washing process and redeposited later.   Actually, redeposition rarely occurs in this manner.   In the first place, unless washing is continued for an inordinately long time in a bath that has little or no dispersing action, only a small proportion of the removed soil will become redeposited.   Secondly, and more important, the soil that redeposits is generally in quite a different state than it was at the time of removal, having meanwhile undergone transformation by action of the bath. The more important types of transformation that soils can undergo after removal are as follows.

Liquid soils that have been removed by roll-back or by emulsification, and that contain more than one component, can gradually change in composition as the components become selectively extracted via solubilization.   This effect occurs, of course, only in baths that contain surfactants.   It can become quite pronounced if the soil consists of polar and nonpolar constituents and the surfactant concentration is above the cmc (39).   Solid soils that are removed as agglomerates generally undergo further deflocculation in the bath, and the different solid species tend to separate and segregate. If the deflocculation is extensive small particles that were part of the aggregate on the substrate but were not in direct contact with the substrate become free in the bath, so that they now have a chance of colliding with the substrate. A certain amount of reaggregation can occur in the bath after initial deflocculation.   The agglomerates formed by this secondary action, which is strictly analogous to redeposition on the substrate, will generally differ in composition from those removed in the initial detersive action.   Mixed liquid–solid soils probably undergo the most significant changes in the bath.   Liquid–solid soil aggregates are frequently attached by liquid–substrate contact. They can be extensively removed by roll-back or by emulsification before any significant separation of the solid soil components occurs.   In the bath, however, by continued action of the surfactant and/or other bath solutes, the solid soil particles can become released from the oily soil and are then free to collide directly with the substrate.

Redeposition can be regarded as a soiling of the substrate while both the substrate and the soils are submerged in the bath.   The mechanisms of attachment do not differ from those already discussed.   Whether or not a particle becomes attached depends on the interfacial energies that prevail at the time of contact, the energy barrier against collision and the kinetic energy and vector velocity with which the particle and the substrate approach each other.   These considerations apply to both liquid and solid particles.

IV. DYNAMICS AND KINETICS OF SOIL REMOVAL

A. General Considerations

In practical systems the rate of soil removal and the time required to achieve satisfactory cleaning vary enormously depending on the type of system being considered. Cleaning a window with a stream of well-selected aqueous detergent can be an essentially instantaneous process. Laundering soiled apparel under ordinary conditions takes in the range of 10–20 min or more. In considering the kinetics of detergency, therefore, the use of model systems is fully as helpful as it is in other aspects of cleaning. From the point of view of kinetics detergency can be broken down into several stages. The first stage is bringing the phases together and establishing the phase interfaces where the action is going to take place. This is what happens when the soiled substrate is first immersed, and the bath displaces air to create the bath–soil and bath–substrate interfaces. In the second stage the newly created interfaces are changing their chemical and energy states, usually by adsorption of bath components; sometimes by penetration of bath components into the interior bulk of solid soil or substrate, altering its bulk as well as its surface character. The third stage of soil removal is the macroscopic, directly observable disappearance of the soil–substrate interface and its replacement by new areas of the soil–bath and substrate–bath interfaces. Each of these stages has its own characteristic rate, dependent in turn on the rates of its own component processes. The three stages, moreover, overlap one another in time. The second stage mentioned above, involving as it does adsorption and diffusion phenomena, is possibly the easiest to consider in classical physicochemical terms. The first and third stages involve phase displacement, which is essentially a macroscopic mechanical process, and merit some introductory discussion.

The displacement of one fluid phase by another, as in wetting or in the roll-back of liquid soil by a bath, can conveniently be referred to as "spreading" and can take place spontaneously or with the aid of externally applied mechanical force. The forces resisting the displacement in either case are the bulk viscosities of the two fluids and the surface or interfacial viscosities of the fluids at the fluid–solid interfaces (40–42). The driving force at any instant in the case of spontaneous spreading is related to the fluid–fluid interfacial tension and the contact angle at the fluid–fluid–solid boundary line. It is given by the expression

$$F = \gamma_{LL'}(\cos \theta_{eq} - \cos \theta_d)$$

where F is the force/cm length of fluid–fluid front, $\gamma_{LL'}$ is the interfacial tension, θ_{eq} is the equilibrium contact angle, and θ_d is the instantaneous or "dynamic" contact angle.   In the case of forced spreading this value of F is augmented by terms which depend on the shape of the advancing fluid–fluid interface near the three-phase boundary line (43).   It is the balance between the resistance and driving forces that determines the overall rate of displacement.   In any event this rate, measured as the rate of advance of the three-phase boundary line along the solid surface, seldom exceeds a few centimeters per second.   It seldom approaches this figure in spontaneous spreading except when θ_d is much greater than θ_{eq}.   In forced spreading, if the traction against the fluid–fluid interface becomes too large the interface will yield, and a bulk volume of one of the fluids will separate to form a droplet.   Since the total force against the interface is thereby diminished the displacement rate is limited.

The displacement of solid soil from a substrate is essentially the disruption of a solid–solid adhesive bond and in the context of this discussion it occurs instantaneously once the combination of interfacial energies and externally applied forces has become favorable.

In discussing the kinetics of detergency we may consider wetting and any other first-stage effects as ancillary.   Similarly ancillary are bulk changes in the substrate or any of the solid soil particles caused by swelling.   The rate of liquid soil removal in the model system is dependent on both second-stage and third-stage effects.   The rate of solid soil removal in the model system is controlled almost entirely by second-stage effects, if we assume that the rate of energy input remains constant from the start of the process.

B. Ancillary Effects

1. Wetting

It has been shown that soil removal and redeposition are the result of a series of more or less independent processes.   The energetics and rates of these processes must be considered in any attempt to explain detersive action.   The first step in most practical detersive processes is wetting the soiled substrate thoroughly with the bath, that is, displacing all the air from the system and establishing the bath–soil and bath–substrate interfaces, and the bath–soil–substrate line boundaries at which the detersive action occurs. Although the theoretical consideration of detergency does not really start until these interfaces have been established, the wetting step is of sufficient practical importance to merit some discussion.   The rate of wetting (air displacement from a solid surface by an advancing liquid front) depends on several factors, the mechanical pressure forcing the liquid to advance, the geometry of the system, the equilibrium contact angles at the liquid–solid–air boundary lines, and the static and dynamic surface tensions of the liquid being among the more important (40).   When there is no external pressure acting, and the only forces tending to advance the liquid front are surface forces the wetting is referred to as spontaneous; otherwise it is referred to as forced. In most practical systems the wetting is forced, although the ratio of external forces to surface forces may vary greatly. Even when the external force is high, as it is for example when a textile fabric is submerged in a bath, the other factors must not be too unfavorable or wetting will remain incomplete for an indefinitely long period. In general the contact angle should be as low as possible while maintaining the surface tension as high as possible. This follows from the fact that the net surface force driving the liquid forward in a capillary system is equal to $\gamma_{LV} \cos \theta$/cm of line boundary, where γ_{LV} is the surface tension of the liquid and θ is the contact angle. Unfortunately, the relationship between contact angle and surface tension (first elucidated by Zisman and co-workers (44)) is such that low contact angles tend to be formed by liquids of low surface tension. Of the two factors contact angle is usually the more important. The surfaces tension of aqueous solutions can be varied by added solutes over about a threefold range (from about 25 to 75 dyne/cm). The contact angle can vary from 0° (cos = 1) to over 90° (cos negative). The correlation between rate of wetting and $\cos \theta$ and the great influence of relatively small variation in $\cos \theta$, has been demonstrated experimentally (45). The dynamic surface tension, and the rate at which the value of the dynamic surface tension decays and approaches that of the static surface tension, has also been shown to correlate with the rate of wetting (46).

Even when other factors are favorable a complicated surface geometry, such as that of a fabric, may cause the retention of some air long after wetting appears to be complete (47), one reason why prolonged soaking before washing aids in soil removal. In general, oily soil will be wet more slowly than a hydrophilic substrate, and such a soil may tend to trap bubbles and pockets of air. Mechanical working of the soiled substrate during submersion in the bath is usually necessary to remove all air.

2. Swelling of the Substrate

Most natural textile fibers, and some synthetics such as viscose rayon, swell to a marked extent in water. This swelling has two effects on the detersive process. First, it alters the nature of the substrate surface making it more like a water surface. Second, it allows diffusion of bath components to the interior of the fiber, where they may be adsorbed and taken out of action or may diffuse to the fiber–soil interface and get directly into the action. Water enters the fiber much more rapidly and easily through clean portions of the surface than through oily-soiled portions. It must then travel laterally through the fiber to swell the portions under the soil. This action takes some time to complete, which is another reason why prolonged soaking prior to actual washing aids the cleaning of fabrics. Swelling is in most cases a diffusion-controlled process, and those factors which accelerate diffusion will accelerate swelling.

C. Adsorption

All the important detersive mechanisms except solubilization depend on attaining a favorable relationship among the various interfacial states and free energies involved in the system. This is true regardless of the chemical nature of soil or substrate. Consider a soiled substrate in which neither the substrate nor any of the soil constituents has appreciable solubility in water. If we immerse this soiled substrate in pure water the substrate–water interface and the soil–water interfaces attain their final equilibrium states the instant the air has been displaced. If the water is capable of loosening the soil to the point where it can be removed by the mechanical or thermal energy available the soil separation will proceed at a rate which depends on the various resistance factors and the mechanical and/or thermal energy input. In the typical detersive bath, which contains solutes that promote soil removal, this is not the case. The final interfacial states (which in the case of a good detergent should favor soil removal more than those provided by a bath of pure water) are attained by adsorption. This is a rate process, and in most detersive systems a long time is needed to attain equilibrium adsorption of all the important solutes, particularly the surfactants and antiredeposition agents. It is unusual for practical detersive operations to run long enough for adsorption equilibrium to be attained. The substrate has usually become clean enough to satisfy the operator, and the washing has been stopped, while physicochemical changes in the system are still proceeding at appreciable rates.

The chain of causes and effects in soil removal can be reduced to simplest terms as follows: both the rate and extent of soil loosening depend on the interfacial free energies. Interfacial free energies depend on the chemical nature, quantity, and state of the adsorbed material. At any instant after adsorption starts the quantity of any single adsorbed species on an interface depends directly on the *rate* of adsorption rather than on the equilibrium adsorption value. Although the importance of adsorption was recognized very early in the history of detergency research, and many data are available on the adsorption isotherms of surfactants and other bath components on various substrates (48–50), relatively little has been published on rates of adsorption of these materials. Most of what has been done concerns rate of adsorption at the liquid–air interface and has already been mentioned in connection with wetting and dynamic surface tension. Attempts have been made to correlate this rate with detergency effects (51, 52), but they have been of relatively limited theoretical value because of the complexity of the detersive systems used.   Rates of adsorption at liquid–liquid interfaces are studied by techniques similar to those used for the liquid–air interface (53). They should be of importance in estimating the rate and extent of liquid soil removal when either the roll-back or emulsification mechanisms are involved.

Relatively little data is available on the rates at which typical detergent bath components are adsorbed onto typical substrates or solid soils.   In an interesting recent study, however, it has been shown that a typical wetting agent is sorbed onto Graphon (graphitized carbon black) much more *rapidly* than a typical detersive surfactant of isomeric structure (54).   This indicates that the quantity of surfactant which must be sorbed before significant soil loosening occurs depends heavily on the chemical structure of the surfactant. It was long ago recognized that the so-called wetting agents, which have very little detersive power at ordinary detergent bath concentrations (about 0.2%), can be excellent detergents at higher concentrations (about 2%) (55).   This may correlate with the fact that the cmc of the wetting agents is generally higher than that of the detergents and that good detergency is not achieved at concentrations lower than the cmc (56).   These studies, like the above-mentioned attempts to correlate detergency with the extent of adsorption at equilibrium, suffer from poor definition of the detersive system.   The typical practical system to which discussions of "wetting agent vs. detergent" pertain is a cotton substrate soiled with a mixture of carbon black and oil. The most relevant simple model system is probably the cotton–carbon black system, but it might also be the cotton–oil system.   In any event until quantitative data become available relating soil loosening in these model systems to the extent and rate of adsorption, it seems likely that any apparent relationships in practical system will be quite tenuous.

D. Energy Input

Externally applied energy is used in almost all practical cleaning operations to increase both the rate and extent of soil removal.   Aside from a few unusual systems, such as those in which electrophoretic effects are used to aid cleaning (57), energy is put into the system in either thermal or mechanical form or both.

From the theoretical point of view the effect of increased temperature on any of the model systems is almost self-evident.   In all systems increased temperature increases the rate of adsorption, thereby bringing the phase interfaces to the favorable energy states more rapidly.   In liquid soil systems increased temperature decreases the viscosity of the soil, facilitating roll-back, emulsification, and solubilization.   Increased temperature increases the rate of diffusion and thereby facilitates any of the ancillary processes that are diffusion controlled, for example, swelling of the substrate.   In solid soil systems high temperatures increase the Brownian motion, which is probably as important a factor as hydraulic action in removing finely particulate soil from the substrate.

Mechanical energy input is important in all three kinetic stages of detergency. In the first stage, and in other ancillary effects in practical systems, mechanical action helps by flexing complex substrates such as fabrics, causing their surfaces to rub over one another and helping to displace soil and air. In the second stage mechanical action helps increase the rate of diffusion by tending to thin the static barrier layers, and correspondingly helps increase the rate of adsorption. Although this second-stage effect is doubtless quite significant in many instances, it is in the third-stage kinetics that mechanical action plays its most evident role.

Considering first the model liquid soil system and the emulsification mode of soil removal, little need be said about the importance of mechanical action. It is emphasized in all cogent discussions of emulsification, both practical and theoretical (58, 59). Solubilization and phase transition are basically second-stage kinetic effects, and are affected by mechanical energy input in the manner mentioned above. In the roll-back mechanism mechanical energy has several effects. In the first place it introduces the external force which acts to speed up forced spreading, that is, the displacement of oily soil by aqueous bath from the solid substrate surface. Secondly, it generates the convective hydraulic currents that cause the bath–liquid soil interface to yield, resulting in the separation of masses of liquid soil remote from the soil–substrate interface. Its third effect is connected with the geometry of the substrate, the bath ratio (ratio of quantity of bath to quantity of soiled substrate), and the value of θ_{SOW}. Consider first the case where advancing θ_{SOW} is 180°, and the oil thus separates from the substrate spontaneously. If the substrate surface is geometrically complex (a textile fabric, for example, or a metal part with bolt holes and reentrant cavities) the separated oil may still be caught and held mechanically on the surface. Mechanical agitation will shake this oil out into the bulk of the bath. If the bath ratio is high, relatively little oil will be shaken back into the holes. A high bath ratio is desirable if maximum benefit is to be derived from good agitation. When advancing θ_{SOW} is 180° it makes little difference how the liberated oil is distributed in the water phase. Whether emulsified or in bulky masses, the oil cannot redeposit on the fabric except by mechanical entrapment.

When θ_{SOW} is less than 180° some mechanical action is needed to liberate the oil even when the substrate is smooth and planar. A liberated oil droplet or oil mass that contacts the substrate can become redeposited. It is therefore important to have a high bath ratio, which minimizes the probability of redeposition. It is also important to have the oil evenly distributed in the form of small droplets throughout the bath and preferably emulsified. Vigorous mechanical action promotes the liberation and emulsification of the oil, and even though it also affords greater chance for redeposition it is, on balance, highly favorable to good cleaning. It is evident that strong agitation contributes more to systems in which $\theta_{SOW} <$ 180° than to those in which $\theta_{SOW} = 180°$, and the requirement for agitation is roughly in inverse proportion to the value of θ_{SOW}.

A certain mechanical energy input is necessary for solid soil removal. In an idealized model system we can conceive of a mechanical force being applied directly to the soil particle. The force required to separate the particle from the substrate will decrease as the ability of the detergent bath to loosen soil increases. Measurements of this type have actually been made, and will be discussed below. In practice the forces tending to separate soil from substrate are applied indirectly, usually via some form of agitation in the bath. The forces cannot be measured directly, but their average magnitude and the maximum value they attain in a given time span are assumed to be roughly proportional to the power input (power = energy/time). The proportionality constant in such a relationship depends enormously on two factors: the absolute size of the particle and the specific form of the mechanical energy input. The smaller the particle, the less probable it is that a random kinetic energy input will be translated into a separating traction (traction = force per unit area) on that particle. Furthermore, the less random and more directed the energy input, the greater the chance of obtaining the required separating traction. Another very important point in this connection has already been mentioned in connection with particle adhesion. In small particles the ratio of the area of true contact to total surface area is high. Since the adhesive traction is presumed to be very high (in the range of the cohesive strength of solids) it follows that in small particles the traction on the nonadherent surface necessary to separate particles from substrate will be much greater than in large particles. A scrubbing brush on solid surfaces, or vigorous flexing of the fabric in textile cleaning, is much more effective than a hydraulic current because it affords far greater traction on those soil particles which it affects. In practical detersive systems the precise form in which mechanical energy is introduced has been the subject of much productive study and development. The design of washing machines for fabrics, and of mechanical apparatus for cleaning solid objects, can have as great an effect on performance as the choice of detergent. An excellent example is the use of ultrasonic generators in the soak tanks used for cleaning intricate metal machine parts. Ultrasonic energy input causes cavitation at the solid–liquid interfaces. When such cavitation occurs next to an adherent soil particle it exerts a strong separating traction on that particle. Boiling of the bath has a similar effect. Those steam bubbles which are nucleated and generated near or on a soil particle can exert a far stronger separating traction than a simple hydraulic current.

It is evident from these considerations that if we attempt to correlate the rate and extent of soil removal with a simple average power input to the system, we can expect only the most tenuous of relationships. The detailed mechanical arrangement and the disposition of soil on substrate are much more important. If these latter factors are kept reasonably constant, however, the effect of power input per se can become evident.

V. EXPERIMENTAL STUDIES ON MODEL SYSTEMS

A major thesis of this discussion has been the highly diversified nature of detergency theory. The fact is that the effects encountered in the art and technology of detergency must be carefully and extensively fragmented before they are amenable to theoretical treatment. The individual fragments, which we have called model systems, are models for *phenomenological* study. When the individual phenomena have been isolated and identified the theories of colloidal behavior can be applied to them. As mentioned previously, most attempts to apply colloid theory to detergency have been limited in their success because the detersive systems which were chosen as dependent variables in the equation were too complicated. We shall refer to these studies only in passing, if at all, despite the fact that over the years they have been of incalculable practical value. Most of them have been adequately covered in earlier treatises and reviews (60–62). Only those studies will be discussed in which the detersive systems are sufficiently simple and well defined to be considered model systems in our terminology, and the selection is intended to be illustrative and representative rather than complete.

A. Liquid Soil Systems

The roll-back mechanism of liquid soil removal was first described by Adam (63). He observed the removal of wool grease from single fibers, measuring the contact angles and their variation with the concentration of detergent in the bath. Similar studies were made by Kling and co-workers (64), using an extended range of oils and surfactant solutions on a variety of fibers. In these early experiments the quantities of oil remaining on the fibers after roll-back were not measured. Stewart and Whewell carried these lines of investigation much further, measuring removal of oil from fabrics and correlating it with contact angle measurements at the fiber–oil–surfactant solution boundary line (65, 66). Oil removal was measured by extraction in the conventional manner, and it was found that considerable amounts of oil were removed by washing even when the contact angles were much greater than zero. A very recent study with the scanning electron microscope shows the appearance of partially rolled back oily soil on textile fibers after incomplete removal in a detergent bath (67). Several other studies have been directed toward observing or identifying a particular mode of soil removal, using a model three-phase system consisting of a substrate, a single-phase oily soil, and an aqueous bath. Among these are the work of Harris and co-workers in solubilization (68, 69), Lawrence on mesophase formation (70), Stevenson on the osmotic effect in swellable substrates (71), and Hamilton and Jennings on film transfer (72).

A large proportion of the more important and more recent work on soil removal, particularly of liquid soils in model systems, has utilized radio-tagged soil components to facilitate precise measurement of soil removal down to extremely low levels of residual oil on the substrate (73, 74). By tagging the different soil components with different tags, of which tritium, carbon-14, and sulfur-35 are the most widely used, any fractionation of oily soil that might occur during removal from the substrate can be observed. A series of studies by Gordon and co-workers has shown clearly that such fractionation does occur, polar oils such as fatty acids and fatty alcohols being removed at a much different rate than are hydrocarbon oils (75, 76). This strongly indicates that solubilization accounted for a significant proportion of the soil removal under their experimental conditions, since neither roll-back nor emulsification would separate the mutually dissolved components of a single phase (77).

If we regard detergency from the purely experimental, macromechanistic point of view there are five major factors that are controlling. These are as follows: (1) the chemical nature of substrate, bath, and soil, respectively; (2) the concentration of each component in each phase. Of special practical importance are the concentrations of the various bath ingredients since these can be controlled in practice to optimize the result; (3) time of processing; (4) temperature; and (5) mechanical energy input. From the micro-mechanistic or molecular point of view the variables of interest are (1) the various intermolecular potentials at the phase boundaries, and their dependence on molecular structure and geometry; and (2) mass and energy transfer and their dependence on the microenvironment (viscosity, temperature, concentration, etc.). Elucidation of the micromechanisms and the relationship between these micro- and macromechanisms is, of course, the heart of colloid science. Besides this writer many investigators in the field of detergency have recognized explicitly that the effects of the various factors can best be worked out in a meaningful manner if the experiments are performed on model systems. This tactic has been adopted not only for oily soils but also for particulate soils by Lange and co-workers, who recently studied the effect of surfactant (dodecyl benzenesulfonate) concentration on the removal of polar and nonpolar oils and soot from wool fibers, relating it to surface tension, electrophoretic mobility, and adsorption (78).

Fort, Billica, and Grindstaff (79) studied the removal of fatty acid, fatty alcohol, hydrocarbon, and triglyceride oils from cellulose, nylon, polyethylene terephthalate, and Teflon FEP fluorocarbon polymer, using aqueous solutions of various typical anionic, nonionic, and cationic surfactants. The substrate materials in their model systems were in the form of flat sheets. The soils were radiotagged with ^{14}C, and the soil concentration on the substrate surface was monitored by an end window Geiger counter. The detergent solutions were used mainly at 0.01 M concentration, at which they all were above their cmc levels. Temperatures and degree of agitation of the bath were varied. Similar studies were performed on woven fabrics made of the same materials as the sheets. The correlation between fabrics and flat sheets proved to be quite close. Although the soil removal values varied quite widely as the variables were changed, it was possible to select conditions which gave reasonably good soil removal for all substrates and soil combinations. In the course of the study it was proved that polar fatty soils at high wash temperatures tend to penetrate into the interior of a polyester substrate, whence it is very difficult to remove them by conventional methods.

Another excellent example of the use of model systems in the study of oily soil removal is given in a publication by Scott (80). This investigator used ^{14}C-tagged octadecane, tripalmitin, stearyl alcohol, and stearic acid on cotton fabric substrates of varying construction, and also studied the effects of detergents, electrolytes, temperature, and agitation on the soil removal. As a comparison model for the fabric structure variations, a chopped cotton fiber substrate was used. The chopped fiber technique for studying detergency was first described several years ago, and has been used very successfully in research on fibrous substrates (81, 82). The fibers, in this case cotton, are chopped to an average length in the range of 2 mm (aspect ratio in the range of 100 to 1). They are soiled by slurrying vigorously in water containing the dispersed soil, and the soil–substrate complex is filtered off with suction, being recovered as a compact mat whose soil content is then determined. The soiled fibers are washed in the detergent bath in the same way they were soiled. The residual soil content in the mat, as well as in the fouled bath and rinsings, is then determined. Scott concluded that the major modes of soil removal in his systems included roll-back, phase penetration, soap formation (chemical mode involving reaction of fatty acid soil with the alkaline bath), and breakup of adherent agglomerates of crystals of the solid fats in his soil. He was able to detail the effect of electrolytes on the various modes of soil removal, and the distribution of soil among yarn surfaces, fiber surfaces, fiber lumens, and the interior cellulosic structure of the fibers.

Using cellophane, polyester film, glass plates, and porcelain plates as model substrates Schwabe and co-workers were able to correlate the degreasing effect of sodium alkyl sulfates with their adsorption. The surfactants were tagged with ^{35}S, and ^{14}C-tagged methyl stearate was used as the soil (83). In a similar study, using this same soil and solutions of sodium tetrapropylenebenzene sulfonate as the detergent, Uhlick and co-workers have determined the effect of surfactant concentration and substrate composition on soil removal. Five different metals, four organic polymers, and three types of hard inorganic surfaces were used as substrates (84).

In systems where oily soils are removed by solubilization and/or emulsification the effects of varying soil, surfactant, surfactant concentration, temperature, and several other factors can be determined reasonably well in the absence of substrate. Such systems can be regarded as fulfilling the model requirements insofar as they are sufficiently simple to allow unequivocal interpretation of the results. A considerable number of studies of this type have been published, particularly by Japanese investigators (85–89).

The kinetics of oily soil removal by surfaces film transfer has been studied by Hamilton and Jennings, using radiotagged tristearin as soil on a stainless steel substrate (90). They found evidence of three different types of tristearin, differing in their rates of removal and their mode of attachment in the soil–substrate complex.

B. Solid Soil Systems

Among the early studies involving model solid systems was that of Compton and Hart on the relationship between the particle size of carbon black and its adhesiveness to cotton (91). This study stimulated much other work on the nature of the soil–substrate adhesive bond. Representative of more recent extensive model studies using carbon black is that of Grindstaff, Patterson, and Billica (92). They used films and fabrics of nylon, cellulose, and polyethylene terephthalate as substrates and ^{14}C-tagged blacks as the soils. Both hydrophobic and hydrophilic blacks were investigated. The general technique was quite similar to that described earlier for oily soils, and the same series of surfactants was used. The substrates were soiled not only with the tagged blacks alone, but also (in a separate series of runs) with mixtures of the blacks and an oily soil. They were able to develop quantitative data on the relationship between soil removal and detergent concentration, detergent composition, temperature, and soil concentration on the substrate surface. They found, not unexpectedly, that hydrophilic carbon was easier to remove than hydrophobic carbon, and that at least part of the effect of bleaches in a laundry bath is to oxidize the soil surface and thereby make it more hydrophilic and easier to remove. The profound effect of substrate geometry on soil removal was demonstrated by comparing cellulose and polyester in film and fabric form. The carbon soils were easier to remove from cellophane than from polyester film, but much more difficult to remove from cotton fabric than from polyester fabric. The presence of oily soil facilitated the removal of the carbon soils, an effect which is frequently encountered in practical laundering.

Various types of clay are known to be important solid constituents of the natural soils that accumulate on garments and household fabrics, and in recent years at least as much detergency research has been done with clay soils as with carbon soils. Powe was one of the early investigators to use clay-soiled swatches to simulate naturally soiled fabrics in practical detergency studies (93). More recently, Gordon and co-workers radiotagged a kaolinite clay by neutron irradiation and used it as the solid constituent of a mixed soil in which the two oily components were tagged with ^{14}C and tritium. They were able to show that a considerable proportion of the clay present on a washed swatch was not there originally, but was deposited by redeposition during washing. They also noted a difference in specific radioactivity between the original clay soil and the clay which remained adherent to the substrate. This was traced to the fact that the clay sample was heterogeneous not only with regard to particle size but also with regard to chemical composition, the composition of the larger particles differing from that of the smaller ones (94).

The differences among clays with regard to their deflocculating behavior has been pointed out by Evans and Camp as a factor in detergency (95). These investigators consider that the deflocculation of agglomerates that are adherent to the substrate is probably a more important effect in practical detergency than separation of individual clay particles from the substrate.

The specific effects of the interfacial free energies at the various soil–bath and substrate–bath interfaces as well as the adhesion forces at the soil–substrate interfaces have been studied by Berch, Peper, and Drake (96). Hydrophobic fibers, in general, tend to retain solid soils more tenaciously than hydrophilic fibers. This is because most commonly encountered soils tend to be hydrophobic, possibly due to the presence of admixed oily soil. Soft plastic substrates retain solid soil more than harder substrates.

One of the most spectacular recent advances in the technique of studying solid soil detergency has resulted from the adaptation of a centrifugal method originally developed for studying the adhesion of paint films and other adherends of small mass per unit of real contact area (97). In this procedure, which has been reviewed in detail by Krupp, the model substrate material forms the outer surface of the rotor of a high-speed centrifuge (98). The model soil particles adhering to this substrate are in the form of small spheres, all of the same material and of as nearly the same size as possible. The liquid medium of interest surrounds the substrate–soil system and rotates with the centrifuge so that it exerts no shearing stress along the substrate–soil interface. The centrifuge is spun at progressively increasing speeds until a critical speed is reached at which most of the particles separate from the substrate. A direct measure of the normal force of adhesion between soil particles and substrate is thus obtained. The nature of the liquid medium has a profound effect on this force. Surfactants and other solutes which have a detersive effect on the soil–substrate system greatly lower the force necessary to remove the soil. In many systems water alone has a similar effect (99). The method has not only been used to study many representative detersive systems, but also the various factors which affect soiling and particle adhesion in air (100). The effects observed in these almost ideal model systems parallel closely and elucidate remarkably those observed in analogous practical detergency experiments.

The measurement and study of adhesion between two different solid materials (analogs of soil and substrate) in a liquid medium (analog of the bath) is basic to an understanding of detergency, and the centrifugal method is by no means the only experimental technique that has been used. Many studies have been directed toward correlating the observed values of adhesive force with calculated theoretical values, and with values of related parameters such as zeta potential. A recent review, emphasizing Russian work in this field, has been published by Zimon (101).

C. Redeposition Systems

The redeposition effect widely observed in practical detergency can be regarded most simply as the opposite of soil removal. It consists in the more or less irreversible transfer of soil particles (which may be liquid or solid) to the substrate surface from their original position completely surrounded by the bath. It has long been recognized (and more recently, demonstrated in well-controlled experiments), however, that the method of introducing the soil into the bath has very distinct effect on the amount transferred to the substrate. If the soil is introduced as soil–substrate complex, then detached from the substrate by the bath's action, then goes back onto the substrate, the effect is called true redeposition. As stated above, this should not occur if the soil is particulate, homodisperse, unagglomerated, and consisting of only one component, conditions seldom encountered in practical laundering. If the soil is free of substrate when introduced into the bath the effect is better referred to as deposition. In general, deposition and redeposition experiments with the same soil do not give the same results (102, 103), an effect which is not surprising and which may be ascribed to any of several different causes.

Deposition is in many ways easier than soil removal to study in model systems. Many studies of the practical soil-suspending properties of carboxymethylcellulose and similar compounds have been done under conditions which would conform to our definition of model, inasmuch as the soil (usually carbon black) was reasonably homogeneous. The radiotracer studies that first elucidated the action of carboxymethylcellulose were done in this manner (104, 105). More recently an extensive series of investigations on the antideposition action of this material has been published by a group at the Unilever Research Laboratory in England. Five different carbon blacks were used, and their rate of sorption by a variety of fibers in surfactant, detergent, and electrolyte baths was measured. Electrophoretic measurements were also made on the blacks and the fibers. The authors conclude that the DLVO theory accounts for the antideposition effect, the carboxymethylcellulose not only charging the solid surfaces on which it adsorbs but also preventing close approach by its large molecular size (106, 107).

The simultaneous deposition of two different pigments onto textile fiber surfaces has been studied by Wagner (108). This system bears directly on practical laundering since more than one solid particulate species is invariably present in natural soil. It was found that one of the pigments is generally sorbed preferentially. This effect is ascribed not only to the difference in surface properties between the pigments, but also to the nonhomogeneous nature of the fiber surface, which exhibits domains of differing surface energy.

True redeposition studies using liquid radiotagged soils have also been made in model systems. Grindstaff, Patterson, and Billica used paired films of polyester and cellophane as substrates, depositing the soil on one of the films and observing its transfer through the bath to the clean film. The quantity of soil on both films and in the bath was monitored continuously, and the effects of variables such as detergent type, detergent concentration, temperature, time, and soil concentration were determined (109). Among the more interesting conclusions of this work was the fact that equilibrium between sorbed and desorbed soil was not attained even after 12 hr at washing temperatures, strongly suggesting that equilibration is not a factor in practical laundering of oily soiled fabrics.

Abbreviations

cmc	critical micelle concentration
NaCMC	carboxymethyl cellulose sodium salt

Subscripts

L	liquid phase
O	oily or nonaqueous liquid phase
OW	oil-in-water (referring to emulsions)
S	solid phase
V	vapor phase
W	watery or aqueous phase
WO	water-in-oil (referring to emulsions)

Symbols

a	particle radius
f	factor for size of sphere
k	Boltzmann constant
m	mass of a particle
n	total number of particles
r	collision radius
t	time
$t_{1/2}$	half life
u	velocity of particles
A	total surface area of a particle
A_c	area of true contact
D	diffusion coefficient
F	force
R	factor for electrical relaxation
T	absolute temperature
V	applied field
W	double layer potential or energy
ϵ	dielectric constant of the medium
γ	interfacial free energy; interface indicated by subscripts
η	viscosity
θ	contact angle; phases at line of contact indicated by subscripts; angle measured in phase indicated by middle subscript
θ_d	dynamic contact angle
θ_{eq}	equilibrium contact angle
ζ	zeta potential

References

1. J. Berch and H. Peper, *Textile Res. J.*, **33**, 137 (1963); J. Berch, H. Peper, and G. L. Drake, Jr., *Textile Res. J.*, **34**, 29 (1964).
2. J. W. Hensley and C. G. Inks, *Textile Res. J.*, **29**, 505 (1959).
3. T. Fort, Jr., H. R. Billica, and T. H. Grindstaff, *Textile Res. J.*, **36**, 99 (1966).
4. F. M. Fowkes, in "Adhesion," *Am. Soc. Testing Mat. Spec. Tech. Publ.* **360**, 1964.
5. H. Stüpel, *Fette, Seifen, Anstrichmittel*, **55**, 501, 583 (1953); N. F. Getchell, *Textile Res. J.*, **25**, 150 (1955).
6. J. Compton and W. J. Hart, *Textile Res. J.*, **23**, 158, 418 (1953); *ibid.*, **24**, 263 (1954).
7. W. Kling and H. Mahl, *Melliand Textilber*, **35**, 640 (1954). T. H. Shuttleworth and T. G. Jones, *Proc. Intern. Congr. Surface Activity*, 2nd, London, 1957, Academic Press, New York, 1957, p. 52.
8. H. Krupp, *Advan. Colloid Interface Sci.*, **1**, 122 (1967).
9. H. Krupp, *Advan. Colloid Interface Sci.*, **1**, 128ff (1967).
10. J. O. Hirschfelder, C. F. Curtiss, and R. B. Bird, *Molecular Theory of Gases and Liquids*, Wiley, New York, 1954.
11. D. Langbein, *J. Adhes.*, **1**, 237 (1969).
12. J. C. Bolger and A. S. Michaels in *Interface Conversion for Polymer Coatings*, P. Weiss and G. D. Cheever, Eds., Elsevier, New York, 1968.
13. C. A. Rader and A. M. Schwartz, *Textile Res. J.*, **32**, 140 (1962).
14. N. K. Adam, *J. Soc. Dyers Colourists*, **53**, 121 (1937).

15. W. Kling, E. Lange and I. Haussner, *Melliand Textilber.*, **25**, 198 (1945).
16. J. Powney, *J. Textile Inst. Trans.*, **40**, 519 (1949).
17. D. G. Stevenson, *J. Textile Inst. Trans.* **42**, 194; *ibid.*, **44**, 12 (1953).
18. W. C. Griffin, *J. Soc. Cosmetic Chemists'*, **1**, 311 (1949); *ibid.*, **5** (4), 1 (December 1954).
19. J. T. Davies and E. K. Rideal, *Interfacial Phenomena*, 2nd ed., Academic Press, New York, 1963, pp. 371ff.
20. P. Sherman, Ed., *Emulsion Science*, Academic Press, New York, 1968.
21. A. M. Schwartz, J. W. Perry, and J. Berch, *Surface Active Agents and Detergents*, Interscience, New York, 1958, p. 467; P. D. Liddiard, *Mfg. Chemist*, **1948**, 202.
22. M. E. L. McBain and E. Hutchinson, *Solubilization and Related Phenomena*, Academic Press, New York, 1955.
23. E. Hutchinson and K. Shinoda, in *Solvent Properties of Surfactant Solutions*, K. Shinoda, Ed., Marcel Dekker, New York, 1967.
24. A. S. C. Lawrence, Chapter 7 in *Surface Activity and Detergency*, K. Durham, Ed., Macmillan, London, 1961.
25. L. Mandell in *Surface Chemistry*, P. Ekwall et al., Eds., Academic Press, New York, 1965.
26. P. A. Winsor, *Chem. Ind. (London)*, **1960** (23), 632.
27. L. M. Prince, *J. Soc. Cosmetic Chemists*, **21**, 193 (1970); J. H. Schulman, W. Stoeckenius, and L. M. Prince, *J. Phys. Chem.*, **63**, 1677 (1959).
28. W. G. Jennings, S. Whitaker, and W. C. Hamilton, *J. Am. Oil Chemists' Soc.*, **43**, 130 (1966).
29. M. C. Bourne and W. G. Jennings, *Food Technol.*, **15**, 495 (1961).
30. M. C. Bourne and W. G. Jennings, *J. Am. Oil Chemists' Soc.*, **42**, 546 (1965).
31. B. Derjaguin and L. Landau, *Acta Physicochem. USSR*, **14**, 633 (1941); see also B. Derjaguin, *Discussions Faraday Soc.*, **18**, 85 (1954).
32. E. J. W. Verwey and J. Th. G. Overbeek, *Theory of the Stability of Lyophobic Colloids*, Elsevier, Amsterdam, 1948.
33. H. R. Kruyt, Ed., *Colloid Science*, Vol. I, Elsevier, New York, 1952.
34. E. L. Mackor and J. H. Van der Waals, *J. Colloid Sci.*, **7**, 535 (1952).
35. H. Lange, *J. Phys. Chem.*, **64**, 538 (1960); *Kolloid-Z.*, **169**, 124 (1960).
36. H. L. Frisch and R. Simha, *J. Phys. Chem.*, **58**, 507 (1954); *ibid.*, **59**, 633 (1955).
37. R. H. Ottewill in *Nonionic Surfactants*, M. J. Schick, Ed., Marcel Dekker, New York, 1967, pp. 658ff.
38. W. Kling and H. Lange, *Kolloid-Z.*, **127**, 19 (1952).
39. B. E. Gordon, J. Roddewig, and W. T. Shebs, *J. Am. Oil Chemists' Soc.*, **44**, 289 (1967).
40. A. M. Schwartz, *Ind. Eng. Chem.*, **61**, 10 (1969).
41. W. Rose and R. W. Heins, *J. Colloid Sci.*, **17**, 39 (1962).
42. T. D. Blake and J. M. Haynes, *J. Colloid Interface Sci.*, **30**, 421 (1969).
43. G. Friz, *Z. Angew. Phys.*, **19**, 374 (1965).
44. W. A. Zisman, *Advan. Chem. Ser.*, **43**, 1 (1964).
45. F. M. Fowkes, *J. Phys. Chem.*, **57**, 298 (1953).
46. I. J. Gruntfest, *Textile Res. J.*, **21**, 861 (1951); H. Lange, *Kolloid-Z.* **121** (3), 130 (1951).
47. E. M. Buras, Jr., C. F. Goldthwait, and R. M. Kraemer, *Textile Res. J.* **20**, 239 (1950); I. J. Gruntfest, O. B. Hager, and H. B. Walker, *Am. Dyestuff Reptr.*, **36**, 225 (1947).
48. R. H. Ottewill in *Nonionic Surfactants*, M. J. Schick, Ed., Marcel Dekker, New York, 1967, pp. 629 ff.

49. K. Shinoda et al., *Colloidal Surfactants*, Academic Press, New York, 1963, Chapter 3.
50. J. J. Kipling, *Adsorption from Solutions of Non-Electrolytes*, Academic Press, New York, 1965, Chapter 15.
51. A. E. Vandergrift and B. J. Rutkowski, *J. Am. Oil Chemists' Soc.*, **44**, 107 (1967).
52. E. J. Burcik, *J. Colloid Sci.*, **8**, 520 (1953).
53. W. Kling and H. Lange, *Proc. Intern. Congr. Surface Activity*, 2nd, London, 1957, **1**, 295.
54. A. C. Zettlemoyer, V. V. Subba Rao, and R. J. Fix, *Nature*, **216**, 683 (1967).
55. A. M. Schwartz and J. W. Perry, *Surface Active Agents*, Vol. 1, Interscience, New York, 1949, pp. 117ff.
56. W. C. Preston, *J. Phys. Chem.*, **52**, 84 (1948).
57. British Iron and Steel Research Assoc., Brit. Pat. 1,061,103 (March 8, 1967).
58. P. Becher, *Emulsions—Theory and Practice*, 2nd ed., Reinhold, New York, 1965.
59. W. C. Griffin in Kirk-Othmer *Encyclopedia of Chemical Technology*, 2nd ed. Vol. 8, Wiley-Interscience, New York, 1965, p. 117.
60. W. Kling, in K. Lindner, Ed., *Tenside-Textilhilfsmittel-Waschrohstoffe*, 2nd ed., Wissenchaftliche Verlag, Stuttgart, 1964.
61. A. M. Schwartz, in Kirk-Othmer *Encyclopedia of Chemical Technology*, 2nd ed., Vol. 6, Wiley-Interscience, New York, 1964.
62. K. Durham in K. Durham, Ed., *Surface Activity and Detergency*, Macmillan, London, 1961.
63. N. K. Adam, *J. Soc. Dyers Colourists*, **53**, 121 (1937); N. K. Adam and D. G. Stevenson, *Endeavour*, **12**, 25 (1953).
64. W. Kling, E. Lange, and I. Haussner, *Melliand Textilber.*, **25**, 198 (1945).
65. J. C. Stewart and C. S. Whewell, *Textile Res. J.*, **30**, 903 (1960).
66. J. C. Stewart and C. S. Whewell, *Textile Res. J.*, **30**, 912 (1960).
67. R. E. Pence and A. L. Wurstner, *J. Am. Oil Chemists' Soc.*, **37**, 147 (1960).
68. M. E. Ginn and J. C. Harris, *J. Am. Oil Chemists' Soc.*, **38**, 605 (1961).
69. J. C. Harris and J. Satanek, *J. Am. Oil Chemists' Soc.*, **38**, 244 (1961).
70. A. S. C. Lawrence, *Discussions Faraday Soc.*, **25**, 51 (1958).
71. D. G. Stevenson in *Surface Activity and Detergency*, K. Durham, Ed., Macmillan, London, 1961.
72. W. C. Hamilton and W. G. Jennings, *J. Colloid Interface Sci.*, **26**, 471 (1968).
73. J. C. Harris and W. H. Yanko, *Am. Soc. Testing Mat. Bull.*, **158**, 49 (1949).
74. B. E. Gordon, *J. Am. Oil Chemists' Soc.*, **45**, 367 (1968).
75. B. E. Gordon, W. T. Shebs, and R. U. Bonnar, *J. Am. Oil Chemists' Soc.*, **44**, 711 (1967).
76. B. E. Gordon, J. Roddewig, and W. T. Shebs, *J. Am. Oil Chemists' Soc.*, **44**, 289 (1967).
77. H. Schott, *Textile Res. J.*, **39**, 296 (1969).
78. C. -P. Kurzendorfer and H. Lange, *Fette, Seifen, Anstrichmittel*, **71** (7), 561 (1969).
79. T. Fort, Jr., H. R. Billica, and T. H. Grindstaff, *J. Am. Oil Chemists' Soc.*, **45**, 354 (1968).
80. B. A. Scott, *J. Appl. Chem. (London)*, **13**, 133 (1963).
81. J. Powney and A. J. Feuell, *Res.*, **2**, 331 (1949).
82. J. Compton and W. J. Hart, *Ind. Eng. Chem.*, **43**, 1564 (1951).
83. K. Schwabe, D. C. K. Schaurich, and D. C. G. Wasow, *Tenside*, **6** (5), 261 (1969).
84. H. Uhlich, K. Schumann, and W. Nowak, *Tenside*, **4** (5), 133 (1967).
85. F. Tokiwa, *J. Phys. Chem.*, **72**, 1214 (1968).
86. F. Tokiwa, *J. Phys. Chem.*, **72**, 4331 (1968).

87. T. Mitsui and Y. Machida, *J. Soc. Cosmetic Chemists*, **20**, 199 (1969).
88. T. Tsunoda and Y. Oba, *Yukagaku*, **18**, 41 (1969); *Chem. Abstr.*, **70**, 69479a (1969).
89. T. Tsunoda and Y. Oba, *Yukagaku*, **17**, 82 (1968); *Chem. Abstr.*, **68**, 88412y (1968).
90. W. C. Hamilton and W. G. Jennings, *J. Colloid Interface Sci.*, **26**, 478 (1968).
91. J. Compton and W. J. Hart, *Textile Res. J.*, **23**, 158 (1953); *ibid.*, **24**, 263 (1954).
92. T. H. Grindstaff, H. T. Patterson, and H. R. Billica, *Textile Res. J.*, **37**, 564 (1967).
93. W. C. Powe, *Textile Res. J.*, **29**, 879 (1959).
94. B. E. Gordon and W. T. Shebs, *J. Am. Oil Chemists' Soc.*, **46**, 537 (1969).
95. W. P. Evans and M. Camp, *Proc. Intern. Congr. Surface Activity*, *4th*, *1964*, **3**, 259 (Gordon and Breach, London, 1967).
96. J. Berch, H. Peper, and G. L. Drake, Jr., *Textile Res. J.*, **34**, 29 (1964).
97. J. W. Beams, J. B. Breazeale, and W. L. Bart, *Phys. Rev.*, **100**, 1657 (1955).
98. H. Krupp, *Advan. Colloid Interface Sci.*, **1**, 208 (1967).
99. W. Kling, *Fette, Seifen, Anstrichmittel*, **69**, 676 (1967).
100. G. Boehme et al., *Z. Angew. Phys.*, **16**, 486 (1964), *ibid.*, **19**, 265 (1965).   *Proc. Intern. Congr. Surface Activity*, *4th*, *1964*, **2**, 429 (Gordon and Breach, London, 1967).
101. A. D. Zimon, *Adhesion of Dust and Powder*, Plenum Press, New York, 1969.
102. W. H. Smith, M. Wentz, and A. R. Martin, *J. Am Oil Chemists' Soc.*, **45**, 83 (1968).
103. J. W. Hensley, *J. Am. Oil Chemists' Soc.*, **42**, 993 (1965).
104. J. Stawitz, W. Klaus, and P. Hoepfner, *Fette, Seifen, Anstrichmittel*, **60**, 94 (1958)
105. J. W. Hensley and C. G. Inks, *Textile Res. J.*, **29**, 505 (1959).
106. P. G. Evans and W. P. Evans, *J. Appl. Chem. (London)*, **17**, 276 (1967).
107. G. A. Johnson et al., *J. Appl. Chem. (London)*, **17**, 283 (1967); *ibid.*, **17**, 288 (1967); *ibid.*, **18**, 235 (1968).
108. E. F. Wagner, *Fette, Seifen, Anstrichmittel*, **68**, 753 (1966).
109. T. H. Grindstaff, H. T. Patterson, and H. R. Billica, *Textile Res. J.*, **40**, 35 (1970).

Friction, Lubrication, and Wear

D. TABOR

Surface Physics Department, Cavendish Laboratory, University of Cambridge, Cambridge, England

I. INTRODUCTION

This survey is divided into three parts, friction, lubrication, and wear, and for convenience each theme is treated as a separate entity.   The literature is enormous and contains papers which range very greatly in quality.   For this reason the choice of references reflects the author's own interests and to some extent his own outlook.

The first part deals with the friction between solids.   It shows that friction arises primarily from adhesion at the points of real contact.   A second factor arises if the asperities on a hard surface produce grooving or cutting in the other surface.   Although these two processes are simple to grasp, the detailed interaction of many other factors greatly complicates the observed behavior.   Perhaps the most important of these is surface contamination or oxide films.

The second part deals with lubrication.   Under favorable conditions the surfaces can be completely separated by a hydrodynamic or elastohydrodynamic film which is able to prevent contact between the surfaces.   Under these conditions the friction is small and the wear negligible.   If, however, the thickness of the film is less than the height of the surface asperities the main factor involved is the formation of a chemisorbed or chemically formed protective film.   A survey of the literature shows that there is very little information concerning the strength properties of these films or of the way in which they are broken down.

The third part discusses the main mechanisms of wear.   Most of these are well understood.   However, wear as a general phenomenon is usually very complex.   This is largely because of the involved way in which the individual wear processes interact with one another.

II. FRICTION

A. Introduction

If two bodies are placed in contact under a normal load W, a finite force is required to initiate or maintain sliding: this is the force of friction and may be designated F_s for static and F_k for kinetic conditions. There are two basic laws of friction. They were first discovered by Leonardo da Vinci (1) (then forgotten), rediscovered by Amontons (2), and rediscovered yet again by Coulomb (3). They are that the frictional force is (1) proportional to the load, and (2) independent of the geometric area of the bodies. These laws are roughly true over a wide range of conditions. There is a third law which states that the kinetic friction is about one third the normal load but this is of much more limited validity.

In what follows we shall make use of the frictional model that has been widely accepted over the last two or three decades (4–6), namely, that friction between unlubricated surfaces arises from two main factors. The first, and usually the more important, factor is the adhesion which occurs at the regions of real contact: these adhesions, welds, or junctions have to be sheared if sliding is to occur. Consequently, if A is the true area of contact and s the average shear strength of the junctions, this part of the friction may be written $F_{\text{adhesion}} = As$. The second factor arises from the plowing, grooving, or cracking of one surface by asperities on the other. We may call this the deformation term P. Then if there is negligible interaction between these two processes we may add them and write

$$F = F_{\text{adhesion}} + F_{\text{deformation}} = As + P \qquad (1)$$

It is clear that the factors of major importance here are the area of real contact A, the strength of adhesion between the surfaces, the shear strength s of the interface, possible interactions between A and s, the deformation component P, and possible interactions between this and the adhesion component of friction. Before dealing with these we shall first consider the nature and topography of solid surfaces.

B. The Nature and Topography of Solid Surfaces

There are many techniques for studying solid surfaces. The structure is best studied with Low Energy Electron Diffraction (LEED) at normal incidence or High Energy Electron Diffraction (HEED) at glancing incidence, or by field ion microscopy though this necessitates the formation of fine tips of very small radius of curvature. All these studies show how difficult it is to obtain pure clean surfaces. The most elaborate steps involving heating in very high vacuum, ion bombardment, and preferential chemical attack may all be needed to remove the last traces of surface contaminant. Even very small quantities of bulk impurity (of order 1 ppm) may diffuse to the surface during the cleaning process. When finally cleaned, a surface can be kept clean in a high vacuum for fairly protracted periods. A safe generalization is that at 10^{-6} torr a monolayer of gas will take about 1 sec to form assuming a sticking coefficient of unity, at 10^{-10} torr about 10^4 sec, that is, over 2 hr.

The topography of surfaces may be studied by optical microscopy especially if a metallographic section is made, or by profilometry, which can give extremely high vertical resolution. Both techniques, however, give only a line section. By contrast, optical interference between the surface and an optical flat gives surface contours. Surface contours can be studied very graphically using the scanning electron microscope (which does not necessitate a replica) or by transmission electron microscopy: this needs a replica but can give extremely high resolution. All these techniques show that most surfaces are not atomically smooth over more than very restricted areas. The outstanding exception is mica, which cleaves along molecular planes over areas of several square centimeters.

C. Metal Surfaces in Air

Metal surfaces, even if they are noble, immediately adsorb oxygen and water vapor if exposed to the air: this film may not be more than a few molecules thick (7). With reactive metals there is initially some chemisorption which soon gives way to chemical combination and the formation of oxides or hydroxides. During the early stages of oxide growth there may be rearrangement of the surface atoms of the metal, which in a more exaggerated form can lead to faceting. The oxide may then grow to a thickness of the order of 50–100 Å by a process of diffusion of metal ions through the oxide or by oxygen ions through the oxide to the metal surface. Some oxides are epitaxial and firmly linked to the substrate; they can impede diffusion. In that case the oxidation soon comes to an end and the material appears to be noncorrosive or even "noble" (e.g., chromium, rhodium). In other cases the oxide is in marked mismatch with the substrate and cracks as it grows, so exposing fresh metal for further oxidation. Oxides may be amorphous or crystalline; they may be smooth or they may grow as crystals and whiskers so that the surface resembles a disorderly array of skyscrapers (8, 9).

D. Mechanically Prepared Surfaces

Mechanically abraded or polished metal surfaces are those frequently used in frictional studies. This is largely because abrasion under running water is an easy and convenient method of removing grease films and similar

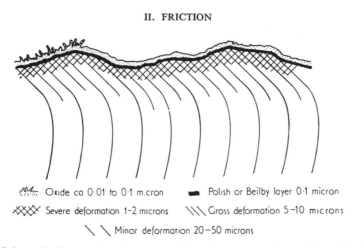

Oxide ca 0·01 to 0·1 m.cron   ▬ Polish or Beilby layer 0·1 micron

Severe deformation 1-2 microns   Gross deformation 5–10 microns

Minor deformation 20–50 microns

Fig. 1. Schematic diagram showing topography and structure of a typical polished metal specimen.

contaminants. Such surfaces are very rough on an atomic scale but if one approximates the asperities to cones, pyramids, or furrows the slopes are small, rarely exceeding a few degrees. The material in the surface is heavily deformed and if polishing has been carried out at high speeds the surface layer may consist of smeared "fudge" of metal, metal oxide, and polishing powder. On top of this layer a new oxide forms which will have a structure and topography depending on the conditions of growth. Below the deformed surface layer the metal usually shows vestigial traces of deformation produced in earlier stages of abrasion (10). A diagrammatic representation of this is shown in Figure 1. It is clear that such surfaces are neither smooth nor simple.

E. The Area of Contact between Surfaces: Analytical Models

The friction between surfaces can arise only at the regions of real contact so that for the two laws of friction to be true the area of contact A must be proportional to the load and independent of the size of the bodies. Such a view seemed completely untenable to the early workers, especially Coulomb (3). The French workers recognized that their surfaces were rough but considered that the contact between them resembled the contact between pieces of a jigsaw puzzle. Consequently the area of contact is the same as the geometric area; it does not depend on the load and increases with the size of the bodies. For these reasons they rejected the adhesion mechanism. They attributed friction primarily to the dragging of one surface up the asperities on the other. If the average slope is θ the coefficient of friction is then $\mu = \tan\theta$ and the load and size of the bodies do not come into the picture. Of course, as Leslie (11) pointed out in 1804, such a mechanism is nondissipative since the sliding body, on the average, remains at a constant horizontal level. The problem was resolved, at least for metal surfaces, twenty or thirty years ago in the following way (4, 5). As we saw above, metal surfaces are never smooth on an atomic scale. When placed in contact the tips of the asperities are deformed, at first elastically; for loads exceeding more than a minute value the elastic limit is exceeded and plastic flow occurs. It turns out that the local plastic yield pressure p_0 is very nearly constant and is comparable to the indentation hardness of the metal. Under these conditions the area of contact for any one asperity bearing a load w_1 is $A_1 = w_1/p_0$ so that for an assembly of asperities the total area is

$$A = A_1 + A_2 + \cdots = \frac{w_1}{p_0} + \frac{w_2}{p_0} + \cdots = \frac{W}{p_0} \tag{2}$$

where W is the total load. The area is thus proportional to the load and independent of the size or smoothness of the surfaces. This conclusion is in harmony with the observation that the sliding of metals is generally accompanied by plastic deformation at the interface and by tearing and shearing of the metals.

During the last decade or so a great deal of interest has been shown in other models involving other types of deformation, particularly elastic deformation. Archard (12), for example, considered the contact between surfaces covered with asperities of spherical shape. The two extreme types of deformation are purely plastic and purely elastic. For purely plastic deformation the area of contact is proportional to the load, as we saw above. For purely elastic deformation the area of each contact will be proportional to $w^{2/3}$. There are now two distinct ways in which elastic deformation can occur:

1. The number of asperity contacts remains constant so that an increase in load increases the elastic deformation of each contact. The area of real contact is then proportional to $W^{2/3}$.

2. The average area of each deformed asperity remains constant and increasing the load increases the number of regions of contact proportionally. Clearly the real area of contact is directly proportional to W.

Archard concluded that in any real situation where elastic deformation occurs the area of contact will be proportional to W^m where m lies between $\frac{2}{3}$ and 1. This is supported by a more detailed analysis. For example, Lodge and Howell (13) considered a spherical surface (radius R) covered with a close-packed array (n/cm^2) of hemispheres of radius r. For elastic deformation the true area of contact turns out to be

$$A = kr^{2/3}n^{1/3}R^{2/9}W^{8/9} \tag{3}$$

If the asperities are covered with still smaller asperities then, as Archard has shown, A becomes proportional to $W^{26/27}$. Thus a multiple-asperity model involving purely elastic deformation tends to give an area almost linearly proportional to the load. Such a model would not give a power of W greater than unity. However, Mølgaard (14) has shown that such a situation is possible over a limited load range if the contour of the surfaces has a suitable geometry. The contour is such that, in effect, there is a collapse from one asperity-covered level to a neighboring level as the load is increased.

A much more penetrating analysis has recently been given by Greenwood and Williamson (15). They consider how the asperities will deform if they have a finite elastic limit. For simplicity Greenwood first considers the behavior of surfaces for which the asperity heights follow an exponential distribution. He shows that whatever the law of deformation this will give an area of contact directly proportional to the load. Physically this means that the *average* size of the asperity contacts remains constant whatever the load so that doubling the load doubles the number of asperity contacts. Even if, say, $x\%$ of the contacts are plastic and the remainder elastic, the same conclusion follows. There will always be $x\%$ plastic. As the load increases the existing contacts will increase in size but new smaller ones will be formed so that the load–area proportionality will remain.

Real surfaces do not, however, show an exponential distribution. A study of surface profiles shows that the distribution is much more nearly Gaussian (Figure 2). The deformation behavior now depends on two main parameters: (1) the surface topography which can be described by the ratio σ/β where σ is the mean deviation of the asperity heights and β the radius of the tips of the asperities (assumed spherical), and (2) the deformation properties of the material as represented by the ratio of the elastic to the plastic properties. This can be written E'/p_0 where E' is the reduced Young's modulus and p_0 is the pressure at which local plastic deformation occurs. Both parameters are dimensionless and the product is termed the plasticity index

$$\Psi = \left(\frac{E'}{p_0}\right)\sqrt{\sigma/\beta} \tag{4}$$

Greenwood shows that if $\psi < 0.6$ the deformation will be elastic over an enormous range of loads. We can see that this corresponds to materials for which p_0 is large compared with E, and/or to smooth surfaces for which σ is small compared with β. In this regime the asperity contact pressure increases somewhat as the load increases but the change is not large. The contact pressure is of order $0.3E'(\sigma/\beta)^{\frac{1}{2}}$ over a very wide range of loads so that the true area of contact is again roughly proportional to the load.   For very smooth surfaces the true contact pressure turns out to be between 0.1 and $0.3p_0$.

For most engineering surfaces $\psi > 1$; the deformation is now plastic over an enormous range of loads and the true contact pressure is p_0.   This is the simple model described above: the area of contact is again proportional to the load.

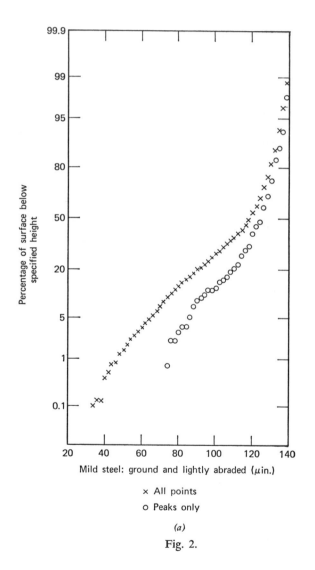

Mild steel: ground and lightly abraded (μin.)

× All points

o Peaks only

(a)

Fig. 2.

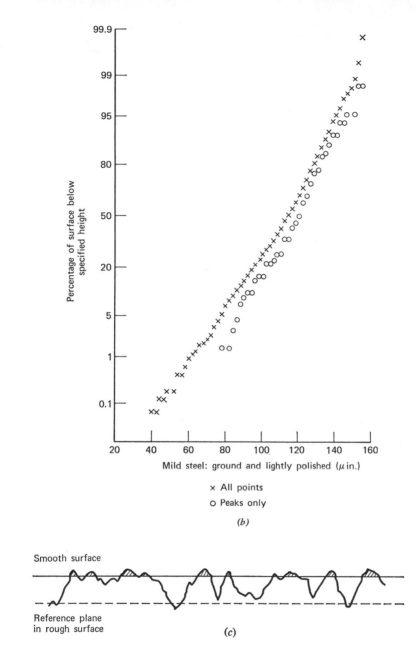

× All points
○ Peaks only

(b)

Smooth surface

Reference plane
in rough surface   *(c)*

Fig. 2. (*a*) Cumulative height distribution for a mild steel surface, ground and lightly abraded. (*b*) Ground and lightly polished. A perfect Gaussian distribution would give a straight line. The results show that both the distribution of all heights (×) and of the peak heights (○) are very nearly Gaussian. (*c*) Contact of a rough deformable surface with an ideally smooth hard surface. The load is supported by the shaded areas.

253

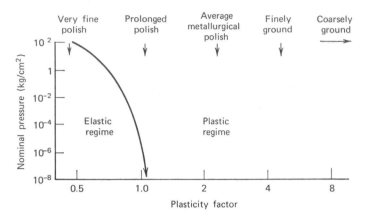

Fig. 3. Graph showing the nominal pressure at which the transition from elastic to plastic deformation occurs. The data, taken from Greenwood and Williamson (15), are for a flat metal of specified roughness, pressed on to a flat ideally smooth hard surface. The criterion for plastic deformation is determined by the plasticity index $\psi = (E/p_0)(\sigma/\beta)^{1/2}$, where E is the reduced modulus, p_0 the plastic yield pressure, σ the standard deviation of the asperity heights, and β the radius of the asperity tips which are assumed to be spherical.

The elastic and plastic regimes are shown in Figure 3 for an aluminum surface ($p_0 \approx 4000$ Kg/cm²). In the elastic regime if the load is high enough plastic deformation may occur. The transition according to Greenwood is rather sharp so that to one side of the line all the asperities are elastic—to the other side they are all plastic. In reality this dividing line ought to be fuzzy.

We conclude that for most engineering surfaces the deformation of the asperities will be plastic and the true area of contact will be given by

$$A = \frac{W}{p_0} \tag{5}$$

For extremely smooth surfaces the deformation may be elastic and the area of contact will be given by $A = \text{load}/p$ where p is of the order $0.1–0.3p_0$.

These papers assume either elastic or plastic deformation. With polymers neither approach is valid. They are viscoelastic materials and the deformation is time dependent as well as being dependent on load and geometry. However, over a fairly wide range the contact area between a hard sphere and a smooth flat specimen of polymer (or between a smooth sphere of polymer and hard flat surface) is given by $A = W^m$ where m is generally between 0.7 and 0.8. It is possible, by making a few reasonable assumptions (16), to incorporate this behavior into the Lodge and Howell model described above. The area of contact A is then given by

$$A = k \, \frac{n^{1-m} r^{2-2m} W^{2m-m^2} R^{2(1-m)^2}}{E^{2m-m^2}} \tag{6}$$

It is seen that for $m = \frac{2}{3}$ (elastic case) this reduces to the Lodge and Howell equation. For $m = 1$ it reduces to an area of contact independent of R and proportional to W:

$$A = k \frac{W}{E} \qquad (7)$$

This corresponds to plastic deformation, and E corresponds to the hardness or yield pressure of the solid.

F. Area of Contact: Experimental

With metals some idea of the area of contact can be deduced using electrical resistance methods (4, 5). The main uncertainty arises from the fact that the electrical conductance of a junction is proportional to the *diameter* of the junction, not to its area. With nonmetals a useful experimental approach is the optical one. If the surfaces are molecularly smooth the optical area determined by interference methods, for example, will be identical with the true area of contact. The only material for which this seems to be applicable is mica (17). For other surfaces there is always some uncertainty as to the difference between the optical and real areas of contact. Adams (18) has carried out a very detailed study of the contact between a "smooth" hemisphere of nylon and a flat glass surface using interference. He finds that A is proportional to W^m where $m = 0.70$. Further, the area of contact does not change when sliding occurs; that is, there is no junction growth (see below) during sliding.

Other optical methods include phase contrast (19) and total internal reflection (20). These methods involve some uncertainty since the optical area includes a noncontacting penumbral region where light is able to cross a small gap. Further, they are limited to transparent materials.

Recently Kendall and Tabor (21) have described an ultrasonic method; a pulse is injected into one of the bodies and the acoustic energy transmitted through the interface into the other body is measured. This can be used for all materials and is not greatly affected by the presence of thin contaminant or oxide films. However the interpretation is not unequivocal since the acoustic admittance of a small constriction is proportional to its diameter, not its area. It is therefore of limited applicability.

A more satisfactory method of determining the area of contact between surfaces could be of great value in friction studies.

G. Breakdown of the Oxide Film

In most practical situations metallic surfaces are separated by thin oxide films. These are greatly deformed at the contact region. If they are ductile they will deform with the metal and inhibit metal–metal contact. If they are brittle they will crack and metal will be able to flow through the cracks (22). At a later stage the oxide will be fragmented particularly if sliding occurs and appreciable metal–metal contact will occur. The durability of the oxide during sliding depends markedly on the relative physical properties of oxide and substrate metal. Unfortunately it is not easy to specify the physical properties of the very thin surface oxide films.

H. The Adhesion Component of Friction

We consider here the contact between surfaces of identical metals under conditions where surface contamination is not serious, that is, nominally clean surfaces in air. What is the meaning of the term "real area of contact A"? It implies that over an area A the atoms on one surface are within the repulsive fields of those on the other: this is the way in which atoms "bear a load." In separating the surfaces either normally or tangentially we must overcome the *attractive* forces between the atoms. This is the origin of the strength of the interfacial junctions formed at the regions of real contact when the surfaces are brought together. Although attempts have been made to describe the frictional process in terms of atomic forces, this is not a very useful approach since real strength properties can often differ very markedly indeed from those calculated from basic atomic considerations. It is more useful to recognize that with metals a process of "cold welding" occurs at the contact regions giving interfacial junctions with a shear strength s. Then the adhesion component of friction can be written simply

$$F = As \qquad (8)$$

so that if A is proportional to the load and independent of the size of the bodies the same will apply to the friction. The coefficient of friction μ may then be written

$$\mu = \frac{F}{W} = \frac{As}{Ap_0} = \frac{s}{p_0} \qquad (9)$$

where p_0 is the plastic yield pressure of the asperities. If the metal does not work-harden appreciably s is roughly equal to the critical shear stress τ of the metal. The yield pressure or hardness p_0 is generally found to be about 5τ (23); consequently $\mu \simeq 0.2$. In practice most metals in air give a value of μ of about 1. The reason for this has been revealed by the experiments of Courtney-Pratt and Eisner (24). They studied the contact between a hemispherical slider and a flat surface where, because of the geometry, the static contact is essentially a single circular region. This could be determined optically or with electrical resistance measurements. For platinum surfaces where oxide contaminants are not present there is very good agreement

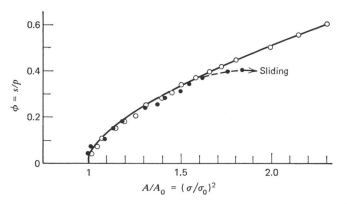

Fig. 4. Tangential force coefficient, ϕ, (where ϕ is the ratio of the tangential to the normal force during microdisplacement) plotted against area of contact A expressed as ratio of initial static area A_0. The ratio A/A_0 is calculated from the electrical conductance measurements assuming metallic contact, so that one may put $A/A_0 = (\sigma/\sigma_0)^2$, where σ_0, σ are the initial and final electric conductance values respectively. $\bigcirc$, clean platinum surfaces; $\bullet$, lubricated platinum surfaces. The full line is the theoretical curve plotted according to equation 10 with $\alpha = 12$. This may be rewritten in the form:

$$1 + \alpha\phi^2 = (p_0/p)^2 = (A/A_0)^2 = (\sigma/\sigma_0)^4$$

between the two determinations. They then applied a tangential force, gradually increasing it until gross sliding occurred. They then found that during the initial microdisplacement of the slider there was a large reduction in the contact resistance. By the time gross sliding took place the area of contact had increased three- or fourfold (see Figure 4). This is because the plastic yielding of the junction is determined by the combined effect of the normal and the tangential stress. If the normal stress on the junction is p and the tangential stress is s, the yield criterion is of the form

$$p^2 + \alpha s^2 = p_0{}^2 \tag{10}$$

where α is a constant with a value of about 10 and p_0 is the static contact pressure (25). When the normal load is first applied the contact region flows plastically under the normal load itself ($s = 0$) and $p = p_0$. As soon as a small tangential stress is applied the equality in equation 10 can be satisfied only if p diminishes. This is brought about by the surfaces sinking together (see Figure 5) so that the area of contact is increased with a corresponding drop in p. This process continues indefinitely under two conditions: (1) if the surfaces are perfectly clean, and (2) if the metals are very ductile. Junction growth then proceeds until the whole of the geometric area of the surfaces is in contact. This constitutes gross seizure and indeed for clean

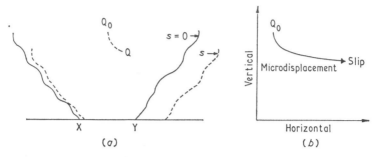

Fig. 5. Effect of combined normal and tangential stresses on the behavior of a soft asperity in contact with a hard flat surface. (a) Under a normal load alone, contact occurs across XY; when a tangential stress s is applied the junction grows as shown by the broken curve and the point Q_0 moved to Q. (b) Schematic diagram showing locus of Q as a tangential stress is increased.

metals in vacuum, coefficients of friction of the order of 10–100 are not uncommon.

The situation is different if the surfaces are contaminated or if the interface is a mixed fudge of oxide and metal so that its shear strength s_i is less than the initial critical shear stress τ of the metals. Junction growth continues until the tangential stress in the interface reaches the value s_i; gross sliding then occurs. This will take place when

$$p^2 + \alpha s_i{}^2 = \alpha \tau^2 \tag{11}$$

If $s_i = k\tau$ where $k < 1$, sliding occurs when

$$\frac{s_i}{p} = \frac{1}{\alpha^{1/2}(k^{-2} - 1)^{1/2}} \tag{12}$$

The coefficient of friction is

$$\mu = \frac{F}{W} = \frac{As_i}{Ap} = \frac{1}{\alpha^{1/2}(k^{-2} - 1)^{1/2}} \tag{13}$$

The way in which μ varies with the strength of the interface is shown in Figure 6, where a representative value of $\alpha = 9$ has been taken. It is seen that for $k = 1$, $\mu = \infty$; this corresponds to gross seizure. For an interface with a shear strength about 95% of τ ($k = 0.95$) sliding occurs for a value of $\mu \simeq 1$. Finally for very small values of k (the situation if sliding takes place in a thin soft surface film of metal or lubricant)

$$\mu = \frac{s_i}{p} \simeq \frac{s_i}{p_0} = \frac{\text{shear strength of interface}}{\text{hardness of metal}} \tag{14}$$

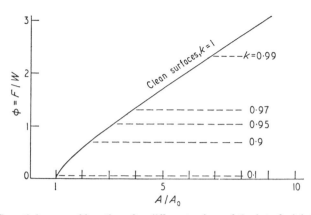

Fig. 6.   Growth in area of junctions for different values of the interfacial shear strength *s*, where *s* is expressed in terms of the critical shear strength τ of the metal ($s = k\tau$).   As the tangential force coefficient ϕ ($= F/W$) is increased, junction growth proceeds until at some critical stage determined by the value of *k* gross slip occurs.   For $k = 1$ junction growth proceeds indefinitely; for $k = 0.95$ slip occurs when the area of contact has grown about threefold and the force coefficient (now equal to the coefficient of friction) has a value of about 1.

Here there is very little junction growth so that the area of contact is essentially the static contact.

The extent of junction growth may, in fact, be estimated from a relation of the type

$$A = A_0(1 + \alpha\mu^2)^{1/2} \tag{15}$$

so that for $\mu = 1$ there is junction growth $A/A_0 \simeq 3$.   This is representative of "clean" ductile metals in air.   For $\mu = 0.1$, $A/A_0 \simeq 1.05$; that is, there is junction growth of about 5%.

It is evident that with ductile materials such as metals, yielding of the junctions depends both on the normal stress and on the tangential stress itself.   They cannot be treated as independent parameters.   Although this picture of junction growth under the influence of combined stresses is borne out by many direct studies the analysis given above must not be pushed too far.

In some cases, particularly if the adhesion is weak, repeated traversals may lead to a flattening and smoothing of the surfaces.   This will favor elastic rather than plastic deformation in the contact zone.   Such effects have been observed in the sliding of low-graphitic carbon (26) and under special conditions in the sliding of contaminated surfaces (15, 27).   It is interesting to consider what happens for elastic contacts during sliding.   If the interface is weak, sliding will occur within the weak surface film when the frictional force $= As_i$. The coefficient of friction will be given by

$$\mu = \frac{F}{W} = \frac{As_i}{Ap_{\text{elastic}}} = \frac{\text{shear strength of interface}}{\text{elastic contact pressure}} \tag{16}$$

If, however, adhesion is strong the interface can presumably fail only by plastic flow of the junctions. Since the static contact pressures are insufficient to produce plasticity the major factor in producing plastic yielding will be the applied shear stress. This means that tangential forces, large compared with the normal load, will be needed before the junctions become plastic, that is, before even microdisplacements occur. As the tangential force is increased beyond this point plastic flow and junction growth will occur in accordance with equation 11. The friction will be high, and the surfaces will be badly torn and roughened, so that in subsequent traversals the deformation will be fully plastic.

We conclude that, although under conditions of normal static loading the asperities may deform elastically, the sliding process itself, if the interfacial adhesion is strong, will lead to appreciable plastic deformation. Consequently elastic deformation in the frictional process is possible only when the tangential stresses are small as in rolling contact or lubricated sliding. It is unlikely that it will be possible in the presence of strong adhesion. It is significant that in the sliding experiments of Midgley and of Archard quoted above, where elastic deformation was deduced, the interfacial shear stresses were relatively low.

Tangential stresses well below those able to produce gross sliding play a very important role in two other fields; in metals they readily lead to fatigue and fretting of the surface asperities (28); with brittle solids they are extremely effective in generating fracture in the surface layers.

I. Adhesion of Solids: Surface Forces

The strength of the interface depends crucially on the adhesion between the surfaces. During the last decade there has been a voluminous literature on adhesion and adhesives, much of which is summarized in books by Weiss (29), Eley (30), and Houwink and Salomon (31). We shall refer only to those aspects which are relevant to the frictional mechanisms. For two perfectly clean specimens of the same metal (e.g., clean gold) the adhesion must necessarily be very strong and the interface will have a strength comparable to that of the metal itself. For dissimilar metals the adhesion is more difficult to specify. It has been suggested that metal pairs which are mutually soluble will be of the right atomic dimensions and electronic configuration to give strong adhesion unless the compounds they form are basically brittle, and that insoluble pairs should give poor adhesion (32).

However, Anderson et al. (33) have found very strong adhesion between gold and germanium, Moore and Tabor (34) found very strong adhesion between indium and diamond, while Machlin and Yankee (35) reported strong welding between metals which are mutually insoluble. In 1956 Bowden and Rowe (36) showed that practically all metal combinations can give strong adhesion if they are sufficiently clean. Indeed Rowe suggested that if strong adhesion is not observed this is due either to contaminant films or to the effect of elastic stresses which are released when the joining force is removed. These conclusions have been supported by the later work of Keller (37) and more recently by Pfaelzer (37a). They have found that very clean surfaces of many diverse metals will stick strongly in a high vacuum (see also Ref. 37b). It may be noted, however, that in the absence of deliberate lubrication iron and silver constitute a very good antiwear combination (38). On the other hand de Gee (39) finds that the wear of iron and silver is crucially dependent on the atmosphere. The most elegant recent work in this field is that due to Buckley (40). He has studied the adhesion of surfaces mounted in a diffraction camera. The structure of the surface layers can be studied by low-energy electron diffraction and the nature of the surface species identified by Auger spectroscopy. This work shows that bonding and transfer occur between all metal pairs when pressed together if they are clean enough. In some cases a monolayer of oxygen on one surface may be transferred by contact to the other if the bond energy conditions are appropriate.

Another factor involved in the adhesion of clean metals is the mutual crystallographic orientation of the clean surfaces. Semenoff (41, 42) suggests that if there is marked mismatch the adhesion will be small; the adhesion can, in his view, be increased by providing energy at the interface, either thermally or by the work of plastic deformation. This idea also merits further study.

The adhesion between metals in air has been studied by Anderson (43) and Sikorski (44). If heavy deformation is imposed on the surfaces to break up surface films, strong adhesions can be obtained with many combinations. Some pairs such as iron–vanadium gave poor adhesion (see above). The general conclusion seems to be that all surfaces will show strong adhesion but that some combinations of materials are more sensitive to surface contamination or to the effect of released elastic stresses. The importance of released stresses, emphasized by Rowe, is consistent with the observation that many practical adhesives fail not because the adhesion is poor but because stress concentrations in the glue line provide a region of weakness (45).

Strong adhesion can occur between nonmetals. The most striking example is that of freshly cleaved mica: two such surfaces placed in contact have an interfacial strength almost as great as that of the original material. Contaminant films of air or water vapor greatly reduce the adhesion (17) and if a long-chain organic molecule is adsorbed on the surfaces there is a further large reduction in adhesion (46).   Many other nonmetals adhere when placed in contact under pressure; for example, two pieces of rock salt can be pressed together at room temperature to form a very strong bond (47). Polymers can adhere strongly under pressure, particularly if the temperature is sufficient to encourage diffusion (48).   All these results are consistent with the observation that in the sliding of clean surfaces there is generally transfer of material from one surface to the other, showing that the interface is at least as strong as one of the sliding pair.   This applies to a wide range of materials: consequently the adhesion component of friction can be estimated on the assumption that s is of the same order of magnitude as τ.

The adhesion between metals is easy to understand.   For identical metals the forces at the interface are of exactly the same nature as those existing between metal atoms in the bulk.   For dissimilar metals (if no alloying occurs) the interfacial forces will probably be an average of the interatomic forces of each of the two members.   Thus the adhesion of a "weak" metal, such as indium, to a much "stronger" metal, such as gold, may be expected to be stronger than the bonds between indium–indium atoms.   Consequently when the metals are pulled apart they will separate within the indium specimen itself, leaving fragments of indium attached to the gold surface.

For ionic solids the interfacial forces will be primarily Coulombic.   For other types of solids the main forces will be van der Waals forces.   Until recently the only dispersion forces that had been measured were the retarded van der Waals forces which operate when the separations are larger than a few hundred angstroms.   It has now been shown directly that for separations less than about 100 Å, normal van der Waals forces operate.   For dielectrics this gives a value of the Hamaker constant of about 10^{-12} dyne (48a, 48b). This implies that for surfaces 5 Å apart, say, interfacial forces of the order 10^8 dyne/cm^2, that is, 100 atm, will be exerted between the two surfaces.

J. The Deformation Term

If a hard asperity plows its way through the surface of a softer metal the plowing force may be easily calculated if adhesion between the surfaces is negligible.   If horizontal and vertical components are taken, it follows that the normal load is supported by the appropriate component of the area of contact while the horizontal force is supported by the material ahead of the slider.   The horizontal force is then equal to the cross-sectional area of the groove multiplied by the yield pressure of the metal (see Figure 7).

This mechanism was first described by Bowden and Tabor (49) in their

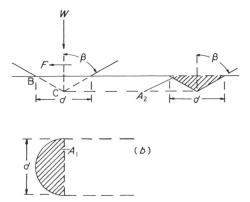

Fig. 7. Diagram showing the grooving of a soft metal when a hard conical indenter slides over it. If interfacial adhesion is negligible and there is no pile up of metal the component A_1 of the area of contact supports the normal load W and the component A_2 resists tangential displacement with a force F. In this simple model $W = pA_1$ and $F = pA_2$ where p is the yield pressure of the softer metal. The effective coefficient of friction due to the grooving mechanism is $\mu = F/W = A_2/A_1$.

original studies of the mechanism of friction. In its simplest form (50) it leads to the result that for a conical asperity of semi-apical angle θ the coefficient of friction due to plowing alone is

$$\mu_p = \frac{2}{\pi} \cot \theta \qquad\qquad (17)$$

so that for a semi-apical angle of 60°, $\mu_p \approx 0.32$; for $\theta = 30°$ (a rather sharp cone), $\mu_p \approx 1.1$.

This approach has been greatly extended and elaborated by Wilman and his colleagues in their studies of the mechanism of wear by abrasive particles. (51). Their experiments show that the rate of removal of metal by abrasion is inversely proportional to the hardness of the metal, a conclusion in close agreement with the results of Krushchov and Babichev (52). It is interesting to note that if we assume that 10% of the volume of the grooves appears as removed metal there is very good quantitative agreement between the calculated and observed abrasive wear rates. Mulhearn and Samuels (53) have suggested that this can be explained in terms of the average orientation of the abrasive particles. Wilman has also studied, using electron diffraction, the orientation of surface layers produced by the abrasive process (54). This and later papers show that an oriented texture is obtained, similar to that produced in compression or in rolling.

With single crystals of metals as well as with single crystals of brittle solids (see Section L) the deformation or plowing mechanism can play an important part in frictional anisotropy.   With rubber (see Section N) and other visco-elastic materials the plowing term is directly related to the hysteretic properties of the material.   This has a rather unexpected bearing on the pulping of wood (54a, 54b); it is found that the energy dissipated by the grinding grits is expended mainly in producing sub-surface thermal softening or fatigue of the lignin which holds the wood fibres together.

The deformation mechanism is also important in rolling friction.   Generally rolling friction arises from two factors: (i) interfacial slip due to differential stretching of surface elements, (ii) deformation of the surface by the rolling element.   It turns out that in general only a small part of the rolling friction is due to interfacial slip: the greater part is due to deformation.   When rolling occurs between, say, a hard ball and a metal surface this deformation may consist of plastic grooving of the metal surface (54c).   If the stresses are not sufficient to produce gross plastic deformation they may produce subsurface plastic deformation as the elegant analysis of Merwin and Johnson has shown (54d).   At an even lower stress level the deformation may involve only elastic hysteresis losses in the metal.   With rubbers (54e) and polymers, hysteretic losses are the main source of energy loss in rolling friction.   A fuller discussion of the role of hysteresis losses in friction is given in Sections N and O.

K. Friction in Very High Vacuum

The friction of solids in air is greatly influenced by the presence of oxide layers or adsorbed gases or other contaminant films.   Earlier work on oxide films by Whitehead (55) and by Wilson (56) show that these films generally but not always reduce the friction.   They may be broken down if the substrate is soft and the deformation severe.   Some studies of the part played by oxides on aluminum have been described by Courtel (57).

Oxides and other contaminants can be removed in two ways.   The surfaces may be heated or bombarded in a high vacuum until the surface films evaporate or decompose.   The earlier work was carried out in a vacuum of 10^{-6} torr; recent work carried out in a better vacuum (10^{-10} torr) shows essentially the same behavior.   As a result of the combined effect of the normal and tangential stresses, the ductility of the metals, and the presence of strong adhesion a vast increase in the contact area occurs and there is gross seizure.   The admission of a small quantity of oxygen or other gases reduces the adhesion and there is a large diminution in friction.

The second method of removing surface films is by repeatedly rubbing in a high vacuum over the same portion of the surface: the films and ruptured or worn away and are not able to reform.   The conditions resemble those occurring between rubbing surfaces in outer space.   The method leaves a clean surface which is also fairly work-hardened by the sliding process.   In spite of the limited ductility of the material the results, broadly speaking, are the same as those obtained in the older method: there is a steady increase in friction with repeated traversals of the friction track. One interesting difference is observed with diamond surfaces. These are difficult to clean by heating in a vacuum since prolonged heating produces graphitization of the diamond surface; in fact the friction in these experiments does not exceed about $\mu = 0.4$. If the diamond surface is repeatedly traversed in a vacuum of 10^{-10} torr at slow sliding speeds so that frictional heating is negligible and graphitization does not occur, the friction rises to a much higher value, about $\mu = 1$ (see Figure 8). In addition the strong adhesion and the increased tangential stress in the interface lead to catastrophic fragmentation of the diamond (58). We shall discuss this again in a later section dealing with the friction of brittle solids.

Buckley and Johnson (59) have carried out friction and wear experiments in a vacuum of 10^{-10} torr after baking out at 200°C. The surfaces are repeatedly slid over one another for periods of the order of 1 hr and it is found that certain alloys and metals give relatively low friction and wear even under these severe conditions. For example, a titanium alloy containing 21% aluminum sliding on a stainless-steel surface gives a friction coefficient μ of only about 0.4; with pure titanium sliding on the same surface there is gross seizure ($\mu \gg 1.6$). The authors suggest that this is connected with the structure of the metal or alloy and particularly with a favorable ratio of the a to c dimension in hexagonal structures, a large $c:a$ ratio giving

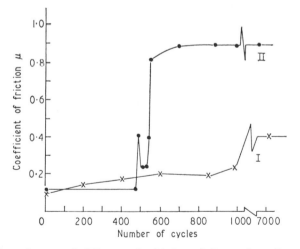

Fig. 8. Effect of repeated sliding on the friction of diamond on diamond in a high vacuum: (I) vacuum of 10^{-8} torr; (II) vacuum of 5×10^{-10} torr. The rise in friction is due to the gradual attrition of surface films: it is accompanied by marked fragmentation of the diamond surfaces (58).

low friction and wear.   A different approach is due to Bowden and Childs (60).   They studied the friction of various metals in a high vacuum and were able to change the mechanical properties of the surfaces by operating over a range of temperatures from 20 to 300°K.   Their results suggested that the friction and wear of clean metals are heaviest if the materials are ductile; the sliding interaction becomes less severe as the ductility is reduced.   This may be associated with an increase in work-hardening rate at low temperatures, a ductile–brittle transition over some critical temperature range, or a phase change.   For example, Powell (61) found such an effect with cobalt which is cubic above 600°K and hexagonal below and shows a marked reduction in friction and wear below this temperature.   These results agree with those of Buckley and Johnson (59) but provide a broader generalized explanation.

A very useful survey of the earlier work in the NASA laboratory by these authors and by Bisson and his colleagues was published in 1960 (62).   It covers a broad variety of subjects such as crystal structure, orientation, order–disorder phenomena, and friction and lubrication behavior under extreme environmental conditions.

L. Friction of Brittle Solids

We deal here with some typical brittle solids such as rock salt, magnesium oxide, glass, diamond and metal carbides.   In spite of their lack of ductility the frictional behavior of these materials resembles that of metals for two basic reasons.   First, there is normally strong interfacial adhesion; second, the hydrostatic stresses around the regions of contact inhibit brittle fracture and although some cracking may occur the deformation is dominantly plastic.   There may even be some junction growth.   However, there is a limit to this.   As the area of contact increases the normal pressure falls off and the ability of the hydrostatic stress to inhibit brittle failure diminishes.   Junction growth comes to an end as the material ceases to be ductile.   It is for this reason, as mentioned above, that even with very clean surfaces μ rarely exceeds a value of about 1.

Brittle crystalline solids can show marked frictional anisotropy.   This is shown most simply by studying the friction of hard sliders over the surface of a single crystal.   When the deformation is gentle the behavior resembles that of ductile materials and metals, the higher friction being associated with the piling up of a hill of work-hardened material *ahead* of the slider.   This is the "bourrelet frontal" studied so elegantly by Courtel and his colleagues (62a, 62b).

When the deformation is predominantly brittle frictional anisotropy again occurs (see Figure 9) and again is largely due to an increase in the plowing term (62c).   However, the high friction observed in certain crystallographic

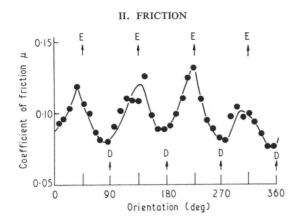

Fig. 9. Seal's results (62c) showing the effect of orientation on the friction of a diamond stylus sliding on the polished cube face of diamond. Along the cube edge directions (E) the friction is high; along the cube diagonal directions (D) the friction is low. The high-friction directions are those of easy abrasion.

directions is due not so much to a piling up of material as to an increase in penetration by the slider into the brittle crystal (63). This mechanism may also account for the frictional anisotropy observed earlier on diamond.

Although the frictional mechanism with brittle solids appears to be due to both an adhesion and a plowing mechanism the wear is usually dominated by cracking and fragmentation rather than adhesion and transfer. In this process the tangential stresses are of primary importance. Figure 10(i), for example, shows the behavior of a glass surface when a hard spherical indenter is pressed onto it with a load of nearly 10 kg. The static load is just sufficient to produce a ring crack around the Hertzian area of contact. If the normal load is reduced to 2 kg no such cracking occurs. However, if now a tangential force of only 1 kg is applied (insufficient to produce sliding) the tangential stress generated in the surface layers is sufficient to produce a cracking over an arc lying just behind the contact area (Fig. 10(ii)). At slightly higher tangential forces, where gross sliding occurs, typical arc cracks are observed over the whole friction track (64). These can naturally be the cause of very heavy wear.

Since then the subject has been developed in theoretical papers by Hamilton and Goodman (65) and by Frank and Lawn (66), and also by more detailed experimental studies on glass by Gilroy and Hirst (67) and on a whole variety of brittle solids by Powell and Tabor (68). The importance of tangential traction in producing surface fragmentation is shown by some results from the latter paper for a titanium carbide sphere sliding on a titanium carbide flat. The static load just necessary to produce ring cracks was 40 kg. If a tangential force equal to 0.16 of the normal load was applied

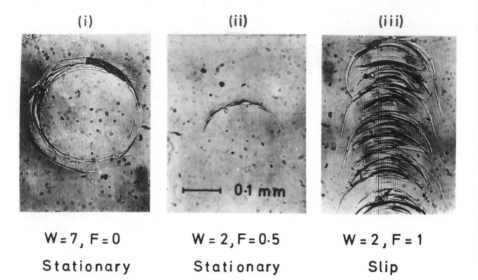

(i)   **(ii)**   **(iii)**

W = 7, F = 0   W = 2, F = 0·5   W = 2, F = 1

Stationary   Stationary   Slip

Fig. 10.   Deformation of glass by a hard spherical indenter (diameter $\frac{1}{4}$ in.): (i) under a static load of 7 kg ring cracks are formed; (ii) under a static load of 2 kg no ring cracks are formed, but if a tangential stress of 0.5 kg is applied an arced crack forms at the rear of the contact region; (iii) if the tangential force is increased to 1 kg so that sliding occurs the friction track is covered with overlapping arced cracks. In (i) and (ii) the slider is moving downward relative to the glass surface.

it was just enough to produce sliding in air ($\mu = 0.16$).   Under these conditions the normal load could be reduced by a factor of 10 and crescent-shaped cracks would still just be formed.   The effect became immensely larger if the surface traction was increased by increasing the coefficient of friction.   This could be easily achieved by removing the films normally present by rubbing the surfaces together gently in a high vacuum.   The friction rose to $\mu = 0.9$ and the normal load necessary to produce crescent-shaped cracks fell from the static loading value (when no tangential force

TABLE I

Load to Produce Cracking for a
Sphere on Flat of TiC

Condition	Load (kg)
Static	40
Sliding ($\mu = 0.16$)	4
Sliding ($\mu = 0.9$)	0.08

was applied) to a value that was 500 times smaller.   The results are summarized in Table I.   Clearly when surface tractions are large cracking may occur for relatively low values of the normal stress.

M. Friction of Lamellar Solids

It is now generally agreed that the low friction of graphite is associated with the presence of adsorbed films.   When these films are removed adhesion is strengthened, the friction rises, and there is an enormous increase in wear (69).   There is still some dispute as to whether the cleavage face in graphite is intrinsically a low-energy surface.   Some experiments by Bryant et al. (70) suggest that this is not so, which would support the view of Rowe (71) that the friction of graphite is due to the fracture or cleavage of crystals and that absorbed gases penetrate to some depth into the lattice and so reduce the cleavage strength of the graphite crystallites.   Most other workers consider that the cleavage face is a low-energy surface (see 71a) and that friction involves the sliding of the crystallites themselves over one another.   The edges are considered to be the high-energy sites where adsorption of gases and vapors readily occurs (72).   On this view any interaction involving edges gives a high friction when the edges are clean, and a low friction when the edges are covered with adsorbed films (see Figure 11).

With MoS_2 it is now generally agreed that the low friction is essentially a property of the structure of the material itself, MoS_2 being extremely weak along the shear planes.   The presence of adsorbed vapor and other

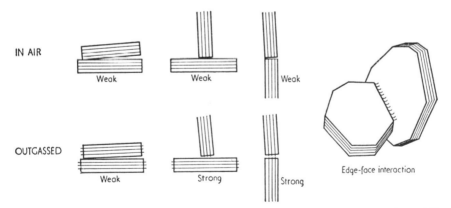

Fig. 11.   The mechanism of graphite friction according to Deacon and Goodman (72). The cleavage face is assumed to be one of low surface energy, the edges of high surface energy.   Sliding occurs between crystallites.   In the presence of adsorbed gases on the edges the friction is always low.   If the adsorbed gases are removed by outgassing the graphite, the only high-friction combinations will be those involving edge interactions.

impurities tends, if anything, to increase the friction (73).   For a recent survey of the frictional properties of MoS_2 see Winer (74).

One of the more interesting developments in this field is the effect of crystal structure on the frictional properties of lamellar solids of the MoS_2 type (chalcogenides).   Some evidence suggests, as with the hexagonal metals and alloys studied by Buckley and Johnson, that a large $c:a$ ratio is advantageous (75).   Experiments by Giltrow (76), however, suggest that the effectiveness of lamellar compounds depends mainly on the extent to which they are stoichiometric; the more perfect their structure, the lower the friction.   A somewhat different point of emphasis has been made by Bowden, Greenwood, and Imai (77).   They stress the importance of interlamellar bonding.   For example, with titanium sulfide interstitial titanium atoms can be incorporated within one lamella to give strong bonding with a neighboring lamella.   This lamellar sulfide has in fact poor antifriction properties.

These friction studies have been accompanied by other investigations including the orientation of surface layers as a result of sliding (54), the formation of blisters (78, 79), the electrical characteristics of carbon contacts during sliding, the packing and adhesion of surface films (80), and the wear and durability of these films in various environments.

Another important line of work is concerned with the formation in situ, by chemical attack of surface films possessing a lamellar structure.   This was first clearly studied in detail by Rowe (81) who showed, for example, that titanium could be effectively lubricated by forming titanium iodide on the surface, and tungsten carbide by forming tungsten chloride on the surface.   This has led to a number of practical applications, in particular the work of Roberts and Owens (82, 83).   They showed that a lubricant containing an activated complex of iodine is a very successful lubricant for titanium and also for chromium.

N. Friction of Rubber

Since sliding friction is basically attributable to the shearing of adhesions at the points of real contact, materials which show marked dependence of mechanical properties on rate of deformation should also show a marked dependence of friction on speed of sliding.   Rubber is such a material.   It consists of long coiled-up chains of molecules attached at various points to one another by cross-links.   When a specimen of rubber is stretched the molecules have to be uncoiled and this provides the main source of the elasticity of the rubber (it is primarily an entropy effect, not a mechanical resistance to bond twisting).   At the same time parts of the molecule have to slide over one another and in this process energy is lost in a manner resembling the viscous losses in a sheared liquid.   This energy loss which accounts for the elastic hysteresis of the rubber appears as heat. The loss characteristics at various temperatures and frequencies of deformation can be superposed by applying an appropriate shift derived by Williams, Landel, and Ferry and known as the WLF transform. All the data then lie on a single master curve.

The frictional behavior of rubber has been studied over a wide range of temperatures and sliding speeds by Grosch (84). By working at speeds below about 1 cm/sec he was able to avoid complications due to frictional heating. His results show that on rough surfaces there is a component of friction due to plowing (see also 84a, 84b) and another component due to adhesion. Both these factors vary with speed and temperature in a manner which directly parallels the known viscoelastic properties of the rubber, and they can be fitted to a "master" friction curve by the use of a WLF transform (see Figure 12). The adhesion component at room temperature reaches its maximum value at a sliding speed v of about 1 cm/sec. The maximum viscoelastic loss at this temperature occurs at a frequency v of about 10^6 cps. If these are to be correlated it implies that, in the sliding process, there is a significant distance λ given by $\lambda = v/v$. This quantity has the value of about 100 Å, which is approximately the length of a segment of the rubber molecule which other experiments show to be involved in relaxation processes.

One of the characteristic features of rubber friction is that, over an appreciable range of conditions, there appears to be no transfer of rubber to the other surface; that is, sliding appears to occur truly at the interface. This suggests that the rubber molecules are temporarily attached to and then detached from the other surface. This has led Schallamach (85) to develop a molecular theory of rubber friction involving bond formation between the rubber molecule and the other surface, dwell time, and stress-activated detachment of the molecule. The treatment is essentially an extension of the Eyring molecular theory of viscous flow and gives reasonably good qualitative agreement with experiment. The quantitative agreement, however, is rather poor.

A different approach is due to Ludema and Tabor (86). They apply the simple adhesion theory of friction and consider the way in which A and s individually vary with temperature and rate of deformation. The area A depends on the elastic modulus which is well described by viscoelastic theory. The shear strength s is not known but the *tear* strength of rubber over a wide range of temperatures and an enormous range of tear rates has been studied by Smith (87) and is found to follow a classical WLF behavior. Multiplying these two parameters gives a relation for $F = As$ which shows a maximum in the friction at roughly the correct sliding speed. However the calculated friction is about ten times larger than the observed. (For other theories see Bulgin et al. (88), Savkoor (89), Kummer and Meyer (90), and Bartenev (91).)

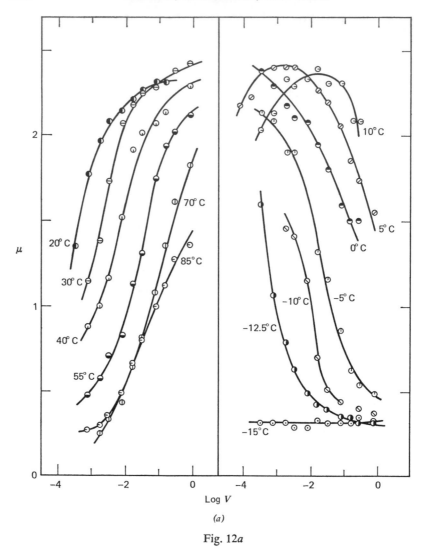

Fig. 12a

Most of the work described above deals with the adhesion component of friction. Greenwood and Tabor (84a) first showed that the plowing term is also directly related to the hysteretic properties of the rubber. This has an important bearing on the lubricated sliding of hard asperities over a rubber surface since the adhesion component becomes very small and the friction is dominated by the plowing term. This has stimulated the use of high hysteresis loss rubbers in automobile tires. On wet or greasy road surfaces the

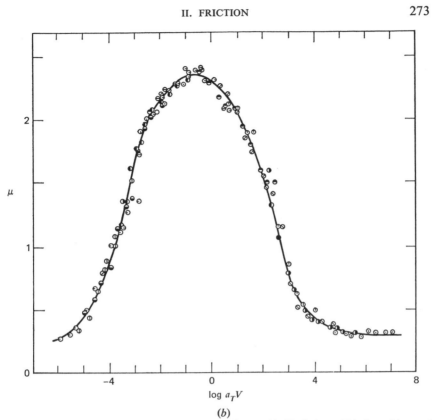

(b)

Fig. 12.   Friction of rubber against a hard surface.   (a) Variation of friction with speed for acrylonitrile–butadiene rubber sliding over a hard surface.   (b) Master curve for the friction data in (a) deduced from the Williams-Landel-Ferry transform using the known viscoelastic characteristics of the rubber (84).

friction is due mainly to the plowing of the tire-tread by the road asperities. Consequently the friction is increased, that is the tire is more skid resistant, if the tread has a high hysteresis loss (84b).   This process will, of course, vary with speed and temperature according to the viscoelastic properties of the rubber (91a).

O. Friction of Rigid Polymers

Rigid thermoplastics such as "Perspex," polyethylene, polyvinylchloride (pvc), and nylon resemble rubbers in their structure except that crosslinking is often absent and in their normal temperature range they are glasslike rather than rubbery.   Their deformation is neither elastic nor plastic, but is time dependent.   For quasistatic experiments this can be ignored and the frictional behavior between sphere and flat or between crossed cylinders can be easily explained.   If the area of contact A varies with load and geometry as given by equation 6 we may write

$$\mu = skW^{1-n}$$

where s is the shear strength of the polymers.   Some typical results from Pascoe and Tabor (92) for crossed cylinders of various radii are shown in Figure 13.   It is evident that at very small loads the coefficient of friction can be very high.   This is often the situation in the textile industry where fibers and yarns rub over one another or over guide pins at relatively small loads.

Adams has carried out a more detailed study of the contact between a hemispherical polymer slider and a flat glass plate using optical interference to study the area of contact A (18).   The results show that ignoring the effect of time, A varies with load according to an empirical law of the form

$$A = k_1 W^m \tag{19}$$

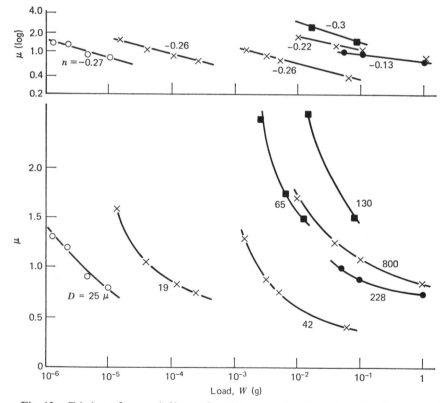

Fig. 13.   Friction of crossed fibers of various diameters ($D\mu m$) as function of load (W) showing that $\mu = k_1 W^{n'}$ where n' lies between -0.13 and -0.3 and where $n' = n - 1$.
○, ptfe; ×, nylon-66; ●, pvdc; ■, Polythene.

when n is of the order of 0.7–0.8.   The sliding friction varies with W according to a law

$$F = k_2 W^n \tag{20}$$

where n is slightly but significantly greater than m.   This implies that the specific shear strength s of the interface increases slightly with increasing pressure.   This has been ignored by most other workers in the field, but recent work by Bowers (92a) on the friction of thin polymer films and by Towle (92b) on the shear strength of bulk polymers at high pressures has demonstrated the importance of this effect.

Cohen and Tabor (16) have shown that certain liquids can plasticize the surface layers of many polymers and so influence their frictional behavior. They also show that small quantities of surface-active molecules dissolved in the polymer can diffuse to the surface and provide effective lubrication; in addition, as the more recent work of Briscoe, Mustafaev, and Tabor (93) shows, the surface film can be replenished, as it is worn away, by diffusion from the bulk.   It is possible that this technique will provide a means of fabricating self-lubricating polymers (93a).

Rigid polymers show loss properties which are frequency and temperature dependent.   It is therefore of interest to see if the frictional behavior reflects these properties in the same way as with rubber.   Much of the earlier work was carried out at "engineering" speeds, so that the interpretation has been greatly complicated by the effects of frictional heating.   This not only influences the strength properties at the contact regions but may also have a profound effect on interfacial diffusion.   However, as a broad generalization it appears that the more rigid the polymer, the less its friction depends on speed and temperature (94).

More recent studies have been carried out at very low sliding speeds (86) where frictional heating is negligible.   It is found that the deformation part of the friction follows very faithfully the viscoelastic properties of the polymer, but that the adhesion part shows very poor correlation.   The results suggest that this is because the conventional study of viscoelasticity is carried out at very small strains and at ambient pressure.   By contrast the material around the friction junctions is subjected to a very high local pressure and the shear strains, before sliding occurs, are enormous.   Consequently, although the sliding friction often varies markedly with speed and temperature, there is no reason why this should reflect viscoelastic properties measured under much gentler conditions.   On the other hand Vinogradov, Bartenev, Elkin et al. (95, 95a) have recently found that with polyethylene the frictional data can be correlated over a wide range of temperatures and speeds.   By considering the individual variations of A and s with these parameters they are able to superpose all the data onto a single master curve.

With polymers the adhesion at the interface is generally strong. Shearing occurs within the polymer itself and there is marked transfer. Under carefully controlled conditions strong interfacial adhesion can occur even with polytetrafluoroethylene (ptfe), though the friction remains small (96). Although experiments show that ptfe of low crystallinity gives a friction that is generally about 10% higher than that observed with highly crystalline material (86), this does not seem to be the main factor. Recent experiments by Pooley and Tabor (96a) show that the low friction of ptfe is essentially a molecular property. A smooth molecule is associated with low friction and transfer. If a few side groups are attached to the molecular chain the friction can be greatly increased. It is interesting to note in this connection that whereas low-density (branched) commercial polyethylene gives marked transfer and a fairly high coefficient of friction, high-density unbranched polyethylene gives very little transfer and a low coefficient of friction comparable with that of ptfe. It is, of course true that in many practical situations the *adhesion* between ptfe and other surfaces is small (97) and this is accompanied by a further small but significant drop in friction.

P. Friction of Natural Fibers

The friction of natural fibers is a special case of polymer friction. The surface of the fiber is covered with fine scales pointing towards the tip and the friction is higher when sliding occurs against the scales than with them. With wool fibers this is particularly marked and the differential friction effect is responsible for preferential migration of the fibers if a woolen fabric is agitated: this is the basic cause of felting. The high friction against the fiber is due to a ratchet mechanism if the other surfaces is hard and contains crevices; it is due to a plowing mechanism by the scales if the other surface is softer.

A great deal of effort has been expended by the wool industry to find a treatment that will reduce the felting or shrinking tendency of wool fibers. All these are aimed at reducing the differential friction. However some treatments increase the with-scale friction and scarcely change the frictional difference. The literature is full of conflicting data and unsatisfactory explanations. A very interesting attempt to explain all the observed data is due to Makinson who has made use of the concepts of Ludema and Tabor (86) in their work on polymer friction. A fascinating survey of her main conclusions is available in a short article in Wear (97a).

R. The General Mechanism of Friction

The friction between solids arises from two main causes. The first is the adhesion which occurs at the regions of real contact. Although there may be some combinations of materials for which adhesion is poor, in general it would appear that most solids will stick strongly to other solids if contaminant films are absent.   These interfacial adhesive forces are as natural as the cohesive forces within the bulk of the solid.   The second factor arises if the asperities on a hard surface produce grooving or cutting in the other. With metals the grooving involves plastic displacement, with brittle solids some cracking or fragmentation, with rubbers and polymers hysteresis losses. The detailed behavior depends on the nature of the solids and their deformation properties, for example, elastic, plastic, viscoelastic.   It also depends on their structure so that those materials which possess well-defined anisotropy may well show anisotropic frictional properties.   In some cases, particularly with materials which have a lamellar structure, the friction may be very low, though this is by no means always the case.   With solids that are markedly viscoelastic the deformation properties are rate and temperature dependent and there is a corresponding variation in friction with sliding speed and temperature.

However, the factor that has the largest influence on friction is the cleanliness of the surfaces.   Thoroughly clean solids, particularly if they are ductile, will tend to give very high coefficients of friction or even gross seizure.   The presence of a trace of oxygen or some other contaminant can bring the friction down to much lower "normal" values.   In practical affairs involving the sliding of metals it is probable that the oxide films normally present constitute the main factor responsible for reducing friction and preventing the occurrence of seizure and heavy wear.

III. LUBRICATION

A. Hydrodynamic Lubrication

Under suitable conditions of geometry, load, and speed sliding surfaces can operate with a continuous film of lubricant between them.   The friction is entirely due to the viscous resistance of the fluid and, in principle, no wear of the rubbing surfaces occurs.   This is the regime of classical hydrodynamic lubrication.

The simplest example is that of a journal rotating in a bearing.   The journal runs slightly eccentrically so that a convergent wedge of oil is formed between it and the bearing.   The variation of friction with viscosity Z, number of revolutions/sec N, and nominal pressure P is shown in Figure 14. This figure also shows how the film thickness, at region of nearest approach, varies with ZN/P.   It is seen that as the viscosity diminishes or the sliding speed falls or the load increases, the thickness diminishes.   The bearing

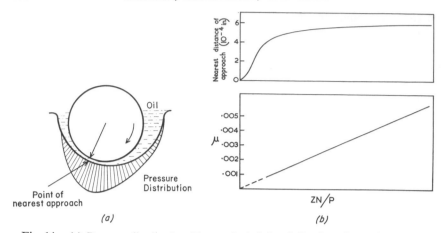

Fig. 14. (*a*) Pressure distribution (shown shaded) in oil film for a journal running in a half bearing. Convergence in the oil film leads to a pressure great enough to support the journal. (*b*) Theoretical curves of hydrodynamic lubrication between journal and bearing. Lower curve, friction; upper curve, distance of nearest approach.

enters a region of danger if the surface roughnesses are greater than the film thickness.

It is clearly desirable to work within the "thick" film region. In practice this means that the speeds must be fairly high, the loads not too high, and the viscosity appropriate to the running conditions. If the lubricant heats up as a result of the shearing process itself the viscosity diminishes according to a relation of the type

$$Z = Z_0 e^{Q/RT} \tag{21}$$

where Q is an appropriate activation energy. To offset this effect "viscosity improvers" are often used. These are long coiled-up molecules which uncoil as the temperature is increased and so tend to raise the viscosity. Another approach is to use a gas (air) as the lubricant. This has the advantages that it is cheap, the viscosity increases with temperature, and chemical degradation is unlikely. However, its viscosity is very low so that the loading must be very small and the speeds very high. Even so, to be of practical use, the film thickness is appreciably smaller than when liquid lubricants are used. Consequently a fine surface finish and very good alignment are needed.

When liquid lubricants are used, penetration of the hydrodynamic film by surface asperities may occur at low values of ZN/P. These asperities may be separated by liquid films only a few molecules thick the properties of which are radically different from those of the bulk liquid. The friction is higher and some wear may occur. In the earlier classical work this was known as boundary lubrication. Under fully hydrodynamic conditions the coefficient of friction is of the order of $\mu = 0.001$ and if the friction rose to $\mu = 0.1$ or more, it was considered that the bearing was operating under boundary conditions. It is now apparent that this view needs drastic revision.

B. Elastohydrodynamic Lubrication (EHL)

The new element that has been introduced into the theory of lubrication is the following. In classical hydrodynamic lubrication the behavior is determined by speed, viscosity, pressure, and the geometry of the system which is assumed to remain constant. It is now apparent that when lubricant film thicknesses become very small the hydrodynamic pressures in the oil film are sufficient to deform the surfaces appreciably. The behavior is then determined by the flow of liquid between the elastically deformed geometry of the surfaces.

A simple example of this (98) is shown for a rubber cylinder sliding over a glass surface in the presence of a silicone fluid (Figure 15). The rubber is optically smooth so that the geometry of the gap between the rubber and the glass may be deduced directly by optical interference methods. The contact region is clearly flattened and shows a convergence (giving load carrying capacity) and a dip at the exit region where the hydrodynamic pressure suddenly falls from its maximum value to atmospheric pressure (Figure 15b). This geometry is typical of all elastohydrodynamic systems. Similar behavior is observed for a rubber sphere sliding over a lubricated glass surface (see Figure 15c).

With metal surfaces, however, a new feature emerges. The rubber surfaces described above operate under a contact pressure of a few atmospheres. With carefully aligned and finely finished metal surfaces (as in rollers or gears) the elastic contact pressures may be of the order of 10,000–100,000 psi. With most organic fluids such as are used as lubricants this has a prodigious effect on the viscosity. If Z_0 is the viscosity at atmospheric pressure, the viscosity at pressure P is given approximately by

$$Z = Z_0 e^{\alpha P} \tag{22}$$

where for most mineral oils $\alpha \simeq 2.10^4$ in²/lb. This leads to the following result:

$$P = 10,000 \text{ psi} \qquad Z = 7Z_0$$
$$20,000 \text{ psi} \qquad Z = 55Z_0$$
$$50,000 \text{ psi} \qquad Z = 22,000Z_0$$

It is seen that at very high contact pressures the oil film is trapped between the surfaces and behaves virtually as a solid waxlike separating layer (99).

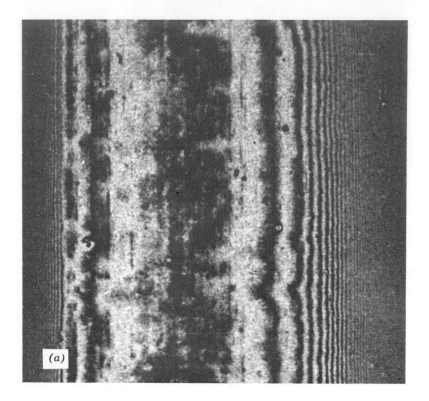

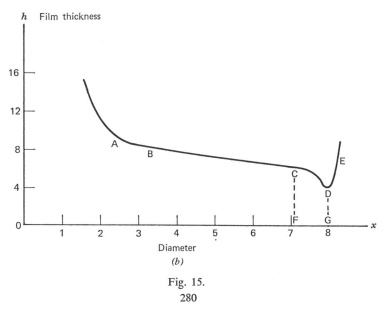

Fig. 15.

280

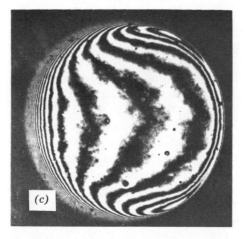

Fig. 15. (a) Interferogram between cylindrical rubber surface and a flat glass plate in presence of a silicon fluid at a sliding speed of 0.15 cm sec. (b) Profile deduced from interferogram. Along the x axis 1 division $= 0.1$ mm and along the h axis 1 division $= 2000$ Å. (c) Interferogram between a spherical rubber surface and a flat glass plate in the presence of a silicone fluid at a sliding speed of 0.1 cm sec, showing wedge-shaped contour at the fluid entrance (on left) and the horseshoe-shaped protuberance on the exit.

This prevents metal–metal contact and explains why many mechanisms, in practice, operate under more severe conditions than classical hydrodynamic theory would allow. This may explain why certain lubricants such as silicones which have lower pressure viscosity characteristics are generally poor lubricants (100). More recent work suggests that another factor may be the non-Newtonian properties of these fluids at very high pressures (100).

One of the difficulties of EHL is that it is now difficult to explain why lubricants ever fail, since the harder they are compressed the more difficult they are to extrude. It has been suggested that high local flash temperatures can desorb or even evaporate the film; or that high rates of shear can actually fracture the film (101). More work on this is necessary. It is clear, however, that a good deal of the earlier observations which were classified as "boundary" lubrication may well correspond to EHL conditions at the asperities. For example, Johnson (102) has studied the behavior of finely polished carefully aligned steel rollers, operating at contact pressures of the order of 50–100 kg/mm²: the EHL film is about 10^{-5} cm thick, that is, greater than the surface asperities, so that pure EH conditions obtain. Under these conditions the coefficient of friction observed with a pure mineral oil is $\mu = 0.06$–0.08. These contact pressures are of the same order as those capable of producing plastic flow of asperities so that the conditions closely resemble those occurring when the classical hydrodynamic film is penetrated by surface asperities. In this sense EHL may well appear to "squeeze" classical boundary lubrication out of existence.

The position, however, is very different if the lubricant contains a small quantity of surface-active material. For example, Naylor has studied the behavior of a typical disc machine in the presence of a pure mineral oil; he has been able to operate the system under ideal EH conditions at a limiting film thickness of less than 200 Å. If now a small quantity of oleic acid is added to the oil the film thickness remains unchanged; furthermore there is no change in the viscous resistance of the oil film. On the other hand, in a practical cam and tappet rig operating at similar pressures and speeds it is found that with the oil containing the small quantity of oleic acid, the load at which scuffing occurs is much higher than with the pure mineral oil itself (100C). We conclude that a very thin film, perhaps only 1 molecule thick, of oleic acid is adsorbed on the metal surfaces: it plays no part in the bulk viscous properties of the system but provides protection to the surfaces when the EH film breaks down. It is evident that we have returned to a type of boundary lubrication very similar to that described in the earlier classical work. We may define it as that type of lubrication which cannot be attributed to the bulk viscous properties of the lubricant (whether the system is operating under hydrodynamic or elastohydrodynamic conditions) but arises from a specific solid–lubricant interaction.

C. The Study of Boundary Lubrication

Archard and Cowking (103) have provided a simplified but very useful analysis of the thickness h of the elastohydrodynamic film formed between a spherical surface of radius R sliding over a flat surface with a speed U_s provided that only elastic deformation occurs. For an oil of viscosity Z_0 and pressure viscosity coefficient α they give for steel surfaces

$$h \simeq (\alpha Z_0 U_s)^{2/3} R^{1/3} \text{ cm} \tag{23}$$

Mechanically prepared surfaces rarely have a surface finish better than a few hundred angstroms so that if the elastohydrodynamic film is to be ruptured h must be appreciably less than, say, 100 Å. It is evident that the speed of sliding must be very low and R and Z_0 must not be too large. For example if $R = 1$ cm, $Z_0 = 10$ cP, a sliding velocity of 1 cm/sec gives $h \simeq 20$ Å.

Generally, boundary lubrication is studied between a curved slider and a flat surface at sliding speeds of order 0.1 cm/sec. The friction is measured and the surface damage studied with an optical or electron microscope. An additional technique of very great value is to make the slider of radioactive material so that transfer onto the flat surface may be determined either with a Geiger counter or by autoradiography.

TABLE II
Transfer of Cd Slider onto Cd Flat

Lubricant	μ	Transfer (10^{-9} g/cm track)
None	0.8	50,000
Cetane	0.6	500
Cetyl alcohol	0.4	100
Palmitic acid	0.07	0.7
Copper palmitate	0.05	0.5

Table II shows typical results obtained for the lubrication of Cd sliding on Cd in air, Load 2 kg, Sliding speed 1 mm/sec at room temperature. All the lubricants were applied neat. It is evident that the greatest reduction in friction and transfer is achieved with a fatty acid or soap. The friction is reduced by a factor of about 20, the transfer by a factor of 100,000 (104).

A further point of general validity is that the reduction in transfer is not mainly due to a reduction in the number of transferred fragments. For example the number of transferred fragments diminishes by a factor of 3–4 although the total transfer is reduced by a factor of 100,000. This leads to a very simple picture: the boundary film reduces the amount of metal–metal adhesion at those asperity contacts where it would otherwise occur (see Figure 16).

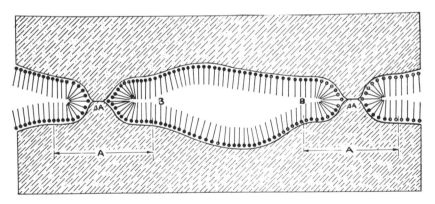

Fig. 16. The sliding of solid surfaces under conditions of boundary lubrication. Mechanism involving breakdown of the lubricant film at small localized regions. The load is supported over an area A, while metallic junctions are formed through the lubricant film over a much smaller area βA. The force to shear these metallic junctions ($\beta A s_m$) in general constitutes part of the friction observed. The remainder of the frictional force is involved in shearing the lubricant film $\{(1 - \beta)A s_l\}$. Further, if the lubricant is a fatty acid it may react with the metal to form a metallic soap.

For well-lubricated surfaces the friction arises *not* from the shearing of the metallic junctions but from the shearing of the lubricant film. The transfer may differ by a factor of 20 without detectably affecting the coefficient of friction. This has an important consequence. In comparing two good boundary lubricants the coefficient of friction is a very unreliable measure of the relative protection provided by the lubricants.

In the earlier work it was generally assumed that hydrocarbons, alcohols, and amines were physically adsorbed on to metal surfaces, whereas fatty acids reacted chemically to form in situ a monolayer of metallic soap, a view generally supported by electron diffraction studies of the orientation of adsorbed monolayers (105, 106). Such studies showed that the nonreactive molecules lost their orientation at temperatures very close to their bulk melting point, whereas the fatty acid monolayers retained their orientation up to a much higher temperature which corresponds approximately to the melting point of the corresponding soap. Again friction experiments showed that the lubricating properties of the fatty acids were maintained (on a reactive metal) to higher temperatures than the nonreactive compounds if sufficient reaction had occurred (see Figure 17).

It is clear that boundary lubrication relies on a protective surface film. We consider here three main classes of film.

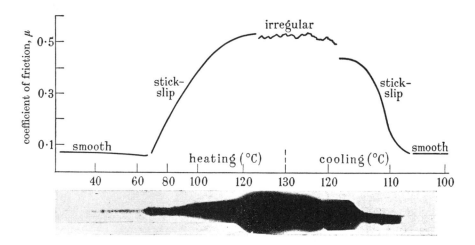

Fig. 17. Friction record and autoradiograph of pick up for cadmium surfaces lubricated with palmitic acid as surfaces are heated and then cooled (104). At 70°C, which corresponds closely to the melting point of palmitic acid, there is marked deterioration in the efficacy of the lubricant film during the first heating. Presumably there has been insufficient reaction between the metal and the acid. After heating to 130°C and then cooling, effective lubrication is re-established at about 110°C which corresponds to the softening temperature of the cadmium soap.

D. Physically Adsorbed Films

The simplest type of physically adsorbed film is a nonpolar hydrocarbon. Recent work by Groszek (107) shows that these may be adsorbed quite strongly if the surface is not too hydrophilic. The molecules lie horizontally on the surface and the interaction energy is high. These films, however, are only a few angstroms thick and have only limited protective properties. For example, recent experiments (107a) on the lubrication of a flat glass surface with n-eicosane (C_{20}) over which a glass hemisphere is slid show that the coefficient of friction ($\mu = 0.2$) is considerably less than for unlubricated surfaces ($\mu \simeq 1$) but increases rapidly with repeated traversals of the surface.

The next simplest type is a long-chain alcohol, amine, or metallic soap. Zisman (108) has studied the lubricating properties of these and similar organic materials adsorbed onto a glass surface using a clean stainless-steel sphere as the slider. The friction results suggest that during the first millimeter or so of sliding the clean sphere picks up molecules from the glass surface so that, under the steady conditions reached, the friction corresponds to the sliding of two solids coated with a close-packed monolayer. (This view must now be somewhat modified in view of recent experiments by Scruton described below in Section H.) The study shows that long-chain acids, alcohols, and amines give a lower friction than the other materials. Fluorinated acids give a slightly lower friction than the hydrocarbon compounds. In general the longer the molecular chain, the more durable and resistant it is to wear. These results are of basic interest but they involve an uncertainty that is typical of all this work: there is no definite measure of the thickness of the film that is actually effective when sliding occurs.

Most workers consider that the physically adsorbed film is only one or two molecules thick. However, Derjaguin and his school in Russia and more recently Cameron and Gohar (109) in Britain have provided evidence for the presence of very much thicker adsorbed films. The explanation of this is still the subject of dispute; it may, for example, be the result of some solubility effect or the formation of micelles at some critical concentration. Cameron and Gohar (109) have found that a long-chain surface-active molecule dissolved in a pure hydrocarbon oil is most effective as a lubricant when the hydrocarbon has the same chain length as the surfactant. Lubrication, in their view, is achieved by a film 10^3–10^5 Å thick of viscosity appreciably higher than the bulk viscosity. They consider that the last molecular layer is rich in surfactant; this influences the structure and enhances the viscosity of the superincumbent liquid. Thermal desorption of the acid reduces its influence and when the acid coverage is less than about one-half, the enhanced viscosity of the lubricant film is lost and seizure occurs. Since other work (110) shows that the boundary layer is itself a mixed adsorbed film of surfactant and hydrocarbon, more work on this is clearly desirable.   The field is further confused by a recent paper of Smith and Cameron (110a) which shows by a very elegant experimental technique that thick films are only formed if chemical reaction can occur, a view in close agreement with earlier experiments of Bowden & Moore (110b): furthermore Cameron states that these thick films are relatively weak in shear.

Some attempts have been made to treat the physical adsorption of the molecule and its lubricating action as a problem in thermodynamics.   We shall consider this in greater detail in discussing below the breakdown of the lubricant film.

E. Chemisorbed Films

Most engineering systems involve oxide-coated metals in the presence of mineral oils.   It is unlikely that marked chemisorption will occur between a hydrocarbon and a metal oxide.   In a running mechanism, however, the oxide may be worn away or cracked, thus exposing fresh metal, and under these conditions chemisorption of the hydrocarbon may readily occur.   In many cases this leads to the breaking up of a carbon–hydrogen bond and the attachment of the dissociated molecule to the exposed metal atom.   In some cases breakup of the molecule may occur leading to a fairly carbon-rich surface layer.   In the presence of oxygen dissolved in the hydrocarbon there will be competitive adsorption.   If oxygen is adsorbed first it will produce an oxide-covered surface and this will preclude reaction with the hydrocarbon. If the hydrocarbon is preferentially adsorbed on the fresh metal sites this may be followed by reaction between the chemisorbed hydrocarbon and oxygen.   Fein and Kreuz (111) have studied the behavior of steel surfaces run together under a hydrocarbon oil and do, in fact, detect the presence of appreciable quantities of oxidized hydrocarbon which can polymerize to form a typical "friction polymer."   This is not the only route by which high-molecular-weight polymers may be formed.   For example, a different mechanism has been proposed by Vinogradov (112) (see below).

The behavior of carboxylic acids (RCOOH) is of greater interest since these materials are often added to hydrocarbon oils to serve as boundary additives.   Unlike the hydrocarbons these substances can chemisorb readily on metal oxides where they form carboxylate ions.   On the other hand if they are adsorbed on the metal surface itself, they split off hydrogen and form a species which appears to involve covalent bonds between the oxygens

and the metal atoms.   The details of this are not established unequivocally.

The behavior probably depends on the reactivity of the metal. It is interesting to note, however, that in the presence of oxygen the covalent species is converted into the carboxylate. This is due to oxidation of the metal and not to changes in the stoichiometric formula of the adsorbed species. For a fascinating account of this field the reader is referred to a survey article by Eischens (113).

F. Chemical Reactions at the Surface

The interaction of organic materials with metal surfaces is now known to involve very complex processes. The early stages have been studied by multiple-reflection infrared spectroscopy especially by Eichens (113) and by mass spectrometry. For example St. Pierre et al. (114) have shown that a perfectly clean aluminum surface reacts violently with a simple hydrocarbon if it contains a double bond. This led them to examine the lubricating efficiency on aluminum of lubricants containing the double $C=C$ bond. Experiments in fact showed that cetene ($C_{15}H_{30}=CH_2$) is far more effective than cetane ($C_{15}H_{31}-CH_3$).

Again Hermance and Egan (115) found that in the presence of platinum or palladium surfaces a wide range of organic vapors will react to form a dark brown carbonaceous deposit. In lubricated sliding experiments on steel Fein and Kreuz (111) observed the formation of similar polymerlike deposits. This phenomenon is probably related to a whole series of experiments by Vinogradov and his school (112) on the role of oxygen in the interaction of hydrocarbons with rubbing surfaces. Vinogradov has shown that the hydrocarbon is cracked and converted into an organic peroxide and that the subsequent behavior is governed by interaction between the metal and the hydrocarbon oxidation products.* The metal is oxidized by the organic peroxides and the continuous formation and removal of the oxide film are the primary cause of wear. If an antioxidant is introduced the metal oxide formation is reduced and, provided the running conditions are not too severe, the wear may decrease. This appears to account for the observed reduction in fretting corrosion if antioxidants are added to the lubricant (116).

If on the other hand the wear is very severe, oxide formation is highly desirable. For example, Vinogradov found that in a very heavily loaded four-ball machine the wear is less in air than in a lubricant from which all oxygen has been carefully excluded.

The interaction of lubricants with oxygen and their further interaction with the solid surface is probably of very wide occurrence. For example Tingle (118) found that a fatty acid would lubricate metals covered with

* Recently Koutkov has found evidence for a similar process in the lubrication of polymers sliding on steel (117).

oxide films but would give very poor lubrication if the oxide were scraped off the surface. In the latter case exposure of the surface to water or oxygen greatly improved the lubrication. Eischens suggests that this may be because the carboxylate species formed on the oxide is a better lubricant than the covalent species. The issue is not clear since it is possible that under Tingle's experimental conditions more than a monolayer was needed for effective lubrication. Probably chemical reaction rather than chemisorption is involved. Another example where the interaction between oxygen, lubricant, and surface is important is the behavior of alkyl silicones (119). These compounds are very stable thermally in the presence of noble metals or in the absence of oxygen. However, in the presence of oxygen and oxide-coated metals marked degradation of the silicone occurs at relatively low temperatures. Ionized oxygen atoms or molecules at the oxide surface break up the Si—CH_3 bond and form a crosslinked silicone polymer on the surface at temperatures below 100°C. Since the oxidation process is due to O^- or O_2^- ions the process is hardly affected by conventional antioxidant additives which usually operate as "chain-stoppers." The silicone polymer is relatively brittle and not very effective as a boundary film but in some circumstances its durability and lubricating action may be considerably improved.

G. Extreme Pressure Lubricants

Apart from the interactions described above there is another class of lubricant whose purpose is to form an inorganic surface layer. These are the extreme pressure lubricants which contain a labile sulfur, chlorine, or phosphorus group. At those contact regions where there is incipient seizure high local temperatures are generated and the lubricant breaks down to form a sulfide, chloride, or phosphate layer. The reaction is by no means simple. For example Godfrey (120) has shown that, on ferrous materials, sulfurized oils form a mixture of iron sulfide and iron oxide, and oxygen diffuses to a considerable depth below the surface. An interesting summary of work in this field has been given by Fein (120a). Chloride films generally give a lower coefficient of friction since they have a lower shear strength than the corresponding sulfide. However they hydrolyze in the presence of moisture and the liberated HCl can cause undesirable corrosion of the system. For this reason chloride additives have fallen out of favor. On the other hand, because the sulfide is not a low-friction film it is often desirable to include some free fatty acid or soap as an additional constituent (see Figure 18). Lubricants which function by reaction must not be capable of dissolving the surface films formed—otherwise, they too will lead to excessive removal of metal by reaction and dissolution.

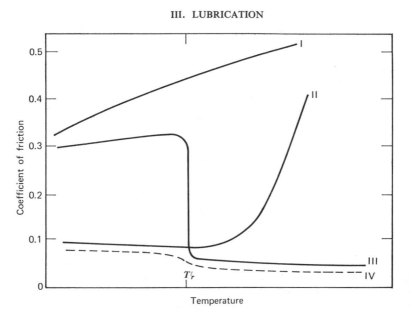

Fig. 18. Frictional behavior (schematic) of various lubricants, as a function of temperature: (I) paraffin oil; (II) fatty acid; (III) EP lubricant which reacts with the surfaces at temperature T_r; (IV) mixture of EP lubricant and fatty acid. The fatty acid provides effective lubrication up to the temperature at which the EP additive reacts with the surface.

H. The Structure and Shear Properties of Boundary Films

Our major ignorance concerning the action of boundary films is threefold. We do not know their composition with accuracy; we do not have precise information as to their structure, and we do not know how sliding and shearing occur.

The composition and structure of films formed from fatty acids are best understood, though even here there is some uncertainty as to the nature of the metallic soap that may be formed by chemical reaction. For example there is evidence that some soaps have a chelate structure (121). Much work has been carried out on monolayers formed from the Langmuir trough or by retraction from the melt or from solution. Their structure has been studied by electron diffraction. In general the chains are oriented with their polar groups attached to the solid surface and the chains normal or steeply inclined to the surface. The lateral attraction between the chains adds greatly to their stability and physical robustness. As the temperature of the system is raised the chains acquire increased thermal motion. Orientation is lost, and at a higher temperature the molecules are desorbed.

The strength properties of these films have been studied by Akhmatov

(122) and his school. They have assembled multiple "sandwiches" of molecular films deposited on polished metal substrates and in this way have been able to determine a number of mechanical properties such as elastic compressibility, shear modulus, and yield stress of the films. A more direct study is due to Bailey and Courtney-Pratt (17), who deposited a monolayer of calcium stearate from a Langmuir trough on to two mica surfaces. The surfaces were pressed together and the force required to shear the interface measured. In this way they showed that the shear strength of the film was of order 0.25 kg/mm². They also showed by optical interference that the bifilm was 45 Å thick, which is approximately twice the length of the molecule.

It is interesting to recall the earlier experiments of Wilson (56) in which a fine needle of stearic acid was slid over a smooth platinum surface. A fine visible track is left on the platinum from which a rough estimate of the contact area may be made. From this the contact pressure and the shear stress during sliding can be calculated. For contact pressures less than 1 kg/mm² the shear strength is comparable with that deduced by Bailey and Courtney-Pratt in their mica experiments where the contact pressure was of the order 0.1 kg/mm². When the contact pressure exceeded 1.5 kg/mm², however, there was a change in shear strength which Wilson attributed to the fact that at lower pressures the molecules slide with their chains perpendicular to the plane of sliding, while at higher pressures the chains are bent over and sliding occurs with the chains parallel to the sliding direction. Because of the finite yield pressure of the stearic acid needle itself it was not possible for Wilson to extend his measurements to higher contact pressures.

This issue is of great importance for the following reason. Consider the behavior of, say, tool steel surfaces and tin surfaces lubricated with long-chain molecules. The hardness of the steel (600 kg/mm²) is 100 times greater than that of tin (6 kg/mm²) so that the contact area under a given load should be 100 times less. If the friction is due to the shearing of the lubricant film trapped at the regions of contact the friction should be 100 times less for steel than for tin. In fact it is only about one-half. The simplest explanation is that the shear strength of the film is roughly proportional to the pressure so that the shear strength increases proportionately as the area of contact diminishes. There is some evidence for this from experiments by Bridgman (123), Boyd and Robertson (123a), and White (123b), and a theoretical calculation due to Cameron (124). The most direct and relevant data have recently been provided by Scruton (125).

In Scruton's experiments a glass hemisphere was slid over a flat glass surface on which monolayers of stearic acid had been deposited from the Langmuir trough or by retraction. Langmuir-trough multilayers were also studied. Because the glass surfaces were fire polished they were very smooth and it is reasonable to assume that the true contact area A was the same as the Hertzian area.   The radius of curvature of the sphere was varied from 0.0037 to 2.4 mm and the normal load from 10 mg to 20 gm: in this way the contact pressure could be varied from about 1 to 300 kg/mm². The frictional force F was found to depend very little on sliding speed (range 0.005 to 0.1 mm/sec) and very little on the number of layers deposited, though there was a tendency for multilayers to give a lower friction than a single monolayer.   Careful examination of the surfaces after the friction experiments, using electron microscopy, showed no evidence for damage to the glass surfaces.   It seems reasonable to assume therefore that the frictional force is a measure of the shear strength s of the lubricant film.   Consequently we may write $s = F/A$, where F is the measured force and A the calculated (Hertzian) area of contact.

Typical results are shown in Figure 19.   It is seen that for contact pressures below about 1 kg/mm² the value of s is fairly constant and agrees reasonably well with the value obtained by Bailey and Courtney-Pratt.   Above this pressure there is a fairly linear increase of s with p.   The results would seem to support the idea of a change in the molecular orientation with pressure

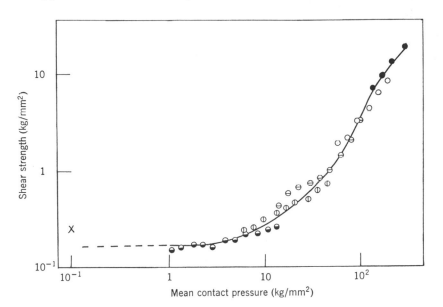

Fig. 19.   Variation of shear strength with contact pressure for calcium stearate layers. 1, 3, and 5 layers deposited on a glass flat by the Langmuir-Blodgett technique.   Experimental points correspond to sliders of radius ●, 3.7 μm; ○, 40 μm; ⊖, 0.1 mm; ⊙, 0.4 mm; ◓, 2.4 mm moving over the glass plate.   The point denoted by × is taken from Bailey and Courtney-Pratt (17).   The results are in fair agreement with those obtained on bulk specimens of stearic acid by Boyd and Robertson (123a) and on metal stearates by White (123b).   The agreement with Akhmatov's (122) results is less satisfactory.

around 1–10 kg/mm² as suggested by Wilson.   However, similar results are found with copper stearate deposited as a relatively thick smear on the glass surface.   Since there is no reason to suppose that copper stearate forms an oriented monolayer this would suggest that the change in shear strength is not due to a change in orientation: it is presumably a characteristic of the material itself.   It is interesting to note that the value of s at a contact pressure of 10 kg/mm² is about the same as that observed by Pooley and Tabor in the slow speed sliding of high-density polythene over clean glass. In their experiments the transferred fragments of polythene could be lifted off the glass and examined in an electron microscope.   Diffraction studies showed that the hydrocarbon chains were aligned with their long chains extended in the direction of sliding.   This suggests that the lubricating action of stearic acid mono- and multilayers is also associated with the sliding of chains over one another with the chains oriented in the sliding direction.

Thin film lubrication can also be achieved by using thin soft metallic films on hard substrates (125a), thin layers of polymers (92a) or metal sulphide films (125b).   In these cases film thickness is important, not only in determining the magnitude of the coefficient of friction but also in influencing the viability of the lubricating film itself.   This is also shown in recent experiments designed to lubricate polymers by incorporating surface active materials within the polymer itself (93, 125c, 125d).   These materials diffuse to the surface and provide lubrication the effectiveness of which depends on the nature of the surfactant and the thickness of the film.   The most effective additive for polythene appears to be oleamide (93) though many other additives have been studied (93a, 125e).

I. The Electric Double Layer

If a surface is immersed in a liquid containing free ions these may be adsorbed to give a charged double layer on the surface.   If two such surfaces are brought together they will experience a repulsive force—this is the classical stabilizing force in colloidal systems.   The thickness of the film depends on the ionic strength and on the pressure to which it is subjected. Direct measurements of this have been described by Roberts and Tabor (125a) in studies of the contact between optically smooth rubber and glass. For a contact pressure of about 1 atm the film thickness is of the order of 120 Å (Figure 20).   If the surfaces are very smooth the film is not penetrated and the resistance to sliding is due only to the viscosity of the liquid film. This study shows that for films below 1000 Å in thickness the viscosity is the same as the bulk viscosity and even for films 200 Å in thickness the viscosity is only marginally increased.   These results show that no long-range order is produced in a liquid by a nearby surface, or if it does exist, the ordered liquid has virtually no additional resistance to shear.

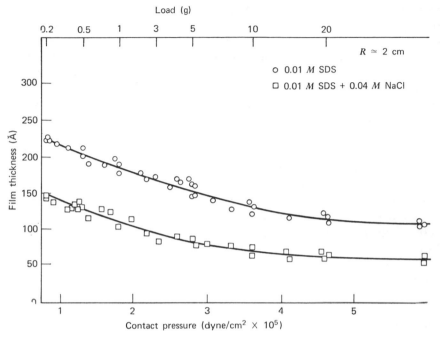

Fig. 20. Variation in equilibrium thickness of aqueous sodium dodecyl sulfate (SDS) films sandwiched between a rubber sphere and glass plate with contact pressure and with solution ionic strength. Photometric measurements were made at the centre of the contact zone and the pressures quoted are the Hertzian pressures at this point; they are 1.5 times the mean contact pressure as found from the load and area of contact.

The presence of charged double layers provides a means of lubricating surfaces if the loading is relatively light. The layer, of course, exists at heavier pressures; for example, other work has shown that at 100 atmospheres it would have a thickness of 10–20 Å. However, for most real surfaces, which are covered with much larger asperities, this is probably not thick enough to serve as an effective lubricant film. Consequently it is unlikely that the charged double layer can provide lubrication for metals though it may well play a part in the lubrication of rubbers or polymers. It is also possible that the charged double layer provides a modest measure of lubrication in body fluids such as saliva or synovial fluid (125b).

J. The Breakdown of the Boundary Film

In 1940 Tabor (126a) studied the boundary lubrication of metals at slow sliding speeds and investigated the effect of heating the surfaces. He found that surface-active materials may provide effective lubrication but that lubrication deteriorates as the temperature is raised; the effect is reversible on cooling (126b). For fatty acids applied neat to the surfaces two stages of deterioration were observed: the first corresponded to melting of the surface film, the second to its desorption (see Figure 17). This study was continued by Frewing (127) who investigated the behavior of various surface-active materials dissolved in a white mineral oil. He again found a reversible change in friction with temperature: an additional factor of great importance was the solubility of the surface film in the superincumbent liquid. The behavior could be described in thermodynamic terms: if the logarithm of the concentration was plotted against the reciprocal of the absolute temperature at which lubricant breakdown occurred a straight line resulted. This idea has recently been revived by Cameron and his colleagues (128) to explain the scuffing of lubricated metal surfaces at some critical temperature. We describe their analysis using a more standard thermodynamic treatment. Consider the behavior of a surface-active material dissolved in a neutral oil at concentration C. For reversible adsorption we may write

$$\Delta F = RT \ln \frac{C}{C_0}$$

where ΔF is the free energy change for transferring by adsorption 1 mole of adsorbate from the bulk at a standard bulk concentration C_0 to a surface concentration defined by a specified coverage. If we take C_0 to be unity and the standard state to correspond to half-coverage we obtain

$$\ln C = -\frac{q_s^{st}}{RT} - \frac{\Delta S_s}{R}$$

where q_s^{st} is the standard isosteric heat of adsorption and ΔS_s is the differential entropy change. Or rearranging,

$$\Delta S_s = \frac{q_s^{st}}{T} - R \ln C$$

If one works with solutions of different concentrations and observes the temperature T_c at which breakdown occurs there will be a linear relation between $1/T_c$ and $\ln C$, provided in all cases the breakdown occurs at the same fractional coverage, that is, ΔS_s is constant. Such a linear relation is found experimentally and they conclude that breakdown occurs when the critical coverage is about $\frac{1}{2}$. It is not at all clear, however, that the equations do, in fact, mean this. Furthermore, there are many other adsorption models which lead to substantially the same equation. For example, if the adsorption is treated as a competitive adsorption between the solvent and the surface-active material a similar equation is obtained although the thermodynamic quantities have a different physical significance.

Cameron et al. (128) identity this breakdown as the critical "scuffing temperature" in a practical operation, for example, in gears or bearings. They believe that this explains why, in high-speed gears, the breakdown temperature increases at higher speeds. There is not enough time during the transit of the gear teeth through the loading cycle for desorption to occur. The process is, of course, complicated by the possible occurrence of elasto-hydrodynamic lubrication particularly at higher speeds (129). Breakdown also depends on the load, the breakdown temperature being lower at higher loads because the lubricant film is subjected to more severe conditions (130). In addition some metal combinations scuff more easily than others—they need a larger fractional coverage to achieve effective lubrication. Again some materials even if they begin to scuff can "heal" more readily than others. Finally the thermodynamic treatment becomes far more involved if chemical reaction (as distinct from physical adsorption) occurs between the surfactant and the solid surfaces. It is clear that the practical situation involves more factors than the simple model they have proposed.

The most sophisticated attempt to apply thermodynamics to lubrication is that due to Rowe (131). He has described a wear mechanism for lubricated sliding in terms of sliding speed, temperature, heats of adsorption, junction growth, and surfactant concentration. His model involves a number of somewhat arbitrary assumptions, but within the range of his experiments he has obtained good agreement between his observations and his predictions.

A completely different approach to boundary lubrication and to its breakdown is due to Fein and Kreuz (132). They define boundary con-ditions as those occurring when the surface roughnesses are bigger than the thickness of the macroscopic elastohydrodynamic film. In that case the surface asperities are deformed and microelasto- or microplastohydro-dynamic lubrication occurs between the asperities themselves. On this view the surfaces may, in fact, never touch and may always be separated by a very thin film of lubricant, the viscosity of which is enormously increased by the high local pressures. However, the high shear stress in the film may be able to tear out portions of the asperities, or plowing may occur, or the asperities may be rapidly fatigued. In this way wear fragments may be detached. Scuffing may occur if the surface of an asperity is so highly extended that portions of it are no longer covered by the lubricant film. These two approaches are typical of the widely differing views held concerning the nature of boundary lubrication. It remains a problem of vital importance in lubrication practice and an open challenge to the professional tribologist.

Since the first draft of this review was written an extremely important paper has been published by Hirst and Stafford (132a) on the breakdown of bound-ary lubricating films using as lubricant a dilute solution of stearic acid in a pure mineral oil. They show that the breakdown or "transition" temperature depends on concentration as was found in the earlier work so that an adsorption process is involved. But they also find that it depends on the stiffness of the friction apparatus, on the surface finish and on the severity of deformation of the surface oxide film normally present on metal surfaces. When this deformation is slight the oxide film is not broken through and provides a substantial measure of protection. The lubricant is not exposed to severe demands and the transition temperature is relatively high. When the deformation is great enough to cause breakdown of the oxide film the whole burden of lubrication is thrown on the lubricant and the transition temperature is low. With one set of surfaces the severity of deformation at constant sliding speed is most easily varied by changing the load. Increasing the load from 0.1 to 10 Kg reduces the transition temperature from 250°C to less than 40°C. The effect of surface finish on transition temperature is complex. In general a smoother surface implies gentler deformation of the surface oxide and a higher transition temperature. There is, however, a limit to this. If the surface finish is too smooth trivial damage, initiated at a surface blemish or even a dust particle, may produce fragments which cannot escape: this will lead to increased damage and early failure of the lubricant. This effect has long been known but the paper as a whole brings out clearly the complex nature of the sliding process and the impossibility of describing lubricant breakdown in terms of a single parameter such as a transition temperature. Similar views have been expressed by Bell and Dyson (132b) and, in a recent paper, by Cameron and Sharma (132c).

In the experimental study of lubricant breakdown three main techniques have been used: the measurement of friction; the measurement of wear or transfer, for example, by radioactive tracers; and the electrical resistance. The latter technique is particularly suitable for studying the behavior of a running mechanism: for example, Courtney-Pratt and Tudor (133) used it to study the lubrication between the piston ring and cylinder wall of an internal combustion engine. If the lubricant film is complete the resistance is very high; if some metal–metal contact occurs the resistance falls to a low value. More recently Furey (134, 135) has revived this technique and has used it to estimate more quantitatively the amount of lubricant breakdown. In this way he has been able to study in a very convenient way the influence of load, speed, surface roughness, and lubricant additive. However, his "quantitative" values of metallic contact can only be regarded as qualitative.

K. Kramer and Rehbinder Effects

We refer here briefly to two areas of work involving surfaces which at various times have attracted considerable attention. The first, generally named the Kramer effect, is concerned with the emission of electrons from surfaces as a result of deformation such as occurs during abrasion or frictional sliding. A very helpful survey by Grunberg (136) describes the main mechanisms involved. One would expect the Kramer effect to play a part in the formation, as a result of physical or chemical attachment to the activated surface, of surface films possessing some lubricating or protective property. However, although a small number of papers have appeared on the Kramer effect since Grunberg's survey was published, little systematic work seems to have been done on its role in frictional and lubrication processes.

The second effect is associated with the name of Rehbinder: it is concerned with the influence of surface-active materials on the mechanical strength of solids. Although not all Rehbinder's observations are fully confirmed it is now clear (see recent surveys by Kramer and Demer (137) and Westwood (138)) that in many cases the adsorption of surface-active materials, especially at surface flaws or cracks, can produce marked reductions in strength. This may well play a significant part in such processes as lubrication, both in sliding and in metal cutting, as well as in Rehbinder's classical field of rock drilling.

L. Weeping Lubrication

There are two further points of applied interest that may be quoted. The first is the observation of McCutchen (139) that porous materials may extrude lubricant when subjected to pressure, thus providing a "weeping" type of lubrication: he has suggested that this may be one of the ways in which the cartilage and the synovial fluid lubricate bone joints. The second is somewhat similar but operates under much higher pressures. If a metal surface is lightly shot-blasted before lubrication it can be subjected to very heavy deformations in subsequent rolling or drawing without the occurrence of scuffing; the lubricant is squeezed out of the cavities during the metal-working operation and prevents metal–metal contact (140). In this way even titanium may be successfully worked.

M. The General Picture of Lubrication

The best lubrication of surfaces is achieved when they are completely separated by a film of fluid as in aerodynamic, hydrodynamic, or elastohydro-dynamic lubrication. If the film is ruptured some additional protection is provided by lubricant films adsorbed at the surface. The poorest protection is provided by simple hydrocarbons; they may be strongly adsorbed but are probably too thin to be effective. Long-chain polar molecules such as amines or fatty acids containing 16 carbons or more are far more effective. They are adsorbed with their polar ends on the surface and their chains steeply inclined or normal to the surface.

At low contact pressures the force to shear these films is very small; it increases as the contact pressure increases and it is probable that the molecules are bent over. The most effective films appear to be those formed by chemical reaction between the metal (or metal oxide) surface and a fatty acid, presumably because the soaps have a higher melting point.

The effect of temperature on these films of amines, fatty acids, or soaps is striking. So long as the adsorbed or chemically combined film is close packed it gives good protection. It reduces metallic contact at those regions where it would otherwise occur. Although the friction may be reduced by only a factor of 20, say, the metallic transfer may be reduced by a factor of 100,000 or more. As the temperature is raised the film melts or loses its close-packed structure. The friction rises by a factor of five and the transfer by a factor of 100. At a still higher temperature the lubricant is desorbed and wherever the surfaces come into contact the film is pushed away and the friction and transfer resemble the behavior of unlubricated surfaces. A schematic presentation of these results for a long-chain compound applied neat to a surface is given in Figure 21. A similar type of failure will occur

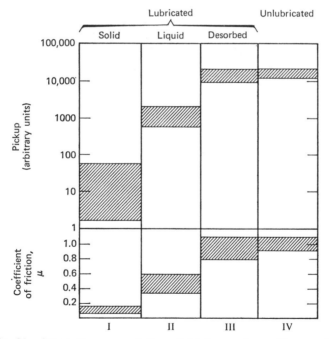

Fig. 21. Schematic representation of friction and metallic transfer for lubricated surfaces when the lubricant film is (I) solid; (II) liquid; (III) desorbed. The behavior when the film is desorbed is practically the same as for unlubricated surfaces (IV).

with all types of adsorbed films—at some temperature the molecules will desorb, particularly if they are soluble in the superincumbent liquid, and henceforth serve no lubricating function. It is probable that, in practice, high temperature flashes are one of the main causes of lubricant failure.

At still higher temperatures (or if the heating is prolonged) other effects become important. Chemical degradation, oxidation, and polymer formation occur. The process is greatly aided by the presence of free oxygen (dissolved in the lubricant) and by catalytic action of the surface itself.

The oxygen normally present in lubricants is often beneficial since it helps to form metal oxides at regions where the oxide is worn away. In some cases, however, organic peroxides can lead to excessive oxide formation and wear. It is evident that in any practical mechanism the situation is very complicated.

Where temperatures are excessive the use of simple organic fluids alone is no longer practical. Labile groups are incorporated into the molecule; these attack the surface at regions of incipient seizure and form an inorganic film, usually of sulfide. These films provide protection up to much higher temperatures.

IV. WEAR

A. Laws of Wear

There are no precise laws of wear. In general, we can make three broad observations. Wear increases with time of running, increases with load, and is less for hard surfaces than for soft. There are many exceptions, however, even to these generalizations.

B. Effect of Load

We first consider the wear of unlubricated metals using a very simple configuration of a pin of a softer metal sliding over a disc or cylinder of hard steel. Typical wear results are shown in Figure 22. Below a critical load the wear is mild and the wear debris is mainly oxide: the worn surface is relatively smooth and the electrical contact resistance is high. Above the critical load the wear rate increases rapidly: the electrical contact resistance is low, the surfaces are appreciably roughened, and the wear debris consists of metal particles or flakes. This is the regime of severe wear.

C. Mechanism of Severe Wear

Severe wear is associated with strong adhesion and the shearing of metallic junctions. Even on this simple model it is clear that the amount of material

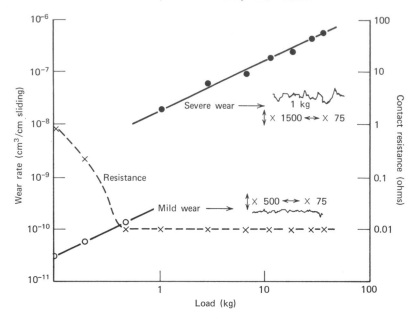

Fig. 22. Wear results (continuous line) for a 60:40 brass pin on a hard steel disc, showing the transition from mild wear at loads below 500 g to severe wear at loads above 1 kg. The electrical contact resistance (broken line) shows a large drop in surface roughness; for mild wear (lower insert) average surface roughness is 20 μ in.; for severe wear (upper insert) average surface roughness is 1000 μ in.

plucked out of the surfaces depends on the location of the plane of shear. In the ideal case, if shear could occur exactly in the interface between the two surfaces, the plucking would be negligible. In most cases shearing occurs a small distance away from the interface within the softer of the two solids. In the sliding of one material on itself adhesion will be strong and the interface, because of work-hardening, will be stronger than the parent solids. As a result fragments will be torn out of both surfaces. For this reason it is generally bad practice to slide similar materials together.

There is of course a clear distinction between the plucking and transfer process and the observed wear. Where surfaces are subjected to repeated traversals over the same contact region the plucked fragments may initially be attached to one surface but may subsequently be back-transferred onto the other. The net wear rate will therefore depend crucially on the back-transfer process and on the final mechanism which detaches a transferred fragment and turns it into a loose wear fragment.

D. The Archard Model of Severe Wear

A very useful model is that due to Archard (141). Consider an individual junction of radius a. If it is circular its area is πa^2 and if the contact pressure p is equal to the hardness or yield pressure of the material the junction supports a load

$$w = p\pi a^2 \tag{24}$$

if junction growth is ignored.

When such a junction is sheared it leaves a fragment of volume proportional to a^3. Assuming the lump to be hemispherical in shape its volume is $\frac{2}{3}\pi a^3$. This fragment is formed in a sliding distance $2a$. Consequently the wear volume per unit distance Z is $\frac{2}{3}\pi a^3/2a = \pi a^2/3$. From equation 24 this gives

$$Z = \frac{\pi a^2}{3} = \frac{w}{3p} \tag{25}$$

This will apply to each junction so that if all the fragments are of geometrically similar shape the total wear volume per unit distance Z will be the sum of the Z's whatever the size distribution of the fragments.

$$Z = \sum \frac{w}{3p} = \frac{W}{3p} \tag{26}$$

This model assumes that all junctions involved in friction produce a wear fragment. If, in fact, only a fraction k contributes to wear

$$Z = k\frac{W}{3p} \tag{27}$$

This model shows that Z is proportional to the load and independent of the size of the bodies: under some carefully controlled experimental conditions these laws are approximately obeyed and equation 27 provides a means of estimating k. If, of course, wear involves not lumps but a surface layer of constant thickness d, a different and more complicated equation results. For junctions of constant diameter $2a$

$$Z = k\frac{d}{2a}\frac{W}{p} \tag{28}$$

This cannot be applied very easily unless both d and a are known. For this reason the simpler model has been much more widely used.

Applying equation 27 to a series of experiments carried out by Archard for a pin sliding on a steel disc at a load of 400 g and a speed of 180 cm/sec, we obtain the results of Table III. There are two basic conclusions. First,

TABLE III

Typical Values of k

Surface	μ	k
Mild steel on mild steel	0.6	10^{-2}
60/40 leaded brass on hard steel	0.24	10^{-3}
ptfe on hard steel	0.18	$2 \cdot 10^{-5}$
Stellite on hard steel	0.6	$5 \cdot 10^{-5}$
Stainless steel on hard steel	0.5	$2 \cdot 10^{-5}$
Polyethylene on hard steel	0.65	10^{-7}

although the friction varies by only a factor of 2 or 3 the wear parameter k varies by a factor of 10^5. Second, only a small fraction of the friction junctions contribute to the wear even for similar metals.

E. The Release of Wear Fragments

Rabinowicz (142) has suggested that repeated traversals will subject a fragment to numerous loading and unloading cycles as it passes in and out of the contact zone. Strain energy will gradually be stored in the particle and at some stage this will be sufficient to provide the interfacial surface energy necessary to detach the fragment. This is an interesting idea which is fully developed in his book entitled *Wear*.

A different approach is that due to Archard (141), Rozeanu (143), and Kragelsky (144). They consider that the wear fragment is finally detached by a fatigue mechanism. Finally Rowe (145) has suggested that the small value of Archard's k for similar metals is due to surface films which prevent the whole of the junction from being completely metallic: on this view really clean surfaces would give a value of k approximately equal to unity. In practice, of course, such surfaces would give gross seizure.

F. Mild Wear

In mild wear most of the sliding occurs within a thin surface film. With metals this is generally the oxide. Even if some metallic contact occurs through the film the plucked metal fragment will be very small and because of its large surface/volume ratio will oxidize very rapidly. Consequently with metals even if there is some metal–metal interaction the wear debris is predominantly oxide.

G. Abrasive Wear

Abrasive wear occurs if a hard particle cuts or grooves one of the rubbing surfaces. The first criterion for appreciable abrasive wear is that the particle should be harder than the surface being abraded. If the Vickers hardness of the particle is more than 1.2 times that of the surface, abrasion can occur fairly readily (146).   If the particle is smooth most of the abrasion will be in the form of plastic grooves (with very little material removed) or in the form of chips and flakes if the surface is brittle.   If the particle has sharp corners or edges and it is appropriately oriented it will cut the surface.   Abrasion then resembles microcutting and the abrasion rates are relatively high.   There is a good deal of experimental work, particularly by Khrushchov (147) in Russia and Richardson (148, 149) in Britain on this aspect of wear.   If the particle is not harder than the surface some abrasive wear can still occur but at a greatly diminished rate.

Abrasion tends to produce a marked change in structure and orientation of the surface layers.   With metals Wilman (150) has shown that the abrasion texture is similar to that produced when the metal is deformed between hard rollers.   Sometimes phase changes also occur.   Because the surfaces are continuously work-hardened by the abrasive process they gradually become more resistant to abrasion.

The best way of avoiding abrasive wear is to fabricate the rubbing surfaces of materials that are extremely hard.   For example, very hard surface layers can be deposited by plasma or flame deposition.   If, however, a small particle of the hard layer becomes detached it can produce very heavy scoring and abrasion of the layer itself.   This leads to a runaway catastrophic situation.   Further, as we saw above a tangential traction greatly facilitates the cracking of hard brittle surfaces.

Although in the chemical industry the wear produced by the flow of slurries is often considered to be abrasive wear, the use of hard coatings may be quite misguided.   In many cases the wear is a combination of abrasion and corrosion and a chemically inert layer may be far more effective.   It also turns out that polymeric materials can often absorb a great deal of deformation energy before they fragment.   For both these reasons polymeric films can often be used very successfully to reduce wear in such applications.

H. Chemical Wear

In mechanisms running in air the rubbing surfaces will always tend to oxidize.   With metals the oxidation product is a surface film which is often hard and may protect the underlying metal from intimate metal–metal contact.   On the other hand it may become detached and act as a hard abrasive.   With hypoid gears where contact stresses and frictional heating are severe it is common to use lubricants containing sulfur or chlorine. These react with the surface to form a protective sulfide or chloride film. But if the lubricant additive is too reactive it can lead to excessive chemical corrosion.

With polymers chemical effects are equally important but more subtle. The abrasion of polymers involves ultimately the breaking of chemical bonds. This is aided by oxidative degradation. For this reason, in some circumstances, the addition of stabilizers to polymers to increase their resistance to oxidative degradation can lead to an appreciable increase in wear resistance. This is particularly marked under those conditions where interfacial adhesion is weak and the wear process is dominated by a fatigue mechanism.

I. Surface Dissolution

In some cases very high wear rates can occur if one of the sliding surfaces is soluble in the other and if the temperature at the interface is high. Elevated temperatures may arise in two ways: first the surfaces may have to run in a hot environment; second, the high temperature may be generated by the sliding process itself. A well-known example is the interaction of tungsten carbide with ferrous materials: above 1100°C tungsten carbide is soluble in iron. Consequently if the interface reaches or exceeds this temperature the tungsten carbide will be worn away by a sort of erosion (Latin: *erodere* = to gnaw away): the carbide is eaten away or consumed by the hot iron. This is well known in the metal cutting of ferrous materials. At very high cutting speeds the wear of tungsten carbide tools is catastrophic (151).

Sometimes the process of surface dissolution may prove to be beneficial. Several years ago Roach, Goodzeit, and Hunnicut (152) suggested that if, in the sliding of metals, surface solubility produced an alloy which was brittle, shear would occur at the interface itself. As a result subsequent wear would be relatively small. There is some evidence to support this view.

J. Fatigue Wear

If solids are subjected to cyclic loading above a certain critical stress they gradually fatigue and fail. Such a process can always occur between sliding surfaces. It is, however, a slow process so that it is usually swamped by adhesive or abrasive wear. Consequently fatigue wear becomes important only when adhesive and abrasive wear are relatively small. For example, in well-lubricated systems adhesive wear may be negligible. If hard particles are excluded from the system abrasive wear may be small. If then the surfaces are continuously subjected to loading and unloading they may gradually fatigue and pieces of the surface may easily be detached. This occurs in sliding systems where asperities on one surface continuously transmit stresses onto the other even though they are completely separated by a lubricant film.

It is clear that asperities of marked curvature will be subjected to larger stresses and will therefore fatigue more quickly than asperities of gentler curvature. Consequently, as Kragelsky (153) has pointed out, the fatigue process will gradually remove the more marked asperities and lead to a more uniform pattern of surface finish. This may well be one of the mechanisms by which "running-in" produces a relatively smooth surface. It predicates, of course, the absence of strong adhesion (15).

Fatigue wear is generally the main cause of failure in ball and roller bearings and is often initiated at a surface flaw or crack. An applied stress may open the crack a little: in the presence of a contaminating atmosphere the crack does not "heal" on removal of the stress. Repeated cycling of the stress will thus gradually produce spalling of a fragment out of the surface. In some cases surface flaws are not sufficiently pronounced to generate surface fatigue. Under such conditions repeated stressing gradually work-hardens the subsurface material. This material may then undergo shear or tensile failure.

Fatigue failure can be minimized by reducing the contact stresses, and by using materials which do not contain surface flaws or other inhomogeneities.

K. Effect of Load and Speed

The effect of load on wear is twofold. First, as the load is increased there will be some increase in frictional heating. This may soften the surfaces and lead to excessive flow of material. This often occurs with heavily loaded gears. On the other hand, as Welsh (154) has shown in his studies of the wear of steels the high temperatures may lead to phase changes and even to the formation of hard nitrides or carbides by reaction with surrounding air or lubricant. In that case the wear rate becomes less at heavy loads than at light loads.

In most engineering situations, however, the main effect of increasing the load is to produce increased deformation of the surfaces. Many engineering metal surfaces are covered with protective oxide films or (if additive lubricants are used) composite oxide–sulfide or chloride films. Severe deformation can disrupt these and expose the underlying clean metal. The chances of metal–metal contact are then greatly increased with the accompanying danger of severe adhesive wear. This change in wear mode is, in effect, the transition described by Hirst and his colleagues (155) between mild and severe wear in unlubricated sliding. Hirst's recent work (132a) suggests that a similar process plays an important role in determining the breakdown of boundary lubricant films.

The effect of speed is also twofold. On the one hand, if an engineering system is designed to run under conditions of hydrodynamic lubrication the hydrodynamic film will form more readily at high velocities. There is a limit to this, however, since the associated increase in shear rate will lead to viscous heating and to a decrease in oil viscosity. A more important factor is the behavior of contacting asperities separated by very thin lubricant films. An increase in speed can produce a large increase in the temperature rise at the engaging asperities. This may be sufficient to disorient, desorb or even evaporate the protective film, leading in turn to severe metal–metal contact. This is one of the major factors responsible for the occurrence of scuffing, though other mechanisms may also be involved.

There is, of course, a different way in which speed may influence the wear of unlubricated solids. If the speed is high enough it may actually melt the surface layers within the region of contact. If the melting is restricted to a very thin interfacial layer this can change gross adhesive wear into a very mild type of material removal.

L. The Overall Mechanism of Wear

The literature on wear is enormous and this brief review cannot do more than touch on some of the more basic mechanisms. These include adhesion and shearing of interfacial junctions, alloy formation at the interface, fatiguing of transferred fragments or of surface asperities, oxidation or corrosion of surface layers, abrasion by extraneous particles or by wear fragments, and cracking of brittle films by combined normal and tangential stresses. Each of these processes is fairly well understood in itself, yet wear as a general phenomenon is usually very complex and almost impossible to quantify. This is partly because the sliding process itself may change the nature of the surfaces either by work-hardening them or changing their roughness or by producing new phases or alloys or structures at the interface. In addition a slight change in running conditions may alter the importance of individual wear mechanisms or change their mode of interaction in an unpredictable way.

Acknowledgment

I wish to express my gratitude to members of the laboratory who have made critical comments on various parts of this review. I am particularly indebted to Dr. B. J. Briscoe.

Symbols

a	radius of individual asperity contact
A	are of contact
A_0	initial contact area, before junction growth occurs
C	bulk concentration of surfactant
C_0	standard bulk concentration
E	Young's modulus
E'	reduced Young's modulus
F	friction force
F_k	kinetic friction force
F_s	static friction force

ΔF	change of Helmholtz free energy
h	film thickness in fluid lubrication
k	Boltzmann constant
k	Archard wear parameter
k, k_1, k_2	arbitrary constants
m	arbitrary constant in load-area relation
n	arbitrary constant
N	number of revolutions per sec
p	contact pressure
p_0	static yield pressure (hardness)
$p_{elastic}$	contact pressure for elastic deformation
P	nominal pressure in bearing
P	plowing component of frictional force
$q_s{}^{st}$	standard isosteric heat of adsorption
Q	activation energy in viscosity-temperature relation
r	radius
R	radius of curvature of surface
R	gas constant
s	shear strength of friction junctions
s_i	shear strength of interface
ΔS_s	standard differential entropy change on adsorption
T	temperature (absolute)
T_c	critical temperature at scuffing
U	relative velocity between two surfaces
w	normal load carried by individual asperity
W	total normal load between surfaces
Z	viscosity
Z_0	viscosity at atmospheric pressure and temperature
α	constant in combined-stress yield-criterion equation
α	pressure coefficient of viscosity
β	average radius of curvature of asperities
β	fraction of load-bearing area that penetrates lubricant film
θ	average slope of surface asperities
θ	semiapical angle of wedge or cone
λ	wavelength
μ	coefficient of friction
μ_p	plowing component of coefficient of friction
ν	frequency
σ	mean deviation of asperity heights
τ	critical shear stress
Ψ	plasticity index

References

1. L. da Vinci, *The Notebooks of Leonardo da Vinci*, English translation by E. MacCurdy, 1938.
2. G. Amontons, *Memoires de l'Academie Royale*, 1699, p. 206.
3. C. A. Coulomb, *Theories des Machines Simples*, 1785 (Memoire de Mathematique et de Physique de l'Academie Royale, Paris).
4. R. Holm, *Electrical Contacts*, Springer, Berlin, 1958.

5. F. P. Bowden and D. Tabor, *Friction and Lubrication of Solids*, Part I, Clarendon Press, Oxford, 1950.
6. F. P. Bowden and D. Tabor, *Friction and Lubrication of Solids*, Part II, Clarendon Press, Oxford, 1964.
7. F. P. Bowden and W. R. Throssel, *Proc. Roy. Soc. (London) Ser. A*, **209**, 297 (1951).
8. G. Pfefferkern, *Naturwissenschaften* **40**, 551 (1953).
9. R. Takaji, *Electron Microscopy, Proc. Regional Conf. Asia Oceania, 1st, Tokyo, 1956*, 297 (1957).
10. L. E. Samuels, *J. Inst. Metals*, **85**, 51 (1956).
11. J. Leslie, *An Experimental Inquiry into the Nature and Propagation of Heat*, J. Mawman, London, 1804.
12. J. F. Archard, *Nature*, **172**, 918 (1951).
13. A. S. Lodge and H. G. Howell, *Proc. Phys. Soc. (London) Ser. B*, **67**, 89–97 (1954).
14. J. Mølgaard, *Proc. Phys. Soc. (London)*, **79**, 516–534, (1962).
15. J. A. Greenwood and J. B. P. Williamson, *Proc. Roy. Soc. (London) Ser. A*, **295**, 300–319 (1966).
16. S. C. Cohen and D. Tabor, *Proc. Roy. Soc. (London) Ser. A*, **291**, 186–207 (1966).
17. A. I. Bailey and J. S. Courtney-Pratt, *Proc. Roy. Soc. (London) Ser. A*, **227**, 500–515 (1955).
18. N. Adams, *J. Appl. Polymer Sci.*, **7**, 2075 (1963).
19. J. Dyson and W. Hirst, *Proc. Phys. Soc. (London) Ser. B*, **67**, 309–312 (1954).
20. I. V. Kraghelsky and V. P. Sabelnikov, *Institution of Mechanical Engineers Conference on Lubrication and Wear*, Institution of Mechanical Engineers, London, 1957, pp. 247–251.
21. K. Kendall and D. Tabor, *Proc. Roy. Soc. (London) Ser. A*, **323**, 321–340 (1971).
22. J. R. Osias and J. H. Tripp, *Wear*, **9**, 388 (1966).
23. D. Tabor, *The Hardness of Solids*, Clarendon Press, Oxford, 1951.
24. J. S. Courtney-Pratt and E. Eisner, *Proc. Roy. Soc. (London) Ser. A*, **238**, 529–550 (1957).
25. J. S. McFarlane and D. Tabor, *Proc. Roy. Soc. (London) Ser. A*, **202**, 244–253 (1950).
26. J. W. Midgley, R. I. Longley, A. Strang, and G. D. Teer, *Proceedings of Institution of Mechanical Engineers Lubrication and Wear Convention*, Institution of Mechanical Engineers, London, 1963, pp. 198–209.
27. J. F. Archard, *Proc. Roy. Soc. (London) Ser. A*, **243**, 190–205 (1957).
28. K. L. Johnson and J. J. O'Connor, *Proc. Appl. Mech. Conv., Proc. Inst. Mech. Engrs.*, **178**, 7 (1963/1964).
29. P. Weiss, *Adhesion and Cohesion*, Elsevier, Amsterdam, 1962.
30. D. D. Eley, *Adhesion*, Oxford University Press, London, 1962.
31. R. Houwink and G. Salomon, *Adhesion and Adhesives*, Elsevier, Amsterdam, 1963.
32. A. E. Roach, C. L. Goodzeit, and R. P. Hunnicut, *Mech. Eng.*, **77**, 350–360 (1955).
33. D. L. Anderson, H. Christensen, and P. Andreatch, *J. Appl. Phys.*, **28**, 923 (1957).
34. A. C. Moore and D. Tabor, *Brit. J. Appl. Phys.* **3**, 299–301 (1952).
35. E. S. Machlin and W. R. Yankee, *J. Appl. Phys.*, **25**, 576–581 (1954).
36. F. P. Bowden and G. W. Rowe, *Proc. Roy. Soc. (London) Ser. A*, **233**, 429–442 (1956).
37. D. V. Keller, *J. Appl. Phys.* **38**, 1896 (1967).
37a. P. F. Pfaelzer, Ph.D. Thesis, Cambridge, 1971.
37b. M. Barquins, D. Maugis, and R. Courtel, *Compt. Rend.*, **272**, 1130–1133 (1971).
38. A. B. Osborn, *R.A.E. Tech. Note No. CPM 69*, 1964.
39. A. W. J. de Gee, *Wear*, **8**, 121–132 (1965).
40. D. H. Buckley, *J. Adhes.*, **1**, 264 (1969).

41. A. P. Semenoff, *Sxvativanye Metallov*, Mashgiz, Moscow, 1958.
42. A. P. Semenoff, *Wear*, **4**, 1–9 (1961).
43. D. L. Anderson, *Wear*, **3**, 253–73 (1960).
44. M. E. Sikorski, *Wear*, **7**, 144–162 (1964).
45. N. A. de Bruyne, *J. Appl. Chem.*, **6**, 303–310 (1956).
46. A. I. Bailey and S. M. Kay. *Proc. Roy. Soc. (London) Ser. A*, **301**, 47–56 (1967).
47. R. F. King and D. Tabor, *Proc. Roy. Soc. (London) Ser. A*, **236**, 250–264 (1956).
48. S. S. Voyutskii, *Auto-adhesion and Adhesion of High Polymers*, Wiley, New York, 1963.
48a. D. Tabor and R. H. S. Winterton, *Proc. Roy. Soc. (London) Ser. A*, **312**, 435–450 (1969).
48b. J. Israelachvili and D. Tabor, *Proc. Roy. Soc. (London)*, in press, 1972.
49. F. P. Bowden and D. Tabor, *J. Appl. Phys.*, **14**, 141–151 (1943).
50. F. P. Bowden and D. Tabor, *Brit. J. Appl. Phys.*, **17**, 1521 (1966).
51. B. W. E. Avient, J. Goddard, and H. Wilman, *Proc. Roy. Soc. (London) Ser. A*, **258**, 159–180 (1960).
52. M. M. Kruschov and M. A. Babichev, *Investigations of the Wear Process in Metals*, USSR Academy of Science, Moscow, 1960 (in Russian).
53. T. O. Mulhearn and L. E. Samuels, *Wear*, **5**, 478–498 (1962).
54. V. D. Scott and H. Wilman, *Proc. Roy. Soc. (London) Ser. A*, **247**, 353–368 (1958).
54a. D. Atack and W. D. May, 1958, Pulp and Paper Magazine of Canada, Conference Paper "Frictional Mechanisms in the Grinding Process."
54b. D. Atack and D. Tabor, *Proc. Roy. Soc. (London) Ser. A*, **246**, 539–555 (1958).
54c. K. R. Eldredge and D. Tabor, *Proc. Roy. Soc. (London) Ser. A*, **229**, 181–198 (1955).
54d. J. E. Merwin and K. L. Johnson, *Proc. Instn. Mech. Engrs.*, **177**, 676–685 (1963).
54e. D. Tabor, *Proc. Roy. Soc. (London) Ser. A*, **229**, 198–220 (1955).
55. J. R. Whitehead, *Proc. Roy. Soc. (London) Ser. A*, **201**, 109–124 (1950).
56. R. W. Wilson, *Proc. Phys. Soc. (London) Ser. B*, **68**, 625–641 (1955).
57. R. Courtel, *Compt. Rend.*, **261**, 3962–3965 (1965); *Bull. Inform. Sci. Techn. Comm. Energ. At.* **90**, 1–29.
58. F. P. Bowden and A. E. Hanwell, *Nature*, **201**, 1279–1281 (1964).
59. D. H. Buckley and R. L. Johnson, *NASA Rept. TND-3235*, 1966.
60. F. P. Bowden and T. H. C. Childs, *Proc. Roy. Soc. (London) Ser. A*, **312**, 451 (1969).
61. B. D. Powell, Ph.D. Thesis, University of Cambridge, 1969.
62. E. E. Bisson and W. J. Anderson, *Advanced Bearing Technology*, NASA, Washington, D.C., 1960.
62a. R. Courtel, *Met. Corrosion-Ind.*, **473**, 1–6 (1965).
62b. R. Courtel, *Compt. Rend.*, **253**, 1758–1763 (1961); **261**, 3962–3965 (1965).
62c. M. Seal, *Proc. Roy. Soc. (London) Ser. A*, **248**, 353–368 (1958).
63. F. P. Bowden and C. A. Brookes, *Proc. Roy. Soc. (London) Ser. A*, **295**, 244–258 (1966).
64. P. R. Billinghurst, C. A. Brookes, and D. Tabor, *Physical Basis of Yield and Fracture*, Conf. Series No. 1, Institute of Physics and Physical Society, London, 1966, Chapter 4.
65. G. M. Hamilton and L. E. Goodman, *J. Appl. Mech.* **33**, 371 (1966).
66. F. C. Frank and B. R. Lawn, *Proc. Roy. Soc. (London) Ser. A*, **299**, 291 (1967).
67. D. R. Gilroy and W. Hirst, *J. Phys. D: Appl. Phys.*, **2**, 1784 (1969).
68. B. D. Powell and D. Tabor, *J. Phys. D: Appl. Phys.*, **3**, 783 (1970).
69. R. H. Savage, *J. Appl. Phys.*, **19**, 1–10 (1948).
70. P. J. Bryant, P. L. Gutshall, and L. H. Taylor, *Wear*, **7**, 118–126 (1964).

310   FRICTION, LUBRICATION, AND WEAR

71. G. W. Rowe, *Wear*, **3**, 274–285, 454–462 (1960).
71a. J. Skinner, N. Gane, and D. Tabor, *Nature Phys. Sci.*, **232**, 195–196 (1971).
72. R. F. Deacon and J. F. Goodman, *Proc. Roy. Soc. (London) Ser. A*, **243**, 464–482 (1958).
73. A. J. Haltner, *Wear*, **7**, 102–117 (1964).
74. W. O. Winer, *Wear*, **10**, 422–452 (1967).
75. G. Salomon, *T.N.O. Nieuws*, **21**, 39 (1966).
76. J. P. Giltrow, *R.A.E. Report No. 66184*, 1966.
77. F. P. Bowden, J. H. Greenwood, and M. Imai, *Proc. Roy. Soc. (London) Ser. A*, **304**, 157 (1968).
78. G. Salomon, A. W. J. de Gee, and J. H. Zaat, *Wear*, **7**, 87–101 (1964).
79. B. P. G. Swinnerton and M. J. B. Turner, *Wear*, **9**, 142–159 (1966).
80. R. R. M. Johnston and A. J. W. Moore, *Wear*, **7**, 498–512 (1964).
81. G. W. Rowe, *Institution of Mechanical Engineers Conference on Lubrication and Wear*, Institution of Mechanical Engineers, London, 1957, pp. 333–3338.
82. R. W. Roberts and R. S. Owens, *Wear*, **6**, 444–456 (1963).
83. R. W. Roberts and R. S. Owens, *Wear*, **7**, 513–515 (1964).
84. K. A. Grosch, *Proc. Roy. Soc. (London) Ser. A*, **274**, 21–39 (1963).
84a. J. A. Greenwood and D. Tabor, *Proc. Phys. Soc. (London)*, **71**, 989–1001 (1958).
84b. D. Tabor, *Engineering (London)*, **48**, 838–842 (1959).
85. A. Schallamach, *Wear*, **6**, 375–382 (1963).
86. K. C. Ludema and D. Tabor, *Wear*, **9**, 329 (1966).
87. T. L. Smith, *J. Polymer Sci.*, **32**, 99 (1958).
88. D. Bulgin, G. D. Hubbard, and M. H. Walters, *Proc. Rubber Technol. Conf., 4th, London*, Inst. Rubber Industry, 1962, pp. 173–188.
89. A. R. Savkoor, *Wear*, **8**, 222–237 (1965).
90. H. W. Kummer and W. E. Meyer, *J. Mater.*, **1**, 667 (1966).
91. G. M. Bartenev, *Dokl. Akad. Nauk SSSR*, **96**, 1161–1164 (1954).
91a. D. G. Flom and A. M. Bueche, *J. Appl. Phys.*, **30**, 1725–1730 (1959).
92. M. W. Pascoe and D. Tabor, *Proc. Roy. Soc. (London) Ser. A*, **235**, 210 (1956).
92a. R. C. Bowers, *J. Appl. Phys.*, **42**, 4961–4970 (1971).
92b. L. C. Towle, *J. Appl. Phys.*, **42**, 2368–2375 (1971).
93. B. Briscoe, V. Mustafaev, and D. Tabor, *Wear*, **19**, 389–414 (1972).
93a. R. C. Bowers, N. L. Jarvis, and W. A. Zisman, *Ind. Eng. Chem.*, **4**, 86 (1965).
94. K. G. McLaren and D. Tabor, *Wear*, **8**, 79–83 (1965).
95. G. V. Vinogradov, G. M. Bartenev, A. I. El'kin, Yu. G. Yanovsky, V. N. Nikolayev, and E. I. Frenkin, *Brit. J. Appl. Phys.*, **2**, 1687 (1969).
95a. G. V. Vinogradov, G. M. Bartenev, A. I. El'kin, and V. K. Mikhaylov, *Wear*, **16**, 213–219 (1970).
96. K. R. Makinson and D. Tabor, *Proc. Roy. Soc. (London) Ser. A*, **281**, 49–61 (1964).
96a. C. M. Pooley and D. Tabor, in press, 1972.
97. L. H. Sharpe and H. Schonhorn, *J. Polymer Sci.*, [B] **2**, 719 (1964).
97a. K. R. Makinson, *Wear*, **16**, 287–292 (1970).
98. A. D. Roberts and D. Tabor, *Wear*, **11**, 163 (1968).
99. D. Dowson and G. R. Higginson, *Elastohydrodynamic Lubrication*, Pergamon Press, Oxford, 1966.
100. D. Tabor and W. O. Winer, *Trans. Am. Soc. Lubr. Engrs.*, **8**, 69–77 (1965).
100a. A. Dyson, *Phil. Trans. Roy. Soc. (London)*, **266**, 1–33 (1970).
100b. H. Naylor and A. Dyson, Private communication.
101. J. F. Hutton, *Proc. Roy. Soc. (London) Ser. A*, **287**, 222–239 (1965).

102. K. L. Johnson and R. Cameron, *Proc. Instn. Mech. Engrs.*, **182,** 307–319 (1967–8).
103. J. F. Archard and E. W. Cowking, *Elastohydrodynamics at Point Contacts*, Institution of Mechanical Engineers, London, 1965/1966.
104. E. Rabinowicz and D. Tabor, *Proc. Roy. Soc. (London) Ser. A*, **206,** 455 (1951).
105. J. W. Menter and D. Tabor, *Proc. Roy. Soc. (London) Ser. A*, **204,** 512–524 (1951).
106. J. A. Chapman and D. Tabor, *Proc. Roy. Soc. (London) Ser. A*, **242,** 96 (1957).
107. A. J. Groszek, *Proc. Roy. Soc. (London) Ser. A*, **314,** 473 (1970).
107a. B. J. Briscoe, private communication, 1971.
108. W. A. Zisman, in Davies, Ed., *Friction and Wear*, General Motors Symposium, Elsevier, 1959.
109. A. Cameron and R. Gohar, *Proc. Roy. Soc. (London) Ser. A*, **291,** 520 (1966).
110. R. T. Mathieson, *Nature*, **186,** 301 (1960).
110a. A. J. Smith and A. Cameron, Disc. of Faraday Soc. (1970) "Thin Films and Boundary Layers," 221–230.
110b. F. P. Bowden and A. C. Moore, *Trans. Faraday Soc.*, **47,** 900 (1950).
111. R. S. Fein and K. L. Kreuz, *Trans. Am. Soc. Lubr. Engrs.*, **8,** 29 (1965).
112. G. V. Vinogradov, V. V. Arkarova, and A. A. Petrov, *Wear*, **4,** 274–291 (1961).
113. R. P. Eischens, *Boundary Lubrication*, American Society of Mechanical Engineers, 1969, pp. 61–86.
114. L. E. St. Pierre, R. S. Owens, and R. V. Klint, *Nature*, **202,** 1204–1205 (1964).
115. H. W. Hermance and T. F. Egan, *Bell System Tech. J.*, **37,** 1 (1958).
116. W. D. Weatherford, Jr., M. L. Valtierra, and P. M. Ku, *J. Lubr. Technol., A.S.M.E.*, **90F,** 42 (1968).
117. A. A. Koutkov and D. Tabor, *Tribology*, **3,** 163 (1970).
118. E. D. Tingle, "Fundamental work on friction and lubrication and wear in Germany," *B.I.O.S. Report No. 1610*, 1947.
119. D. Tabor and R. F. Willis, *Wear*, **13,** 413 (1969).
120. D. Godfrey, *World Petrol, Congr.*, *5th, N.Y.*, *1959*, Section VI, 345 (1959).
120a. R. S. Fein, "Interdisciplinary Approach to the Lubrication of Concentrated Contacts, NASA Symposium 1969," *NASA SP-237*, 489–527 (1970).
121. M. J. D. Low, K. H. Brown, and H. Inoue, *J. Colloid Interface Sci.*, **24,** 252 (1967).
122. A. S. Akhmatov, *Molecular Physics of Boundary Lubrication*, Israel Program for Scientific Translations, Jerusalem, 1966.
123. P. W. Bridgman, *Rev. Mod. Phys.*, **18,** 1 (1946).
123a. J. Boyd and B. P. Robertson, *Trans. ASME*, **67,** 51 (1945).
123b. J. R. White, *Lubrication Eng.*, **10,** 340 (1954).
124. A. Cameron, *Trans. Am. Soc. Lubr. Engrs.*, **2,** 195 (1960).
125. B. Scruton, Ph.D. Thesis, Cambridge, 1971; B. Scruton, D. Tabor, and R. F. Willis, in press, 1972.
125a. F. P. Bowden and D. Tabor, *J. Appl. Phys.*, **14,** 141–152 (1943).
125b. E. F. Finkin, *Wear*, **18,** 231–241 (1971).
125c. S. C. Cohen and D. Tabor, *Proc. Roy. Soc. (London) Ser. A*, **291,** 186–207 (1966).
125d. S. E. Horne and J. J. Suarez, *Soc. Polythene Engrs. J.*, **25,** 34 (1969).
125e. A. J. G. Allan (private communication).
125f. A. D. Roberts and D. Tabor, *Proc. Roy. Soc. (London) Ser. A*, **325,** 323–345 (1971).
125g. A. D. Roberts, *Nature*, **231,** 434–436 (1971).
126a. D. Tabor, *Nature*, **145,** 308 (1940).
126b. D. Tabor, *Nature*, **147,** 609 (1941).
127. J. J. Frewing, *Proc. Roy. Soc. (London) Ser. A*, **182,** 270 (1944).

128. T. C. Askwith, A. Cameron, and R. F. Crouch, *Proc. Roy. Soc. (London) Ser. A*, **291**, 500 (1966); W. J. S. Grew and A. Cameron, *Proc. Roy. Soc. (London)*, in press, 1972.
129. R. S. Fein, C. N. Rowe, and K. L. Kreuz, *Trans. Am. Soc. Lubr. Engrs.* **2**, 50 (1959).
130. R. M. Matveevsky, *Wear*, **4**, 292 (1961).
131. C. N. Rowe, *Trans. Am. Soc. Lubr. Engrs.*, **9**, 100 (1966).
132. R. S. Fein and K. L. Kreuz, *Interdisciplinary Approach to Friction and Wear, SP-155*, NASA, San Antonio, 1967, pp. 358–376.
132a. W. Hirst and J. V. Stafford "Transition Temperatures in Boundary Lubrication". Paper presented at meeting of Instn. Mech. Engrs., 5th April 1972.
132b. J. C. Bell and A. Dyson, Papers 8 and 9, Instn. Mech. Engrs. Second Symposium on Electrohydrodynamic Lubrication, Leeds (U.K.), 11–13 April, 1972.
132c. A. Cameron and J. P. Sharma. In press (1972).
133. J. S. Courtney-Pratt and G. K. Tudor, *Proc. Inst. Mech. Engrs. (London)*, **155**, 292 (1946).
134. M. J. Furey, *Trans. Am. Soc. Lubr. Engrs.*, **4**, 1 (1961).
135. M. J. Furey, *Trans. Am. Soc. Lubr. Engrs.*, **6**, 49 (1963).
136. L. Grunberg, *Brit. J. Appl. Phys.*, **9**, 85–93 (1958).
137. I. Kramer and L. J. Demer, *Progr. Mater. Sci.*, **9**, 131–199 (1961).
138. A. R. C. Westwood, *Ind. Eng. Chem.*, **56**, 14–25 (1964).
139. C. W. McCutchen, *Nature*, **184**, 1284–1285 (1959).
140. P. R. Lancaster and G. W. Rowe, *Wear*, **2**, 428–437 (1958-9).
141. J. F. Archard, *J. Appl. Phys.*, **24**, 981 (1953).
142. E. Rabinowicz, *Friction and Wear of Solids*, Wiley, New York, 1965.
143. L. Rozeanu, *Wear*, **6**, 337–340 (1963).
144. I. V. Kraghelsky, *Friction and Wear*, Butterworths, London, 1965.
145. C. N. Rowe, in *Interdisciplinary Approach to Friction and Wear*, P. M. Ku, Ed., NASA, Washington, D.C., 1968, p. 310.
146. D. Tabor, *Proc. Phys. Soc. (London) Ser. B*, **67**, 249 (1954).
147. M. M. Khrushchov, *Institution of Mechanical Engineers Conference on Lubrication and Wear*, Paper 46, 1957.
148. R. C. D. Richardson, *Wear*, **10**, 291 (1967).
149. R. C. D. Richardson, *Wear*, **11**, 245 (1968).
150. H. Wilman, *Wear*, **14**, 249 (1969).
151. E. M. Trent, *Proc. Roy. Soc. (London) Ser. A*, **212**, 467 (1952).
152. A. E. Roach, C. L. Goodzeit, and R. P. Hunnicut, *Am. Soc. Mech. Engrs.*, Paper 54-A-61, 1954.
153. I. V. Kragelsky and V. S. Kombalov, *Wear*, **14**, 139 (1969).
154. N. C. Welsh, *J. Appl. Phys.*, **28**, 960–968 (1957).
155. W. Hirst, "Lubrication and Wear," *Proc. Inst. Mech. Engrs. (London)*, **182**, Part 3A, 281 (1967–1968).

Author Index

Numbers in parentheses are reference numbers and show that an author's work is referred to although his name is not mentioned in the text. Numbers in *italics* indicate the pages on which the full references appear.

Adam, N. K., 8(95), 16(95), 41(95), *75,* 212, 234, *241, 243*
Adams, G. J., 64(179), *77,* 88(30), 131(30), 134(30), 158(30), *189*
Adams, N., 255, 274, *308*
Ahlbeck, R. A., 108(87), *190*
Akhmatov, A. S., 289–290(122), 291, *311*
Albert, A., 107(81, 82), 123(111), *190, 191*
Alexander, A. E., 7(92,93), 8(96), 25(126), 43(138), 49(126,157), *75, 76,* 82(10), 84(13), 97(10), 105(73,76), 111(73), 112(73), 113(94), 114(97), 123(94), 133(73), 158(73,169), 159(186,189,190), 160(186), 175(94), *189, 190, 192*
Alfrey, T., 34(130), *76*
Amontons, G., 247, *307*
Anderson, D. L., 261, *308, 309*
Anderson, W. J., 266(62), *309*
Andreatch, P., 261(33), *308*
Archard, J. F., 250, 251, 259(27), 282, 301, 302, *308, 311, 312*
Archer, R. J., 164(199,200), *192*
Arkarova, V. V., 286(112), 287(112), *311*
Arnold, J. D., 107(80), *190*
Aron, C., 84(17), *189*
Askwith, T. C., 294(128), 295(128), *312*
Atack, D., 264(54a,5), *309*
Avient, B. W. E., 263(51), *309*

Babichev, M. A., 263, *309*
Bailey, A. I., 255(17), 262(17,46), 290, 291, *308, 309*
Barquins, M., 261(37b), *308*
Bart, W. L., 238(97), *244*
Bartenev, G. M., 271, 275, *310*
Bateman, J. B., 19(114), *75*
Beams, J. W., 238(97), *244*
Becher, P., 158(172), 172(217), 232(58), *192, 193, 243*

Bell, J. C., 296, *312*
Benson, J. C., 166(206), *193*
Berch, J., 199(1), 215(21), 238, *241, 242, 244*
Beredjick, N., 83(12), *189*
Berliner, C., 3(52,53), 49(53), 50(53), *74,* 102(57,59), 115(57), *190*
Bernett, M. K., 86(20), *189*
Betts, J. J., 8(104), *75*
Billica, H. R., 207(3), 236, 237, 240, *241, 243, 244*
Billinghurst, P. R., 267(64), *309*
Bird, R. B., 210(10), *241*
Bisson, E. E., 266, *309*
Biswas, A. B., 82(8,9), 84(9), 95(40), 167(40), 171(213), *189, 193*
Biswas, B., 36(131, 132), 69(131), *76,* 131(130,131), 133(130–132), 136(130, 131), 137(131), 158(179), *191, 192*
Blake, T. D., 227(42), *242*
Blakey, B. C., 51(163), *76*
Blanck, M., 138(136), *191*
Boehme, G., 239(100), *244*
Boháčkova, V., 49(152), *76,* 81(4), *188*
Bolger, J. C., 210(12), *241*
Bonnar, R. U., 235(75), *243*
Bourne, M. C., 219(29, 30), *242*
Boussinesq, J., 3(16), 20, 24, 47, *73*
Bowden, F. P., 265(58), 266, 267(63), 270, 286, 292(125a), *308–311*
Bowers, R. C., 275, 292(92a, 125e), *310, 311*
Boyd, E., 3(22), *73*
Boyd, G. E., 7(89–91), 49(159), *75, 76,* 91(32,33), 92(32), 93(32,33), 95(33), 142(32), 171(32), 178(33), *189*
Boyd, J., 290, 291, *311*
Breazeale, J. B., 238(97), *244*
Bressler, S. E., 57(175), *77*
Bridgman, P. W., 290, 311

313

Subject Index

Cumulative Author Index, Volumes 1-5